METHUEN'S
MONOGRAPHS ON
CHEMICAL SUBJECTS

———

General Editors: H. J. Emeleus, F.R.S.
D. W. G. Style, and R. P. Bell, F.R.S.

CHAIN REACTIONS

An Introduction

Chain Reactions

AN INTRODUCTION

F. S. Dainton, F.R.S.

Vice-Chancellor, University of Nottingham.
Formerly Professor of Physical Chemistry, University of Leeds

LONDON: METHUEN & CO. LTD.
NEW YORK: JOHN WILEY & SONS INC.

First published, 8 November, 1956
Second edition 1966
© *1966 by F. S. Dainton*
Printed and bound in Great Britain
at the Pitman Press, Bath
Catalogue No. (Methuen) 12/4095/63
2.1

CONTENTS

PREFACE TO FIRST EDITION

IN 1913 there appeared in the *Zeitschrift für Physikalische Chemie* the classic paper by BODENSTEIN in which the idea that reactions might proceed by a chain of subsidiary reactions was first proposed. Since that date the subject has developed rapidly and is now a well-established branch of reaction kinetics. Despite this, and despite the immense range of chemical recations which proceed by a chain mechanism, only one book concerned exclusively with the subject has been written. This very useful book, by SEMENOV, was published as long ago as 1935 and for several years there has been a need for a shorter book in the English language in which the emphasis was on the underlying principles, rather than on the hypothetical reaction schemes currently in fashion to account for the detailed properties of individual reactions, and which would include some of the important advances made in the last twenty years. The present volume is an attempt to fill this gap and to provide an introduction to the subject for the university student, either undergraduate or postgraduate, who already has some acquaintance with the general principles of reaction kinetics.

It is the author's hope that the book will not only serve this purpose but also stimulate further reading in the rapidly expanding original literature in this fascinating field of study. For this and other reasons only a few reactions have been discussed as such (in the last two chapters) and these have been chosen solely to illustrate the principles and methods elaborated earlier. Accordingly, the accounts of these reactions are far from exhaustive and do not include all the recent findings. Instead it has been considered preferable to include in the bibliographies some references to review articles in which more recent work is described and which are convenient starting points for further reading.

It is impossible to write so brief a book, involving much compression and arbitrary selection without the inadvertent obtrusion of inaccurate or misleading statements and infelicitous expressions. The author has been saved from many of his original sins both of omission and commission by many friends who from time to time have kindly read parts of the manuscript. These include Drs. P. G. Ashmore, E. Collinson, J. A. Davies, K. O. Kutschke, P. P. Manning and A. F. Trotman-Dickenson. To them he offers his grateful thanks; they should be dissociated from the many blemishes which the book doubtless still possesses. To his own pupils in the teaching of whom he has learnt much, he also gives grateful acknowledgement.

PREFACE TO SECOND EDITION

WHILST there has been no substantial modification of the basic theory of chain reactions since the first edition was published in 1956 considerable advances have been made in (*a*) the application to more complex mechanistic situations, (*b*) the experimental methods for studying reactions, and (*c*) the understanding of the factors governing the rate of uni- and bi-molecular reactions. Moreover, it has become increasingly apparent that the quantitative study of chain reactions, especially those of addition polymerization afford a most valuable weapon in the armory of the chemist who wishes to gain insight into the detailed mechanism of proton-, hydride- and atom-transfer reactions of ions and free radicals. In this edition some account has been taken of these advances but the general pattern of the book has been preserved. Once again I am indebted to colleagues and students for helpful comments. One of the latter has pointed out to me that the power of the methods described in Chapters IV and V is best appreciated by applying them to systems other than those described in the book. I have therefore added some exercises to the end of Chapter IV.

LIST OF IMPORTANT SYMBOLS

(In order of first appearance)

CHAPTER I—(*contd.*)

z.p.e.	=	'zero point' or 'residual' energy $= \frac{1}{2}\Sigma h\nu$
h	=	Planck's constant, erg sec.
ν	=	vibration frequency (sec^{-1})
$\ddagger$	=	subscript or superscript denoting transition state
D	=	bond dissociation energy, k. cal mole^{-1}
E_{calc}, A_{calc}	=	energy of activation and frequency factor as defined by equation (I.13)
v	=	velocity
F	=	partition function
$\overset{r}{\Pi}x_R$	=	product of r terms of the type x_R
κ	=	transmission coefficient
A	=	Helmholtz Free Energy
S	=	Entropy
p_i	=	degeneracy of the ith quantum level
ε_i	=	energy of the ith quantum level
I	=	moment of inertia, gm cm^2
ρ	=	rotational symmetry factor

CHAPTER II

P_l	=	lower pressure limit to ignition
P_u	=	upper pressure limit to ignition
S.R.	=	slow reaction
B	=	energy of activation of branching reaction
π	=	the third or 'thermal' explosion limit
n (as a subscript)	=	number of monomeric segments in a given polymer molecule
$\overline{M}_n$	=	number average molecular weight
O.P.	=	osmotic pressure
$\overline{M}_w$	=	weight average molecular weight
c	=	concentration
η	=	viscosity

CHAPTER III

q	=	heat of reaction $= -\Delta H^{\circ}$, k. cal mole^{-1}
$m_j{}^*$	=	polymer chain containing j monomeric segments and capable of further growth
m_1	=	monomer
m_n	=	polymer containing n units of monomer

CHAPTER IV

k_p	= rate constant of a propagation reaction
$\bar{t}$	= $(k_1[R])^{-1} = 1\cdot443 \times$ half-life of a chain centre in the propagation reaction with reactant R having a rate constant k_1.
I, F, G, W	= Rate and coefficients defined by equation (IV.5)
τ	= average time between initiation and termination of a chain
$k.c.l.$	= kinetic chain length
k_t	= rate constant of a mutual or quadratic termination reaction
ϕ_1	= quantum yield of the primary act, in initial centres per quantum
I_{abs}	= intensity of actinic light absorbed in quanta or einsteins per sec. per litre
γ	= quantum yield

CHAPTER V

n	= concentration of reaction centres
θ	= the rate of initiation of reaction chains
f	= the coefficient of linear branching = $f_0\,e^{-\frac{B}{RT}}$
F	= the coefficient of quadratic branching
g	= the coefficient of homogeneous linear termination
δ	= the coefficient of homogeneous quadratic termination
x	= space coordinate
d	= diameter of a cylindrical or spherical reaction vessel
$\bar{n}$	= volume average concentration of centres
α	= average thermal velocity
$\bar{z}$	= average number of collisions between propagation steps
$\bar{\Delta}$	= average displacement
$I.P.$	= induction period due solely to the time development of the chain
ϕ	= net linear branching factor
Γ	= the constant in the approximate wall termination rate expression

ϕ'	= net quadratic branching factor
λ	= fraction of chains terminated linearly
τ_g	= lifetime of linearly terminated chains
τ_δ	= lifetime of quadratically terminated chains
$\bar{R}$	= average rate under intermittent irradiation
Pr_l, Pr_d	= amounts of product formed during t_l and t_d respectively
t_l	= period of illumination
t_d	= period of darkness
R_0	= rate without sector, i.e. continuous light
n_l	= centre concentration at end of light period
n_d	= centre concentration at end of dark period
x	= exponent in equation $R_0 \alpha I_{abs}^x$
b	= $t_l/\tau_\delta = t_l(\theta\delta)^{\frac{1}{2}}$
f	= $(t_l + t_d)/t_l$

CHAPTER VI

ε	= chain terminating efficiency of vessel wall

CHAPTER VII

k_t'	= rate constant of linear termination ($= g$ of Chapter V)
k_t	= rate constant of quadratic termination ($= \delta$ of Chapter V)
$\overline{DP}_n$	= number average degree of polymerization
k_{de}	= rate constant of unimolecular catalyst decomposition
k_{in}	= rate constant of reaction between primary species and inhibitor
k_i	= rate constant of reaction between primary species and monomer, i.e. initiation
k_t''	= rate constant of primary radical termination
k_r	= rate constant of retardation reaction
k_{tr}	= rate constant of chain transfer reaction
k_d	= rate constant of depropagation
T_c	= ceiling temperature
r_α, r_β	= monomer reactivity ratios $= k_{\alpha\alpha}/k_{\alpha\beta}$ and $k_{\beta\beta}/k_{\beta\alpha}$ respectively

INTRODUCTION

WHEN a chemical reaction proceeds by a chain mechanism most of the reactants are transformed into the products by so-called *propagation* reactions with certain intermediates called chain centres. The essential feature of a propagation reaction is that the chain centre which is destroyed is replaced by a new chain centre. The new chain centre, which may differ chemically from the original centre, is, by definition, able to take part in another propagation reaction or a series of propagation reactions, in the course of which a centre of the first type is regenerated. A simple example of this behaviour is afforded by the two propagation reactions ((1) and (2) below) involved in the photosynthesis of hydrogen chloride gas.

$$(1) \qquad \underline{Cl} + H_2 \rightarrow HCl + \underline{H}$$

$$(2) \qquad \underline{H} + Cl_2 \rightarrow HCl + \underline{Cl}$$

In this reaction the chain centres are chlorine atoms and hydrogen atoms.* The power of chain centres to enter into reactions which result in their regeneration as well as in the conversion of reactants to products enables the propagation reactions to be repeated many times, and, under favourable conditions, thousands of product molecules may be formed from one initial centre which is produced in, or introduced into, the reactant mixture. Such a sequence of reactions is called a reaction chain. Occasionally a centre may be involved in an especially favourable encounter with a reactant and instead of only one new centre being formed, two or more centres may be produced, each of which is capable of propagating a reaction chain. Such a reaction is called a *branching* reaction and will cause the chains to proliferate, the number of centres to increase and the overall reaction to accelerate. Acting in opposition to the propagation and branching reactions are the chain *termination* processes in which centres are converted into species which are incapable of propagating the chain. This removal of centres may occur

* Throughout this book the chain centres in chemical reactions other than addition polymerization will be underlined.

heterogeneously or homogeneously and may involve one or two chain centres. It will be obvious that even when the conditions for chain propagation and branching are optimum, no chains will exist in the system and hence no reaction will occur unless there is some mechanism for the formation of centres which is independent of the propagation and branching reactions. The reactions in which the first centres of reaction chains are created are called the *initiation* reactions, and, as will be seen, may be very diverse in character. A very convenient classification is to call the initiation reaction the primary process or primary act, and to refer to the subsequent reactions of propagation, branching and termination as the secondary processes.

The interplay of the characteristic part-processes of initiation, propagation, branching and termination determines the overall kinetic behaviour of a chain reaction. The identification of these constituent reactions, and the determination of their velocity constants are therefore of prime importance and are the major aims of most investigations in this field. The order of presentation of the material in this book has to a large extent been dictated by these facts. Since the individual chain steps are often simple homogeneous uni-, bi-, or ter-molecular processes it has been necessary to review briefly the kinetics of simple homogeneous reactions which may occur in gaseous or liquid systems. Chain reactions often display kinetic properties not shown by non-chain reactions and these differences are next discussed because they may be exploited as experimental criteria for the recognition of a chain mechanism. The same features often impose novel experimental methods of investigation, and a brief account of experimental methods therefore follows. The largest section is concerned with a discussion of the chemical nature of the various types of constituent chemical reactions which may be involved in chain reactions together with an outline of the kinetic consequences of combining these constituent steps in different ways. Finally, a few important groups of reactions are considered in a little greater detail, in order to illustrate the application of the experimental and theoretical methods. This order is not the historical one. No apology is made for this, since the historical approach is not necessarily the approach of greatest didactic value, and in the field of chain reactions the codification of the theoretical treatment achieved by HINSHEL-WOOD and SEMENOV and their co-workers just about thirty years ago, has provided an intellectual framework for the student which will enable him to place in correct perspective the vast amount of kinetic data published both before and after this date. It will be clear that the debt of any worker in this subject to these two authors is very considerable.

CHAPTER I

HOMOGENEOUS REACTIONS WHICH DO NOT INVOLVE CHAINS

THE observed rates of many chemical reactions may often be represented by an expression of the form

$$\text{rate} = k^{\circ}_{\text{obs}} \cdot e^{\frac{-E_A}{RT}} [A]^{\alpha}[B]^{\beta} \quad . \quad . \quad . \quad . \quad \text{(I.1)}$$

in which $\alpha, \beta, \ldots$ are the orders of reactions with respect to the reagents A, B, . . . The individual orders are often small integers and the sum $\Sigma(\alpha + \beta + \ldots) = n$ is referred to as the overall order of the reaction. The quantity

$$k^{\circ}_{\text{obs}} \cdot e^{\frac{-E_A}{RT}} = k_{\text{obs}}$$

is called the velocity constant, or specific rate constant and when k°_{obs} is constant over the temperature range of investigation, the reaction obeys the Arrhenius law for the variation of the rate with temperature. E_A is the Arrhenius activation energy usually expressed in k. cal mole^{-1}, R is the gas constant, and T is the absolute temperature.

The distinction between the order, which is an experimentally determined quantity, and the molecularity is important. A reaction is said to be uni-, bi-, or ter-molecular according as the 'activated complex' is constituted from one, two, or three reactant molecules respectively. The exact meaning of the term 'activated complex' will appear later; for the present it suffices to define it as the unstable entity formed from the appropriate number of reactant molecules, which it exceeds in internal energy by an amount $\Delta E^{\ddagger}$ (see later) and capable of changing into the products without further acquisition of energy. Whilst the overall order and molecularity are often identical, as for example in the bimolecular, second order reaction

(3) $$(C_2H_5)_3N + C_2H_5I \rightarrow (C_2H_5)_4N^+I^-$$

this is not always the case and there are many unimolecular processes which under certain conditions are second order. In general, for simple homogeneous reactions, the overall order may exceed but is never less than the molecularity.

The values of the order, k_{obs}° and E_A are obtained from measurements of the change of reactant concentration with time, for different initial concentrations of reactants at each of several temperatures. The experimental means employed to determine instantaneous values of the reagent concentration are diverse, often involving titration for solution reactions, manometric and gas analysis measurements for gas reactions, and where more convenient, the measurement of some physical property (e.g. thermal conductivity, optical density, viscosity, volume etc.) of the reaction mixture which is related to its composition. In very fast reactions it may be desirable to use flow or pulse methods. Details of these methods may be found in references 1 and 2. The analysis of the data is carried out by three main methods.

(1) The half-life method in which the reciprocal of the time for 50 per cent change ($t_{\frac{1}{2}}$) is plotted against the initial concentration. When all the reactants are initially present in the same concentration (a) and the stoichiometry is suitable, $t_{\frac{1}{2}}$ is inversely proportional to a^{n-1} and hence n and k_{obs} may be evaluated.

(2) The reactant concentration against time curves are frequently linear in the first stages of the reaction and in these cases the tangents to these curves at the origin may be determined with accuracy. n and k can then be calculated from the relation that the initial slopes of these curves are equal to ka^n.

(3) The third main method is to plot an appropriate function of the initial and instantaneous reagent concentrations against time. In practice the order is often known before such plots are made, but this method removes the uncertainty often experienced in methods (1) and (2) of the precise time of starting the reaction.

A plot of $\log_{10} k_{obs}$ against T^{-1} should then give a straight line of slope $= - E_A/2 \cdot 303R$. However, there is a considerable number of reactions for which the simple Arrhenius Law, i.e. k_{obs}° independent of temperature, does not hold and there are a few cases for which the curve $\log_{10} k_{obs}$ against T^{-1} is neither linear nor of negative slope. In certain cases the explanation of such anomalous behaviour is simple, namely, that some of the reactants form an intermediate compound with evolution of heat and that this compound is really one of the reagents, and combines with another reagent to form the activated complex. k_{obs} measured as the observed rate divided by (reactant concentration)^n will then be proportional to $e^{\frac{-E_A - \Delta E}{RT}}$, in which $-\Delta E$ is the exothermicity of the reaction in which the intermediate compound is formed and E_A is the Arrhenius activation energy of the reaction between this intermediate and another reagent to form the observed product. It is perhaps not without significance that in the termolecular reactions which behave anomalously, two of the three molecules are identical, paramagnetic, and are known to form a dimer[3] (and in one reaction, $2NO + O_2 \rightarrow 2NO_2$, all three are paramagnetic).

The Collision Theory. In all bimolecular reactions the rate of reaction cannot exceed the collision rate of the molecules which comprise the activated complex. The simple collision theory leads to the following values of the collision rates (Z) in collisions c.c.$^{-1}$ sec^{-1}:

(a) Between dissimilar molecules A and B

$$_A Z_B = \left(\frac{8\pi kT}{\mu}\right)^{\frac{1}{2}} {}_A\sigma_B{}^2 n_A n_B \qquad . \quad . \quad (I.2)$$

where n_A and n_B are the numbers of A and B molecules per cubic centimetre; μ is the reduced mass in grammes defined by $\mu = m_A m_B/(m_A + m_B)$; k is the Boltzmann constant in ergs deg^{-1} molecule^{-1}; and $_A\sigma_B$ is the mean collision diameter $= (\sigma_A + \sigma_B)/2$ in centimetres, σ_A and σ_B being the collision diameters deduced from the study of transport phenomena in the gases A and B.

(b) Between the same molecules A

$$_A Z_A = 2 \left(\frac{\pi kT}{m_A}\right)^{\frac{1}{2}} \sigma_A{}^2 n_A{}^2 \qquad . \quad . \quad . \quad (I.3)$$

and since the average velocity, c_A of A molecules is $\left(\frac{8kT}{\pi m_A}\right)^{\frac{1}{2}}$ we may write

$$_A Z_A = \tfrac{1}{2} \sqrt{2} \pi \sigma_A{}^2 c_A n_A{}^2 . \qquad . \quad . \quad . \quad (I.4)$$

Collision rates calculated by means of equations (I.2) and (I.4) are usually far larger than the observed reaction rates, and this fact combined with the observation that Arrhenius' Law is generally obeyed for these reactions whereas the collision rate is proportional to the square root of the temperature, leads to the conclusion that only those collisions result in reaction for which the energy of the pair of colliding molecules is at least equal to a value E/N where N is Avogadro's number. Provided only two square terms* are required to define this energy, the fraction of collisions which are fruitful is $e^{\frac{-E}{RT}}$ and hence for a bimolecular reaction showing second order kinetics the velocity constant on the collision theory, k_{coll}, is given by

$$k_{coll} = Z_0 \, e^{\frac{-E}{RT}} \qquad \ldots \ldots \quad (I.5)$$

where Z_0 is the collision rate at reactant concentrations of 1 mole litre^{-1}. At 27°C the value of Z_0 for a reaction between molecules of molecular weight $= 30$ and collision diameter $= 3$ Å would be about 10^{11} moles litre^{-1} sec^{-1}. The values of k_{obs}° (in litre mole^{-1} sec^{-1} units) are frequently of this order of magnitude, but many cases are known for which the agreement between theory and experiment is very poor. It has therefore become the practice[4] to introduce a probability factor P defined by the equation (I.6).

$$k_{obs} = P \cdot Z_0 \cdot e^{\frac{-E}{RT}} \qquad \ldots \ldots \quad (I.6)$$

In applying this equation it must be remembered that $E = E_A - \frac{1}{2}RT$.† The values of P which have been observed cover a wide range. For example $P \ll 1$ for many association reactions such as the dimerization of olefins, the Diels-Alder reaction and the reaction of organic halides with tertiary amines or disulphides to form quaternary ammonium halides or sulphonium halides. It is a weakness of the collision theory that a unified treatment

---

* For a given co-ordinate, potential and kinetic energy can often each be represented by a term in which the variable is squared, e.g. kinetic energy as $\frac{1}{2}mv^2$ (m = mass, v = velocity), potential energy in a system in which the force is proportional to the displacement, as $\frac{1}{2}fx^2$ (f = force constant, x = displacement). The total energy of molecules, both internal and external, is often the sum of terms of this kind and each such term is called a 'square term'. The number of such terms corresponds to the number of modes of storage of energy.

† From equation (I.1), $E_A = RT^2 d \ln k_{obs}/dT$ and from equation (I.6) since $Z_0 \propto \sqrt{T}$, $E = \dfrac{RT^2 d \ln k_{obs}}{dT} - \frac{1}{2}RT$

of the wide range of the observed P values does not seem to be possible. Instead, additional hypotheses must be employed such as the necessity for the collisional process to satisfy special configurational or steric conditions often peculiar to individual reactions and not readily amenable to quantitative treatment.

Bimolecular reactions in solution present further problems. In order to apply the collision theory, a model of solutions must be assumed. A common assumption was that the dissolved re-agents behave just as they would do in the gas phase at the same temperature and concentration. Some support for this view is provided by the fact that certain reactions proceed at the same rate in the gas phase as in solution in certain so-called 'inert' solvents, which are usually non-polar liquids like carbon tetra-chloride and cyclohexane. The reactions mentioned in the previous paragraph are in this category. On the other hand, there are also some reactions of which the velocity constants are greatly different in the gas phase and in solution and many others which, although they cannot be investigated in the gas phase, proceed at very different rates in different solvents. Analysis of the data reveals that both E_A and k_{obs}° may be influenced by the solvent, and some classification of these influences is possible.

Although the total collision rate of two solute molecules in a liquid is comparable to that which they would have in the gas phase at the same concentration there is a difference between the collision mechanisms in the two phases which has two important consequences. After collision in the gas phase they immediately separate and the next collision which each makes is with a different molecule. A pair of solute molecules in a liquid which have just collided will be closely surrounded by solvent molecules and before the solute molecules can separate, temporary gaps in this solvent "cage" through which a solute molecule can pass must be created by the random movements of the solvent molecules. A period of time therefore elapses before the solute molecules can diffuse away from one another and during which they will make many collisions with one another[5]. It is useful to refer to the rate of *first* meeting of solute molecules as the *encounter* rate. It would be expected that the encounter rate would be proportional to the diffusion coefficient, D, of solute molecules through the solvent and hence, inversely proportional to the viscosity of the medium. For uncharged spherical solute molecules A and B present at concentrations of 1 mole l^{-1} their encounter rate is $4\pi_A\sigma_B DR/1000k$,[6] which for $_A\sigma_B = 3$ Å and $D = 10^{-5}$ cm^2 sec is about 4×10^9 l. mole^{-1} sec^{-1}. This is almost thirty times smaller than Z_0 for the same molecules in the gas phase and this factor represents the extent to which the solvent molecules impede the movement of the solute molecules. The total collision rate will be the product of the encounter rate and the number of repeated collisions in the solvent "cage" per encounter. The first consequence of this "cage effect" is that when the energy of activation is so low that the collisions per encounter exceed $e^{E/RT}$ the reaction rate is the encounter rate. Such reactions, which include the combination of atoms and radicals, are referred to as *diffusion controlled* and their rate will depend on temperature in the same manner as D varies with temperature. The second consequence relates to the unimolecular breakdown of a solute molecule into atomic or radical fragments, each of which will make several collisions with one another before they ultimately separate. It follows that if the energy of activation for their recombination is low enough only a fraction of the atoms or radicals initially formed will escape into the bulk solvent, the remainder reacting inside the cage[5].

There are relatively few genuine third order reactions, and the first difficulty which is encountered in trying to give a satisfactory account of these reactions on the collision theory basis is the difficulty of deriving a satisfactory formula for the collision rate. It is usual to regard a ternary collision as occurring when the third molecule strikes a pair of molecules which may be deemed to be in binary collision. The ternary collision rate is then the binary collision rate between the collision pairs and single molecules. To complete the calculation the instantaneous concentration of the collision pairs must be known, which in turn requires a knowledge of the time during which two colliding molecules may be regarded as constituting a collision pair. A crude treatment is to equate this time to the period for which the two molecules of the collision pair are in such close proximity that a third molecule cannot pass freely between them; the time is then roughly equal to the mean collision diameter divided by the average relative velocity. More refined methods have been described, e.g. by TOLMAN, all leading to approximately the same answer, namely, that the ratio of the ternary and binary collision frequencies in a gas is roughly equal to the ratio of the molecular diameter to the mean free path. For many gases at room temperature and atmospheric pressure this ratio is $\sim 10^{-3}$ and it would therefore be concluded that when genuine termolecular processes occur with measurable velocity under these conditions, the energy of activation must be small. All the known examples are in harmony with this conclusion.

The best known examples, which are incidentally also those of most importance in chain reactions, fall into one or other of two groups. The first group consists of the reactions between two nitric oxide molecules and a third diatomic molecule H_2, O_2, Br_2 or Cl_2. Although all these reactions are kinetically third order, the value of E based on the fraction of the collisions which at any given temperature are fruitful is considerably at variance with the value $E_A = RT^2 \cdot d(\ln k_{obs})/dT$. In some cases, e.g. the reaction $2NO + O_2 \rightarrow 2NO_2$, there is experimental evidence that part at least of the difference between E and E_A is due to the reaction proceeding in two stages, the first being the exothermic formation from two molecules of a weak intermediate compound, and the second being the reaction of this compound with the third molecule. When this mechanism is operative the difference between E and E_A must be at least equal to the heat of formation of the intermediate. In other third order reactions the evidence for intermediate compounds is insubstantial and the discrepancy is inexplicable in terms of the simple collision theory, although readily accounted for by the transition state theory. The second group of termolecular reactions are the so-called 'third body' reactions, in which simple radicals, or ions, or atoms combine to form a molecule of low atomicity, e.g. $2H \rightarrow H_2$, $H + OH \rightarrow H_2O$, $Br + Br \rightarrow Br_2$. Such reactions provide the termination reaction for certain chain processes, and may be summarized in the equation

$$(4) \qquad \underline{A\cdot} + \underline{B\cdot} + M \rightarrow AB + M^*$$

where A and B are the simple chain carriers and M is a third molecule which serves as an acceptor for part or all of the energy of formation of AB. If M were not present at the collision AB would decompose. The efficiency of a molecule M acting as a third body is not always unity, but varies with the chemical nature of M in a somewhat similar manner to the variation of the ability of M to quench resonance radiation. When such atom or radical recombination reactions take place in liquids the solvent molecules often fulfil the role of third body and since more than one third body is therefore present at every collision it is to be expected that the combination rate would equal the encounter rate. The possibility of any appreciable activation energy being necessary is very unlikely and this conclusion cannot be very far removed from the truth in most cases. For example, RUSSELL and SIMONS[7] have found k_{obs} for the recombination of gaseous iodine atoms in the presence of added gases such as He, A, N_2, CO_2, $(CH_2)_6$ to *decrease* by a factor of about 2 for a temperature rise from 20 to 127°C.

Apart from providing unlimited 'third bodies' it is difficult to obtain any evidence for the effect of solvents on termolecular reactions. This is due to the fact that the only termolecular reactions which have been investigated in the gas and solution phases are those in which very reactive species such as halogen atoms have been reactants. In such cases this reactivity, which imposes the necessity for a third body, may also cause the atoms to react with the solvent. For instance, chloroform would be a medium in which the three body process

$$(5) \qquad Cl\cdot + Cl\cdot + CHCl_3 \rightarrow Cl_2 + CHCl_3{}^*$$

would probably be relegated to a subsidiary role compared with

$$(6) \qquad Cl\cdot + CHCl_3 \rightarrow HCl + \cdot CCl_3$$

Unimolecular Reactions. The initiation step in many chain reactions is frequently written as a unimolecular bond fission and is treated as kinetically first order. However, all unimolecular reactions are not necessarily first order but may follow a higher order. The anticipation of this phenomenon was one of the early triumphs of the collision theory and will therefore be briefly stated.

When a molecule has acquired by collision an energy greater than or equal to the activation energy it is said to be *energized*. Such an energized molecule may well not be able to pass over into products until it has undergone further changes when it may be described as being in an *activated* state. The activation process may involve the attainment of a particular configuration of the atoms in the molecule or of a particular distribution of its energy amongst various internal modes. In any event there will be a lapse of time between energization and activation and when this time interval is comparable with the interval between collisions only a proportion of the energized molecules will become activated and decompose. The remainder will lose some energy by collision with normal reactant molecules and will then have insufficient energy to react. Such collisional transfers of energy from energized molecules are often referred to as *deactivation* but would really be better described as *de-energization*. This mechanism may be represented by (7), where R represents

(7)

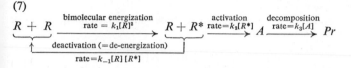

a reactant molecule, R^* an energized molecule, A an activated molecule, Pr the products and k_1, k_{-1}, k_2, and k_3 are rate constants. When $k_3[A] \gg k_2[R^*]$ the rate of product formation is $k_2[R^*]$ and when this is constant, a condition most nearly attained in the early stages of the reaction, $[R^*]$ must be constant and hence $d[R^*]/dt = 0 = k_1[R]^2 - k_2[R^*] - k_{-1}[R][R^*]$. This is essentially the LINDEMANN theory of unimolecular reactions[8] and leads to the rate expression

$$d[Pr]/dt = k_1 k_2 [R]^2 / (k_2 + k_{-1}[R]) \quad . \quad . \quad (I.7)$$

This theory predicts that at low concentrations where $k_2 \gg k_{-1}[R]$ the reaction rate will be $k_1[R]^2$, i.e. the reaction will be second order and at higher concentration where $k_2 \ll k_{-1}[R]$ the reaction will be first order in character, proceeding at a rate $= k_1 k_2 [R]/k_{-1}$. Many gaseous reactions were discovered by HINSHELWOOD and others for which this change of order with pressure seemed to occur. Moreover it is reasonable to suppose that the activational time lag which is proportional to k_2^{-1} would be longer the more complex the molecule. A corollary to this supposition is then that at a suitably chosen pressure the decomposition of simple molecules would be expected to be second order and the pyrolysis of complex molecules to be first order. The early measurements seemed to bear this out: for example, whereas formaldehyde and acetaldehyde follow the second order law, higher aldehydes, ether, ketones, and azo compounds fall into the second category.

The theory would seem to be well adapted to include the

possible effects of non-reacting diluents, e.g. other gases such as H_2 or He, or solvent molecules. Thus, representing the diluent molecule as M, supposing it to be able to activate R and deactivate A (equations (8) and (9)),

(8) $\qquad R + M \rightarrow R^* + M$, velocity constant k_3,

(9) $\qquad R^* + M \rightarrow R + M$, velocity constant k_{-3},

and adding these processes to those summarized in equation (7), we deduce

$$\frac{d[Pr]}{dt} = \frac{k_2[R]\{k_1[R] + k_3[M]\}}{k_2 + k_{-1}[R] + k_{-3}[M]} \qquad \text{. . . .} \quad (I.8)$$

The first order character of the reaction may thus be maintained in the reactant concentration range where $k_{-1}[R] < k_2$, provided $[M]$ is sufficiently large for $k_3[M] > k_1[R]$ and $k_{-3}[M] > k_2$. It has been found that hydrogen in general, and a few other non-reactant gases in special cases, can in fact maintain the first order behaviour to lower reactant pressures than would be the case in their absence. Further, it is usually the case that, provided no ions are involved, chemically inert solvents appear to have little influence on first order reactions and that changes of order consequent on dilution of the reacting solution are not observed. This is particularly true for simple bond breaking processes such as the dissociation of molecules into radicals referred to at the beginning of this discussion of unimolecular reactions, and for isomerization reactions. This result is that expected if the Boltzmann distribution is maintained, since $k_1/k_{-1} = k_3/k_{-3}$ = the fraction of molecules with an energy $\geqslant E$.

More detailed experimental investigations of unimolecular gas reactions revealed two weaknesses of the Lindemann theory. It is readily deduced from equation I.7 that k_1 equals the value of the pseudo first order rate constant (defined as $(d[Pr]/dt)/[R]$) at infinite pressure divided by the reactant concentration at which the pseudo first order rate constant has half this value. In many cases the values of k_1 so obtained are very much larger than $Z_0 e^{-E/RT}$. HINSHELWOOD and FOWLER and RIDEAL pointed out that this discrepancy could be accounted for, at least partially,[9] by the fact that the fractional number of molecules possessing energy $\geqslant E$ distributed in all possible ways amongst s square terms is given by

$$e^{\frac{-E}{RT}} \left\{ \frac{(E/RT)^{\frac{s}{2}-1}}{\left(\frac{s}{2}-1\right)!} + \frac{(E/RT)^{\frac{s}{2}-2}}{\left(\frac{s}{2}-2\right)!} + \ldots \right\} \quad . \quad . \quad . \text{ (I.9)}$$

The term in brackets may often be much greater than unity. For example at $327°C$ when $\frac{s}{2} = 9$ and $E = 60$ k. cal mole^{-1}, this term has the value $2 \cdot 5 \times 10^5$. Since s will increase with molecular complexity k_1 will be much larger than $Z_0 e^{-E/RT}$. A further conclusion is that if k_{-1} is independent of temperature and only the first and largest term in brackets is considered, E_A is related to E by equation (I.10). In the case cited E_A is therefore $51 \cdot 0$ kcal.

$$E_A = E - \left(\frac{s-3}{2}\right) RT \quad . \quad . \quad . \quad . \text{ (I.10)}$$

s is generally found by trial and error and is often close to the number of vibrational modes which the energized molecule can possess. The second shortcoming of the Lindemann theory is that whereas equation I.7 indicates that $[R]/(d[Pr]/dt)$ should be a linear function of $[R]^{-1}$ experimental data plotted in this way always give a curve which is convex to the $[R]^{-1} = 0$ axis. This difficulty may be met if the rate of activation increases with the amount of energy which the energized molecule has in excess of the energy of activation. Two different concepts of the activational process have been proposed to account for this. The first, which will be referred to as the KRR theory, is due to KASSEL and RICE and RAMSPERGER[10] and incorporates the idea that energy is continually being exchanged between the vibrational modes of the energized molecule and that reaction can only take place when a critical increment of energy E' has become localized in the bond(s) which ultimately break(s). The other, proposed by SLATER[11], excludes the notion of energy flow and is based on the concept that an energized molecule can only be regarded as being in the activated state when some designated co-ordinate reaches a critical value. Despite the distinct conceptual difference between the KRR and SLATER theories, both imply that the rate of attainment of the critical condition will increase with the amount of excess energy possessed by R^* according to equation (I.11), where E^* is the energy of R^*. Both theories lead to a

$$k_2 = \nu(1 - E'/E^*)^{\frac{s}{2}-1} \qquad . \qquad . \quad (I.11)$$

dependence of the pseudo first order rate constant on pressure which is quite close to experimental observation in those cases which have been thoroughly investigated. In the KRR theory ν is the vibration frequency of the bond ultimately broken whereas in the SLATER theory it denotes the weighted root mean square of the frequencies of all the normal vibrational modes of R^*.

In recent years the pioneer researches of KISTIAKOWSKY and his colleagues[12] have indicated how the validity of these theories may be tested. It appears that the molecule, methylene or carbene, in its excited singlet state, designated $CH_2(S)$, can add to double bonds or insert between the atoms in a C, H bond. As illustrated below, addition of $CH_2(S)$ to the double bond of an alkene will yield a molecule which is identical with that formed by insertion in the isomeric cycloalkane, the only differences being (*a*) that the internal energy of the former molecule will exceed that of the latter by an amount exactly equal to the difference in internal energy between the alkene and cyclo alkane and (*b*) that the two molecules will be initially energized in slightly

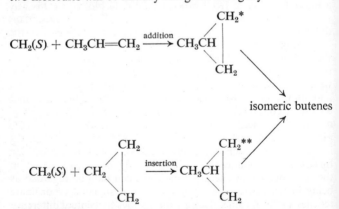

different regions. Despite these differences both molecules rearrange to give the four isomeric butenes in the same relative amounts which strongly supports the view that energy does move inside energized molecules. Furthermore by using a deactivation reaction as a reference process the values of k_2 for these two molecules can be compared and related to the thermal reaction in which the substituted cyclopropane is energized by collision. The results provide general confirmation of equation (I.11) and indicate that v frequently lies in the range 10^{12} to 10^{14} sec^{-1}.

The important conclusion to be drawn from the study of unimolecular reactions is that they provide ample justification for the expectation that the rates of homogeneous decomposition reactions in the gas phase will vary with pressure according to the KRR theory and that the corresponding types of reaction in solution will be kinetically first order. There are many such reactions which involve homolysis of covalent bonds of molecules

$$(10) \qquad (C_6H_5COO)_2 \to 2C_6H_5COO \cdot \to 2\underline{C_6H_5} \cdot + 2CO_2$$

and which serve as initiation processes in chain reactions, or of

$$(11) \qquad\qquad C_2H_2Cl_3 \cdot \to C_2H_2Cl_2 + \underline{Cl} \cdot$$

radicals, e.g. which constitute depropagation processes. However, whilst the yield of the products from each activated molecule formed in the gas phase will be 100 per cent the cage effect will restrict the yield in solution reactions to lower values.

The Transition State Theory. In the collision theory attention is focused on the collision rates and energy of activation, and detailed inquiry is only rarely (see ref. 10) made into the structure of the reacting molecules and the precise nature of the activated condition. In the transition state theory the emphasis is completely altered. The method requires firstly, that the changes in energy and configuration of the system as it passes from reactants to products *via* the activated complex shall be calculated, and secondly, that the rate constant be then evaluated by applying the formulae of statistical mechanics.

Using the methods first devised by LONDON and by PELZER and WIGNER[13] and subsequently applied to many systems by EYRING and POLANYI and their collaborators[14], it is, in principle, possible to calculate the energy of a small assembly of atoms in any possible spatial arrangement. The method is semi-empirical: e.g. assumptions have usually to be made as to the relative contributions made by Coulomb and Exchange forces to the total binding; and the results are only quantitative in the simplest cases. Nevertheless the necessary changes in configuration of the participating atoms for a reaction to occur with the least input of energy can usually be mapped. Such energy contour maps for reactions are to be found in reference 14. In some cases the 'reaction path' is very simple, e.g. for many reactions of the type

(12) $A + BC \rightarrow AB + C$

the route of least potential energy is the approach of A to B and the in-phase retirement of C from B such that the three atoms ABC are always collinear. The reaction between atomic chlorine and molecular hydrogen, the exceedingly important chain propagation reaction (1), is a case in point. The chlorine atom approaches along the axis of the hydrogen molecule, in which the hydrogen atoms are originally 0·75 Å apart. The potential energy of the system rises, gently at first, but more steeply as the chlorine approaches within about 2 Å of the hydrogen atom to which it ultimately becomes attached and the H,H bond begins to be stretched. Marked separation of the hydrogen atoms does not develop until the chlorine is within about 1·5 Å from the hydrogen atom and is accompanied by a fairly sharp rise of the energy to a maximum value of 11·6 k.cal at which energy the configuration is Cl   H   H

•←-----1·30----→•←------1·40----→•

Beyond this point the decrease of potential energy due to formation of the H,Cl link more than compensates for the increase in potential energy due to stretching of the H,H bond. The 'energy profile' of the reaction, i.e. the graph of the potential energy as ordinate against the value of a coordinate which represents the progressive change in the arrangement of the atoms of the reactants as the latter are converted to products can then be constructed. This coordinate is referred to either as the 'reaction path' or 'decomposition coordinate'. The principal features of an energy profile for an endothermic reaction are shown in Fig. I.1. The 'transition state' or 'activated complex' of the reaction is the maximum energy configuration ($\ddagger$ in Fig. I.1). The energy difference between the transition and initial states (R) is sometimes called the 'classical' activation energy (E_c) since in its evaluation, no account is taken of the fact that vibrating systems possess residual energy even at the absolute zero $= \Sigma \frac{1}{2}h\nu_i$ where

v_i is the frequency of the ith vibration and the summation is effected over all vibrations for the given atomic assembly. The actual activation energy $(\Delta E_0^{\ddagger})$ defined as the difference in

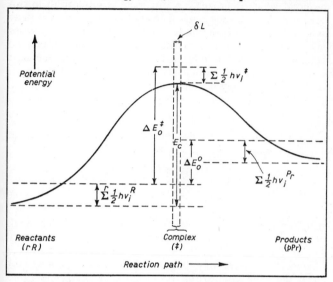

Fig. I.1. The energy profile of an endothermic reaction $rR \rightarrow pPr$

internal energy at absolute zero of temperature between the transition state and the reactants is then given by equation (I.12).

$$\Delta E_0^{\ddagger} = E_c + \Sigma \tfrac{1}{2}hv_i\ddagger - \overset{r}{\Sigma}\tfrac{1}{2}hv_i^R \qquad . \quad . \quad (I.12)$$

where the superscripts $\ddagger$ and R denote transition and initial states. In the case under consideration (reaction (1)), $E_c = 11 \cdot 6$ k.cal, $\overset{r}{\Sigma}\tfrac{1}{2}hv_i^R = \tfrac{1}{2}hv_{H\ldots.H} = 6 \cdot 2$ k.cal, and $\Sigma\tfrac{1}{2}hv_i^{\ddagger} = 5 \cdot 1$ k.cal and hence $\Delta E_0^{\ddagger} = 10 \cdot 5$ k.cal which may be compared with the experimental value of the Arrhenius activation energy of $E_A = 6 \cdot 5 \pm 0 \cdot 5$ k.cal. The disparity between E_A and $\Delta E_0^{\ddagger}$ is typical of the degree of agreement which is commonly obtained in these calculations and often provokes adverse comment which finds its ultimate expression in the view that empirical rules relating E_A to some reaction property are a more valuable guide to the magnitude of E_A than $\Delta E_0^{\ddagger}$. One such rule which has wide validity, is that in reactions summarized by equation (12), $E_A < 0.1\, D_{B...C}$, where $D_{B...C}$ is the dissociation energy of the bond which is broken. Whilst there is some truth in this view, it must be remembered that E_A and $\Delta E_0^{\ddagger}$ are not strictly comparable. E_A is based on the assumption that the Arrhenius Law (I.1) is valid, i.e. k_{obs}° is not temperature dependent and therefore $E_A = RT^2\, \mathrm{d}(\ln k_{\text{obs}})/\mathrm{d}T$. We shall see in the next section that although the velocity constant deduced from transition state theory may be put in the form

$$k_{\text{calc}} = k_{\text{calc}}^{\circ} \cdot e^{\frac{-\Delta E_0^{\ddagger}}{RT}}$$

k_{calc}° is a function of, and not independent of, temperature. If, at a given temperature, k_{calc} is put in the form

$$k_{\text{calc}} = A_{\text{calc}} \cdot \exp\left(\frac{-RT^2\, \mathrm{d}(\ln k_{\text{calc}})}{\mathrm{d}T} \right) = A_{\text{calc}} \exp\left(\frac{-E_{\text{calc}}}{RT} \right)$$

$$\cdots \quad \text{(I.13)}$$

then, for many reactions, particularly those possessing weak vibration frequencies in the complex, E_{calc} will differ very considerably from $\Delta E_0^{\ddagger}$. Examples are known for which such differences are relatively large, and others are known for which the valid comparison between E_{calc} and $\Delta E_0^{\ddagger}$ indicates better agreement than the invalid comparison between E_A and $\Delta E_0^{\ddagger}$.

On this theory the reaction velocity is merely the rate at which the activated complexes are transformed into products and it is calculated as follows. The concentration (molecules c.c.$^{-1}$) of activated complexes is obtained by assuming that complete thermodynamic equilibrium exists between these species and reactants[15]. We may then write for an 'r-molecular' reaction

$$(11) \qquad\qquad rR \underset{v_2}{\overset{v_1}{\rightleftharpoons}}\ \ddagger\ \overset{v_3}{\longrightarrow} Pr$$

in which v denotes a reaction velocity and $v_1 = v_2 \gg v_3$. It is known from statistical mechanics that

$$K_{\ddagger} = \frac{[\ddagger]}{[R]^r} = \frac{F_{\ddagger}}{\prod\limits^{r} F_R} \cdot e^{\frac{-\Delta E_0^{\ddagger}}{RT}} \quad \text{(molecules c.c.}^{-1})^{1-r} \quad . \quad \text{(I.14)}$$

where F denotes the partition function of a species after extraction, i.e. division by, the term $\frac{eV}{N} e^{-\varepsilon_0/kT}$ where ε_0 is the zero point energy. For the purpose of calculating $F_{\ddagger}$ it is important to remember that the activated complex is a normal molecule except in the respect that d E/d (reaction path) $= 0$ and therefore what in a normal molecule would be a coordinate of vibration has, in the activated complex, become a translational coordinate. For this reason $F_{\ddagger}$ will contain one less vibrational term than the total partition function of a stable molecule of the same atomicity and shape, and one more (i.e. a fourth) translational term which will refer to translation along the infinitesimal length δl of the reaction path at the maximum potential energy. Assuming that the total energies of both the transition state and reactants are equal to the sum of their respective nuclear, electronic, translational, rotational, and vibrational energies, their partition functions can be written as the product of the partition functions of all the individual modes of energy storage. We may then extract from $F^{\ddagger}$ the term $(2\pi m_{\ddagger}kT)^{\frac{1}{2}}\delta l/h$ for translation along the element δl of the reaction path and write

$$K_{\ddagger} = K_{\ddagger}' \frac{(2\pi m_{\ddagger}kT)^{\frac{1}{2}}\delta l}{h} = \frac{F_{\ddagger}'}{\overset{r}{\Pi}(F_R)} e^{\frac{-\Delta E_0^{\ddagger}}{RT}} \frac{(2\pi m_{\ddagger}kT)^{\frac{1}{2}}\delta l}{h} \quad . \quad (I.15)$$

The frequency with which molecules pass through the configuration of the transition state in a given direction is the average translational velocity $(= (kT/2\pi m_{\ddagger})^{\frac{1}{2}})$ in this coordinate, divided by the distance δl which defines the state. Making the necessary substitutions we obtain

$$\frac{d[Pr]}{dt} = v_3 = [\ddagger] \left(\frac{kT}{2\pi m_{\ddagger}}\right)^{\frac{1}{2}} \frac{1}{\delta l} = \frac{kT}{h} K_{\ddagger}' [R]^r \quad . \quad (I.16)$$

and hence

$$k_{calc} = \frac{kT}{h} . K_{\ddagger}' \text{ (molecules c.c.}^{-1})^{1-r} . \text{sec}^{-1} \quad . \quad (I.17)$$

In this discussion, the possibility that even after reaching the transition state a system may revert to the initial state has not been considered. Depending on the shape of the energy contours in the vicinity of the top of the energy barrier and the masses of the reactants a greater or less proportion of the molecules which are activated may not be converted to products. This is recognized by introducing a transmission coefficient (κ), the detailed evaluation of which is difficult even in simple cases, into equation (I.17) which then becomes

$$k_{\text{calc}} = \kappa \cdot \frac{kT}{h} \cdot K_{\ddagger}', \qquad 1 > \kappa > 0. \quad . \quad . \quad (\text{I.18})$$

Equation (I.18) can lead to useful results in two ways, (a) and (b) below.

(a) The Arrhenius activation energy calculated from the transition state theory and denoted by E_{calc} will be given by equation (I.19).

$$E_{\text{calc}} = RT^2 \, \text{d}(\ln k_{\text{calc}})/\text{d}T = RT^2 \left\{ \frac{\text{d}(\ln T)}{\text{d}T} + \frac{\text{d}(\ln K')}{\text{d}T} \right\} \quad (\text{I.19})$$

Using the form of the isochore appropriate to the variation of a concentration equilibrium constant with temperature we obtain equation (I.20) in which $\Delta E^{\ddagger}$ is the increase in internal energy associated with the conversion of r moles of R into 1 mole of

$$E_{\text{calc}} = RT + \Delta E^{\ddagger} . \quad . \quad . \quad . \quad (\text{I.20})$$

activated complex, each in their standard concentration states at temperature T. $\Delta E^{\ddagger}$ is related to the corresponding enthalpy increment $\Delta H^{\ddagger}$ by the relation (I.21) in which $\Delta V^{\ddagger}$ is the associated volume increment. For solution reactions $\Delta V^{\ddagger} \simeq 0$ and

$$\Delta H^{\ddagger} = \Delta E^{\ddagger} + P\Delta V^{\ddagger} \quad . \quad . \quad . \quad (\text{I.21})$$

for gas reactions $\Delta V^{\ddagger} = (1 - r)RT/P$ and therefore we obtain the equations (I.22). If we express the equilibrium constant in terms of this enthalpy increment $\Delta H^{\ddagger}$, which is sometimes called

$$\left. \begin{array}{l} E_{\text{calc}} = \Delta H^{\ddagger} + RT \text{ for solution reactions} \\ E_{\text{calc}} = \Delta H^{\ddagger} - (1 - r)RT + RT \text{ for gas reactions} \end{array} \right\} \quad (\text{I.22})$$

the heat of activation, and the entropy of activation $\Delta S^{\ddagger}$, equation (I.18) can be rewritten in the form (I.23)

$$k_{\text{calc}} = \kappa \frac{kT}{h} \, \text{e}^{\frac{\Delta S^{\ddagger}}{R}} \, \text{e}^{\frac{-\Delta H^{\ddagger}}{RT}} \quad . \quad . \quad . \quad (\text{I.23})$$

and substituting for $\Delta H^{\ddagger}$ from (I.22) we arrive at (I.24). Taking the energies of activation on the transition state theory and

$$\left.\begin{array}{l} k_{calc} = \kappa \dfrac{kT}{h} e \cdot e^{\frac{\Delta S^{\ddagger}}{R}} e^{\frac{-E_{calc}}{RT}} \text{ for solution reactions} \\[3mm] k_{calc} = \kappa \dfrac{kT}{h} e^{r} \cdot e^{\frac{\Delta S^{\ddagger}}{R}} e^{\frac{-E_{calc}}{RT}} \text{ for gas reactions} \end{array}\right\} \quad (I.24)$$

collision theory as identical, i.e. $E = E_{calc}$, a comparison of equation (I.6) with equations (I.24) can be made and leads to the expression for PZ_0 given in equation (I.25).

$$\left.\begin{array}{l} PZ_0 = e\kappa \dfrac{kT}{h} e^{\frac{\Delta S^{\ddagger}}{R}} \text{ for bimolecular solution reactions} \\[3mm] PZ_0 = e^{\ddagger}\kappa \, e^{\frac{\Delta S^{\ddagger}}{R}} \text{ for bimolecular gas reactions} \end{array}\right\} \quad (I.25)$$

Insertion of numerical value for Z_0, e and kT/h indicates that for bimolecular reactions in which the probability factor, P, and the transmission coefficient, κ, are both unity, i.e. for so-called "normal" bimolecular reactions, the entropy of activation in converting 2 moles of reactants to 1 mole of activated complex, each at a concentration of 1 mole l.$^{-1}$, will have a value close to -12 cal deg^{-1} at room temperature.

Since Z_0 and ΔH can undergo only relatively minor variations as any experimental condition is changed, any large changes of P are to be ascribed to alterations in the entropy of activation. For example, solvents for which the entropy of solution of the activated complex is greater than the entropy of solution of the reactants will increase $\Delta S^{\ddagger}$ and hence P. Such solvents may of course also alter $\Delta E^{\ddagger}$, but since the entropy of solution of the reactants can either be measured directly or estimated from empirical rules if the heat of solution is known and since the entropy of solution of the complex can sometimes be inferred from the solubility relationships of stable molecules of similar type, the influence of the solvent on P can be correlated with their effect on thermodynamic functions and, in some cases, may even be predicted[16].

2

The concept of entropy of activation is also useful for qualitative purposes and one notable advantage over the collision theory is in the field of bimolecular reactions. In the collision theory the reactant molecules, whatever their atomicities and shapes, are merely regarded as spherical particles, and the entropy change in passing from the reactants to the activated collision pair is merely that to be associated with the replacement of three translational degrees of freedom by two of rotation.* On the transition state theory, however, account is taken of the internal degrees of freedom of the reactants and the changes these undergo on reaction, and we find for instance that in bimolecular association reactions between non-linear polyatomic molecules the formation of the activated complex generally involves the net replacement of three translational and three rotational degrees of freedom by five vibrational degrees of freedom. At temperatures in the range 0° to 500°C such a change is accompanied by a decrease of entropy and we therefore expect that the P factor for such reactions will be very small, as is found to be the case (see p. 4).

(*b*) The alternative method which is also the one most frequently employed is to write equation (I.18) in the form

$$k_{\text{calc}} = \kappa \, \frac{kT}{h} \cdot e^{\frac{-\Delta E_0^\ddagger}{RT}} \, \frac{F_\ddagger{}'}{\overset{r}{\Pi}(F_R)} \quad \text{(molecules c.c.}^{-1})^{1-r} \text{ sec}^{-1} \quad . \quad \text{(I.26)}$$

bearing in mind that

$$F = \frac{N}{eV} \sum_0^\infty p_i \, e^{\frac{-\varepsilon_i}{kT}} \quad . \quad . \quad . \quad . \quad . \quad \text{(I.27)}$$

in which p_i is the degeneracy of the ith state of energy ε_i in *excess* of the ground state which has the energy ε_0; and to substitute the values of F directly. In making these substitutions it generally suffices to assume no interaction between the various forms of energy (electronic, vibrational, etc.) in the

---

* This may easily be seen by applying the Transition State Theory to the bimolecular reaction between two single atoms A and B which form an activated complex of interatomic distance r, when equations (I.25) become identical with the collision theory equations (I.5) and (I.2) provided $\kappa = 1$, and r is identified with the collision diameter $_A\sigma_B$.

molecule, so that the form of F for a non-linear molecule of mass m containing n atoms is then

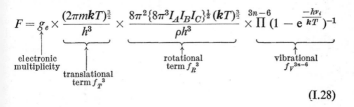

$$F = g_e \times \frac{(2\pi m kT)^{\frac{3}{2}}}{h^3} \times \frac{8\pi^2 \{8\pi^3 I_A I_B I_C\}^{\frac{1}{2}}(kT)^{\frac{3}{2}}}{\rho h^3} \times \prod^{3n-6} (1 - e^{\frac{-h\nu_i}{kT}})^{-1}$$

electronic multiplicity — translational term f_T^3 — rotational term f_R^3 — vibrational f_V^{3n-6}

(I.28)

In equation (I.28) the internal rotational term has been neglected and the nuclear spin factor has been deliberately omitted because these factors always cancel in $K'_{\ddagger}$ unless there is a change in the number of ortho and para molecules. g_e is obtained from the electronic spectrum; the principal moments of inertia can be found from the infrared or microwave spectra or calculated from the known configuration of the molecule; ρ is the number of indistinguishable orientations in a complete rotation, and ν_i is the vibration frequency of the ith vibration and is usually obtained from spectral data. There are $3n-6$ vibrations for each reactant and $3n_{\ddagger}-7$ in the activated complex. Unless there are any very weak vibrations ($\nu/c < \sim 200\ \text{cm}^{-1}$) the vibrational terms are generally unity at room temperature, the rotational term is considerably larger, and the translational term is the largest.

When the appropriate f values have been substituted many useful generalizations appear, of which the following deserve special mention:

(i) The ratios f_T/f_R and f_R/f_V are, as mentioned in the previous paragraph, greater than unity, and are usually greater than the ratio of two f_T values or two f_R or f_V values for two different molecules. The value of $\dfrac{F^{\ddagger}}{\overset{r}{\prod}(F_R)}$ will therefore be very much smaller for bimolecular association reactions involving polyatomic molecules than for two atoms; and since it can be shown (footnote, p. 20) that the collision and transition state theories lead to almost the same k° value for the latter case, we conclude that the P factor for the former must be small. We have thus reached the same conclusion as was obtained by method (a).

This agreement is to be expected because

$$S = R \ln F' + R \left(\frac{\partial \ln F'}{\partial \ln T}\right)_V \quad \cdots \quad (\text{I.29})$$

where

$$F' = \frac{FeV}{N} \, e^{\frac{\varepsilon_0}{kT}}$$

and the second term in (I.29) is generally less important than the first.

(ii) Many chemical reactions consist of the unimolecular rupture of the molecule into two fragments at a weak bond. Assuming that the activated complex resembles the reactant in all respects except for the conversion of this vibrational degree of freedom into one of decomposition, equation (I.26) becomes

$$k_{\text{calc}} = \kappa \cdot \nu \, e^{\frac{-\Delta E_0^{\ddagger}}{RT}} \quad \cdots \quad (\text{I.30})$$

where ν is the frequency of vibration of the bond concerned. Since ν is generally of the order 10^{12} to 10^{13} sec^{-1} we expect the frequency factor (k_{obs}°) of reactions of this type to have this magnitude. This assumption was implicit in the earliest methods of determining bond dissociation energies by pyrolysis[17] and has received extensive *a posteriori* justification from the extension of these methods and from many other experiments[18].

(iii) As may be seen from equation (I.28), f values are a function of the temperature and $\dfrac{F^{\ddagger}}{\Pi F_R}$ is also temperature dependent. The greater the molecularity (r) of the reaction the more steeply will this term decline as the temperature is increased. $E_{A(\text{calc})}$ will thus be less than $\Delta E_0^{\ddagger}$ and in termolecular reactions the decline in rate due to this cause may outweigh the increase in rate due to the positive (but small) value of $\Delta E_0^{\ddagger}$. Those characteristics of termolecular reactions which appeared so anomalous in the collision theory (see p. 7) thus receive a ready interpretation.

The value of the transition state theory in the study of chain reactions is due to the fact that many of the initiation, termination and propagation reactions involve atoms or radicals and are of a simplicity which renders them amenable to investigation by this method. Even when the quantitative agreement between theory and observation is not good, the theory is still useful in that it permits greater insight into the details of the reaction process and therefore permits a correspondingly better assessment of the competing claims of various elementary reactions to be part of a chain process.

REFERENCES

1. MELVILLE, H. W. and GOWENLOCK, B. G.: *Experimental Methods in Gas Reactions.* Macmillan, London (1964); FRIESS, S. L., LEWIS, E. S. and WEISSBERGER, A.: *Investigation of Rates and Mechanisms of Reactions,* Interscience, London, Second edition (1963); CALDIN, E. F.: *Fast Reactions in Solution.* Blackwell, Oxford, (1964).

2. HINSHELWOOD, C. N.: *Kinetics of Chemical Change.* Oxford (1940); FROST, A. A. and PEARSON, R. G.: *Kinetics and Mechanism.* John Wiley, London, (1961); BENSON, S. W.: *The Foundations of Chemical Kinetics.* McGraw-Hill, London, (1960).

3. D'OR, L., DE LATTRE, A. and TARTE, P.: *J. Chem. Phys.,* **19,** 1064 (1951).

4. For a detailed discussion see MOELWYN-HUGHES, E. A.: *Kinetics of Reactions in Solution,* 2nd edition. Oxford (1947).

5. FRANCK, J. and RABINOWITCH, E.: *Trans. Faraday Soc.,* **30,** 120 (1934).

6. SCHMOLUCHOWSKI, M. V.: *Z. phys. Chem.,* **92,** 129 (1917).

7. RUSSELL, K. E. and SIMONS, J. E.: *Proc. Roy. Soc.,* A, **217,** 271 (1953).

8. LINDEMANN, F. A.: *Trans. Faraday Soc.,* **17,** 599 (1922). See also CHRISTIANSEN: *Reaktions kinetiske Studier,* p. 50. Copenhagen (1921).

9. See HINSHELWOOD, C. N.: *Proc. Roy. Soc.,* A, **113,** 230 (1926); FOWLER, R. H. and RIDEAL, E. K.: *Proc. Roy. Soc.,* A, **113,** 570 (1926).

10. KASSEL, L. S., *J. Phys. Chem.,* **32,** 225 (1928); RICE, O. K. and RAMSPERGER, H. C., *J. Amer. Chem. Soc.,* **49,** 1617 (1927); **50,** 617 (1928).

11. See SLATER, N. B.: *Theory of Unimolecular Reactions,* Methuen, London (1959) in which the author outlines the theory which he developed over the preceding twenty years.

12. FREY, H. M. and KISTIAKOWSKY, G. B., *J. Amer. Chem. Soc.,* **79,** 6373 (1957); BUTLER, J. N. and KISTIAKOWSKY, G. B., *J. Amer. Chem. Soc.,* **82,** 759 (1960); FREY, H. M., *Proc. Roy. Soc.,* A, **251,** 575 (1959); *Trans. Faraday Soc.,* **56,** 1201 (1960); **57,** 951 (1961).

13. LONDON, F.: p. 104 of Sommerfeld Festschrift, *Probleme der modernen Physik*, Leipzig (1928); PELZER and WIGNER: *Z. phys. Chem.*, **B, 15,** 445 (1932); WIGNER: *ibid.*, **B, 19,** 203 (1932).

14. For further details the reader is advised to consult the following: (*a*) POLANYI, M.: *Atomic Reactions*, Williams and Norgate, London (1933); (*b*) EYRING, H., GLASSTONE, S., and LAIDLER, K. J.: *Theory of Rate Processes*, McGraw Hill, New York (1941).

15. This assumption first made by MARCELIN, R.: *Ann. Physique*, **3,** 164 (1915), is not always necessary, see e.g. HIRSCHFELDER, J. O.: *J. Chem. Physics*, **16,** 22 (1948), and ZWOLINSKY, B. J. and EYRING, H.: *J. Amer. Chem. Soc.*, **69,** 2702 (1947).

16. For a review see BELL, R. P.: Tilden Lecture, *J. Chem. Soc.*, **629** (1943).

17. BUTLER, E. T. and POLANYI, M.: *Trans. Faraday Soc.*, **39,** 26 (1943).

18. See, e.g. SZWARC, M. and WILLIAMS, D.: *Nature*, **170,** 290 (1952).

CHAPTER II

DISTINGUISHING FEATURES AND SPECIAL EXPERIMENTAL METHODS

SOME of the processes involved in chain reactions may, and occasionally do, take place at interfaces between phases, e.g. termination and initiation of chains may occur at the walls of the reaction vessel or on the surface of catalytic or inhibiting powders; however, the greater proportion of the product molecules are usually formed in the gas or liquid phase and in this sense chain reactions may be regarded as homogeneous. Nevertheless, chain reactions differ in many respects from the homogeneous reactions discussed in Chapter I. These differences can often be used as distinguishing criteria and are often sufficiently large to compel the investigator to adopt new experimental methods. These methods will be described in the second part of this chapter.

1. Distinguishing Features

(a) The P factor of chain reactions is usually much greater than unity and conversely, when the P factor of a reaction is found to be large, reaction chains may be the cause. A photochemical chain reaction will have a quantum yield equal to the product of the average chain length and the quantum yield of the primary act; and the only explanation for large quantum yields is that the reaction is propagated by long chains. Many examples of this behaviour will be found in the following pages.

(b) The excessive speed of chain reactions may in some cases (particularly combustion), lead to the reaction becoming explosive. It is noteworthy that the transition from steady reaction rate to explosion as some parameter such as pressure or composition is varied is very abrupt, i.e. the explosion boundary is well defined. Such explosion boundaries have varied shapes and may enclose further explosion regions which differ from the first in properties such as the colour and temperature of the flame and the products formed. A simple explosion diagram is that appropriate to $2H_2 + O_2$ mixtures. When the total pressure is plotted against temperature (Fig. II.1) the explosion region appears as an unsymmetrical peninsula extending towards low temperatures. Such ignition peninsulae are quite common and may even be detected in vestigial form in the more complicated combustion systems in which several types of explosion may be recognized. In Fig. II.2 the ignition characteristics of 50 per

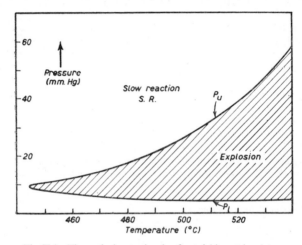

Fig. II.1. The explosion peninsula of a stoichiometric mixture of hydrogen and oxygen in a cylindrical pyrex reaction vessel of internal diameter 4·3 cm. Unpublished data of the author

cent propane-oxygen mixtures as determined by NEWITT and THORNES[1] exemplify the complexity of hydrocarbon combustion.

It is a useful generalization that there is always a lower pressure limit (P_l) and often an upper pressure limit (P_u). When both are found the lower limit decreases slightly with increase in temperature, but the upper limit is much more dependent on temperature, and may increase with temperature according to the exponential relation $P_u = P_u{}^\circ \, e^{\frac{-B}{RT}}$ where B is a constant for a mixture of given composition.

(*c*) In all non-chain processes in which the temperature remains constant the rate of disappearance of reactants falls off

with time, the highest rate being observed at the beginning.*
The general shape of the rate-time curve is given by the broken

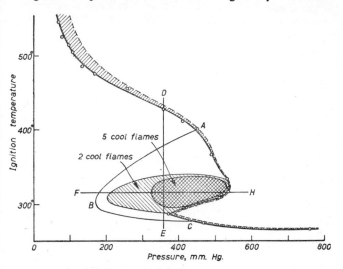

Fig. II.2. The flame and explosion boundaries of an equimolar mixture
of propane and oxygen. The isobar *DE* and isotherm *FH* may be
ignored. In the unhatched area and outside the explosion zone one
cool flame is observed which at low temperatures is preceded by an
induction period of several minutes. In the area ▓ the reaction mixture
becomes luminous immediately after admission to the reaction vessel,
and this luminosity is succeeded by four or five cool flames at intervals
of several seconds. In the area ▓ the luminosity is succeeded by one cool
flame at low temperatures and at high temperatures two cool flames
may be observed. In the unhatched area no successive phenomena are
evident. The strip hatched ▓ represents a region in which intense
luminosity develops on admission of the mixture and is succeeded by a
bright blue flame. In the unhatched area within this explosion zone, the
initial luminosity is followed by the bright yellow flame usually
associated with true ignition. (Taken from Fig. 2 of ref. 1)

* The rate of formation of products is not always the same as the rate
of consumption of reactants. In consecutive non-chain reactions of the
type $A \to B \to C$, in which each step has a comparable velocity constant,
$\dfrac{-\,\mathrm{d}[A]}{\mathrm{d}t}$ will decrease with time according to curve 1, Fig. II.3, but $\dfrac{\mathrm{d}[C]}{\mathrm{d}t}$
will begin at zero, rise through a maximum and then fall to zero
asymptotically.

curve 1 in Fig. II.3. Chain reactions on the other hand begin at
zero rate, rise to a maximum and then fall, as illustrated by the
curves 2 and 3 of Fig. II.3. Curve 2 indicates a very rapid
increase of rate in which very high values are momentarily

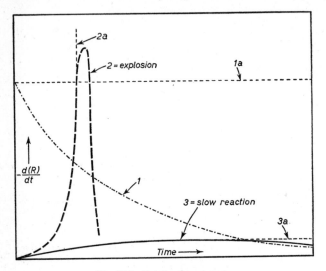

Fig. II.3. Rate *vs* time curves

(1) — . — . — typical non-chain reaction
(2) ▬ ▬ ▬ ▬ explosion due to branched chain reaction
(3) ▬▬▬▬▬ chain reaction in which termination rate exceeds
rate of any branching

1a, 2a, 3a - - - - - curves predicted for systems 1, 2 and 3 respectively
when reactant concentration maintained at initial
value

attained, and this corresponds to an ignition. Such reaction
systems may momentarily reach very high temperatures, be
luminous, be accompanied by an audible click and possibly cause
detonation. Curve 3 represents a much slower chain reaction in
which the maximum rate is not reached until after a considerable
time interval, but the maximum rate is maintained for an
appreciable period before slowly falling off. This behaviour is
typical of the regions in Fig. II.1 marked *S.R.* (slow reaction)

outside the explosion region, and when the maximum velocity is attained rapidly and remains constant for an appreciable period it is called the steady state, or stationary state, velocity. It is this rate which is usually used in determining the reaction kinetics. A further difference between slow reactions and ignitions is apparent from Fig. II.3. In the early stages of a very rapid or explosive reaction the rate often increases exponentially with time and in this region log (rate) plotted against time gives a straight line the slope of which increases the further the explosion region is penetrated. In the slow reactions the curve (2) is commonly convex to the time axis. In passing, we may note that there is much evidence to suggest that the decrease in rate which ultimately occurs is due to the fall in concentration of reactants, and that if this concentration could be maintained constant the explosive reaction would be continually accelerated (curve 2a) and slow reactions approach a limiting rate asymptotically (curve 3a).

(d) Since the initial rate of a chain reaction is zero, an interval must elapse before an appreciable amount of reaction has occurred, or an appreciable reaction rate attained, i.e. before the onset of the reaction is detected. This time interval is called the *induction period* and it is one of the more immediately striking features of some chain reactions. In the oxidation of hydrogen sensitized by NO_2 or $NOCl$, induction periods of 2–3 minutes are observed during which no detectable pressure change occurs and after which either an explosion or a slow reaction may ensue[2].

(e) Most chain reactions are extremely susceptible to acceleration or retardation by traces of other substances. This fact introduces many complexities of behaviour. As an example of positive catalysis we have the lowering of the spontaneous ignition temperature of a mixture of 100 mm of hydrogen and 50 mm of oxygen from 580°C to 330°C by the addition of 0·1 mm of nitrosyl chloride[2]. Moreover the same substance may be a positive catalyst for one group of reactions and a negative catalyst for others. Thus 0·1 mm nitrosyl chloride added to 400 mm of an equimolecular mixture of carbon monoxide and chlorine will reduce the rate of photosynthesis of phosgene at room temperature by a factor of 35[3].

Trace substances which have anticatalytic action are usually referred to as inhibitors or retarders, according to whether they reduce the rate to immeasurably small values or permit reaction to occur with measurable but diminished velocity.* This distinction is one of degree only and depends merely on the greater capacity of the inhibitors as compared with the retarders, to prevent the initiation of chains.† An important difference between negative catalysts arises when these substances are very efficient chain terminating agents. If the negative catalyst is not reduced in concentration during the experiment (because it is rapidly regenerated in some side reaction) the retardation is maintained throughout the run. This is the case with nitrosyl chloride in photochlorination.[3] On the other hand if the retarding agent is destroyed as the reaction proceeds, the rate will be small at the beginning and increase until the retarder is destroyed, when the value of the rate appropriate to the pure reactants is attained. The effect is thus to produce a time lag resembling the induction period of case (*d*) above but entirely different in origin. Well known examples of this behaviour are the action of traces of ammonia on the photosynthesis of hydrogen chloride, the action of dissolved oxygen on polymerization in aqueous media and the time lags introduced into the photopolymerization of vinyl acetate by addition of small amounts of benzoquinone (see (2) (*e*) (ii)).

Even when absolutely pure reagents are used it may not be possible always to avoid effects due to trace catalysis or inhibition, since in some systems the catalyst or retarder may always be generated as a by-product of the main reaction. In the photopolymerization of methyl methacrylate, for example, it has been suggested that certain anomalous features of the reaction including a long-lived photo after-effect are due to traces of a substituted *p*-xylyl diradical formed by the condensation of two monomer molecules[4]

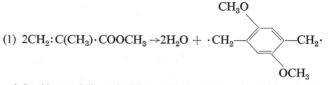

(1) $2CH_2:C(CH_3)\cdot COOCH_3 \rightarrow 2H_2O + \cdot CH_2{-}\langle\ \rangle{-}CH_2\cdot$

* In this case it is preferable to refer to the time lag before reaction is detected as an inhibition period, reserving the term induction period for lags in inhibitor-free systems.

† Arguments have been advanced to classify retarders as those substances which do not react with the active centres formed in the initiation process. This point is expanded in Chapter VII, sections 2 and 3.

Whilst these effects, when due to adventitious impurities, can be a source of considerable annoyance, they may also be turned to advantage in commercial and laboratory practice. For instance, there can be few industrial polymerization processes in which a catalyst is not used and few polymerizable monomeric compounds which are not protected against premature polymerization during storage by small quantities of a stabilizing agent. Similarly, antioxidants such as phenolic compounds or derivatives of aromatic amines may be used to prevent atmospheric oxidation of aqueous solutions of sulphites or to minimize the formation of gums in fuels and lubricating oils.

(*f*) Sensitivity to changes of shape of the containing vessel, particularly at low pressures, is a characteristic of gaseous chain reactions. Usually, a decrease in radius of the reaction vessel, whether spherical or cylindrical, serves to reduce the reaction rate and may convert an explosion into a slow reaction. For equimolar mixtures of hydrogen and chlorine of total pressure less than 30 mm Hg, TRIFONOV[5] found the rate of the photochemical reaction to be proportional to the square of the diameter of the cylindrical reaction vessel. Many other chain reactions are known which, unlike true heterogeneous reactions, are almost completely suppressed by packing the reaction vessel with fibrous material such as glass wool. The nature of the surface is also a determining factor and soda glass, pyrex, quartz, metallic or salt-coated vessels of identical shape are frequently associated with different rates and explosion limits for the same reaction. The effect of an increase of the vessel diameter is invariably to displace the limit to lower values, and frequently a simple quantitative relationship has been found. Thus the lower pressure limits (P_l) in the oxidation of hydrogen[6] and phosphorus[7], in the absence of foreign gases, all conform to the expression

$$P_l \cdot d = \text{constant} \qquad \ldots \quad \text{(II.1)}$$

where d is the vessel diameter.

At higher pressures these surface effects are much less marked and there is evidence that in some cases a chain reaction cannot proceed in the absence of a surface. ALYEA and HABER[8] found this to be the case with crossed streams of hydrogen and oxygen, which would not inflame until a piece of quartz was introduced into the gas stream although the conditions were so arranged that the gas mixture of that composition, temperature, and pressure would have exploded in a reaction vessel. Perhaps firm conclusions should not be drawn from this experiment concerning the role of surface until more is known about the mixing attained in the intersecting reactant streams.

(g) Foreign gases which are chemically unchanged in a chain reacting gas mixture often modify the reaction kinetics. At low pressures the action is frequently catalytic but at high pressures they generally exert a retarding action. In the hydrogen-oxygen reaction for example it was established by GRANT and HINSHEL-WOOD[9] that under certain conditions the upper limit (P_u) of $2H_2 + O_2$ mixtures in a cylindrical reaction vessel was reduced by the addition of argon and helium according to the formula

$$2P_u + 0.67P_A = \text{constant} = 2P_u + P_{He} \qquad . \quad (II.2)$$

but it is also known that at the same temperature addition of 10 mm N_2 to 3 mm $2H_2 + O_2$ changes a non-luminiscent slow reaction into an ignition.*

(h) Chain reactions are rarely of simple order; and non-integral orders which change with vessel shape or other experimental parameters are very common. Many examples will be found in the succeeding pages.

In addition to the properties (a) to (h) above, chain reactions may show other phenomena which in themselves are perhaps less suggestive of chain processes. The formation of polymeric materials, the presence of free radicals and atoms (detected by, say, effects on metallic mirrors or parahydrogen) as intermediates, flame propagation through cold gases from arc and spark sources, fall into this category. In using these properties diagnostically we must be aware that any one reaction will not necessarily show all the phenomena here detailed, although several reactions do display most of them. It is a remarkable fact that the Chain Theory in its present stage can offer an adequate explanation of such diversity of behaviour.

2. Special Experimental Methods for the Study of Chain Reactions[11]. Because of the ease with which chain reactions may be modified by traces of other substances (see paragraph 1 (e)) extreme care must be taken to avoid contamination of the reactants if reproducible results are to be obtained. Even when

* At higher pressures than P_u a change of mechanism causes foreign non-reactant gases to exert a catalytic action. Details of this complex action are given by WILLBOURN and HINSHELWOOD[10].

rigorous conditions of purity have been complied with, it is sometimes found that the results vary with the previous history of the reaction vessel, e.g. the number of previous runs which have been carried out in it, and the quality and time of pumping during evacuation of the vessel between runs. When these

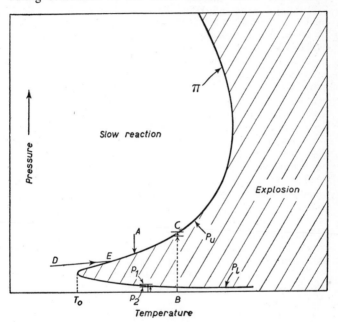

Fig. II.4. Methods of determining the explosion boundary

variations are not systematic, it is necessary to resort to the unsatisfactory expedient of a standard procedure. In all investigations involving explosions, precautions should be taken to avoid injury due to shatter of the apparatus. Observation of the reaction vessel should be indirect whenever possible and suitable screens interposed between the observer and his apparatus.

(a) *Determination of Explosion Boundaries*. An explosion boundary of average complexity is shown diagrammatically in Fig. II.4. P_u and P_l have already been defined, π is sometimes referred to as the 'thermal' or 'third' limit.

(i) *The lower limit* (P_l) is usually measured by 'admission' methods. If the reaction below the lower limit is very slow and if the explosion is not preceded by a long induction period two methods are possible. In the first, the premixed gases are allowed to leak into the reaction vessel through a standard capillary. The pressure in the reaction vessel builds up steadily until the lower limit is reached when a sharp break in the pressure-time curve is observed. If the explosion is luminous, its onset at this pressure may be confirmed visually. This method is particularly valuable in the study of very small pressure limits ($\sim 10^{-2}$ mm Hg) such as are found in the oxidation of phosphorus; because very slow admission rates are possible. In the second method, the reactants may be admitted to the reaction vessel at a pressure below the lower limit and then slowly compressed. This method has not been widely employed.

Even when long induction periods and relatively fast slow reactions are characteristic of the reaction, the lower limit may be determined with reasonable accuracy by premixing the reactants at a temperature at which they do not react and then admitting them as rapidly as possible through a wide bore tap to the evacuated reaction vessel. By repetition of this procedure at a variety of pressures, two neighbouring pressures (p_1 and p_2 in Fig. II.4) may be found which differ only slightly, and between which P_l is located. Many oxidation processes, e.g. of hydrogen, hydrocarbons, and H_2S have been investigated in this way.

(ii) *The upper limit* (P_u) may be measured by admission and withdrawal methods, or by determination of the ignition temperature.

Withdrawal methods involve the preparation, in the reaction vessel, of a mixture of the desired composition at a pressure exceeding P_u (say A in Fig. II.4), followed by slow reduction of the pressure until explosion occurs. This is the converse of the leak method used for measuring lower limits and has been very widely employed. The only difficulties arise in preparing the initial mixture when explosions or fast reactions must be avoided. Usually one reactant is admitted to a partial pressure greater than P_u so that addition of the second reactant does not cause the composition and pressure to pass through the explosion region. A disadvantage of the method is the short time which may be permitted for the gases to mix in systems in which the rate of the slow reaction above the upper limit is appreciable.

When the partial pressure of one component is restricted by the presence of a solid phase as in the oxidation of phosphorus, such a mixing technique cannot be used and the solid is cooled to a temperature below the lowest ignition temperature (the tip of the peninsula, T_0 in Fig. II.4) before adding the oxygen. The reaction vessel and contents are then brought to the required temperature and the withdrawal begun.

If, at the desired temperature and composition, the induction periods for pressures up to and just exceeding P_u (*BC* in Fig. II.4) are much larger than the time of admission from a premixer, then the bracketing admission method can be applied to determination of the upper limit as well as of the lower one. Upper limits for NO_2 or $NOCl$ sensitized explosion of $2H_2 + O_2$ mixtures in the temperature range 350–400°C have been measured in this way[3].

In some cases it is convenient to determine ignition temperatures, i.e. to raise a given reactant mixture as quickly as possible to a predetermined temperature and pressure (path *DE* in Fig. II.4. Note that this is *not* parallel to the temperature axis). Bracketing would then allow most of the explosion boundary to be determined (P_u, P_l, and π). The rise in temperature may be produced by sudden immersion in liquid baths or by adiabatic compression using either a metal piston, as for example in TIZARD and PYE's investigation of the oxidation[12] of CS_2, or mercury as in MELVILLE's work on the reaction between nitrous oxide and hydrogen[13]. Results obtained by the compression method should be cautiously interpreted since explosion, doubtless in part due to the temperature rise, may also be partly due to local increases in the concentration of reaction centres. BUCKLER and NORRISH have observed this latter effect in the oxidation of carbon monoxide sensitized by traces of hydrogen[14].

(iii) *The thermal limit* (π): In principle, measurement of this limit is no more difficult than measurement of the lower limit. In practice, in the only case where extensive observations have been made, viz. the hydrogen-oxygen reaction, considerable difficulties are encountered. These obstacles arise because the reaction rate at pressures between P_u and π is often considerable and rises to very high values near the thermal limit. There is therefore a chance that the system will become self heating and explode. Further, the amounts of water formed before the explosion occurs may be considerable, and since water causes a marked autocatalysis and a pronounced decrease in the third limit this is a complicating factor. The combined effect of these two influences is that at a given temperature mixtures of hydrogen and oxygen will explode over a wide range of pressures (say 50 mm Hg) if left long enough in the reaction vessel[10]. The explosion occurs after a delay, during which reaction is observed to be taking place, which is smaller the higher the pressure. The definition of the limit is therefore entirely arbitrary and must be referred to a stated interval of time between addition of the oxygen to the hydrogen and the ensuant explosion. Considerable increase in precision may be achieved by coating the walls of the vessel with potassium chloride, which brings about a large decrease in the rate of reaction below this limit. All the methods described above refer to static systems. Flow methods could be used but dangers of back-firing and the necessity of long reaction tubes with systems with long induction periods has resulted in a marked preference for static methods. All the examples referred to have been chain reactions, but reactions are known which may not involve chains but which explode above a certain pressure because the rate of heat generation exceeds the rate of heat loss. For such thermal explosions the determination of the lower and only limit does not involve any novel principles.

(b) *Determination of Induction Periods and Steady State Rates.* Induction periods are taken as the time between admission of the reactants to the reaction vessel, or in photo- and radiation-chemical reactions, from the moment of exposure to the radiation, to some definite stage in the reaction. When the reaction is explosive, the reaction rate prior to explosion is often so slow and the transition to explosion so rapid that the onset of explosion determined either visually, or audibly, or by sudden pressure change, is used to mark the end of the induction period. When a slow reaction rate follows the induction period the time is taken variously as that at which the reaction is just detectable (by pressure change in gaseous reactions or by the first turbidity in the polymerization of water soluble vinyl compounds to insoluble polymers); or the time at which the maximum rate is attained. In many cases the uncertainty about the starting time from which the period is to be measured is a factor affecting the accuracy.

Steady state rates are measured by the methods which apply to normal reactions. In photochemical chain processes it is particularly important to know the dependence of the rate on the intensity of the absorbed light and the intermittency of the illumination. The usual photochemical methods are employed.

(*c*) *Non-steady State Rates in Non-explosive Reactions.* It will be seen in Chapter V that in unbranched photochemical chain reactions, the precise form of the rate-time curves (*a*) prior to the attainment of the steady state and (*b*) immediately following cessation of illumination (the so-called 'after effect') is highly significant. These periods of growth and decay are often quite short and are best studied by measuring the time dependence of the small temperature rise or fall by which they are accompanied. Usually the temperature rise is not measured directly but some property of the system related to the temperature. In gaseous systems pressure changes may be followed[15], in solution changes of volume, dielectric constant, and refractive index have been successfully used[16].

(*d*) *Measurement of Reaction Velocities during Explosion.* This cannot often be very effectively accomplished, although accurate measurements of rapid pressure changes can be achieved by employing low inertia gauges. At low pressures, i.e. less than atmospheric, gauges of the glass membrane variety such as that used by KOWALSKY[17], or the glass Bourdon gauge as improved by FOORD[18] may be employed. At higher pressures more robust distortion gauges, e.g. piezo electric quartz crystals, may be used. In all cases the extent of the displacement of the movable part of the gauge is registered on a rapidly moving film suitably time based after suitable amplification by a light lever or electrically. Few investigations of this sort have been made on low pressure explosions.

(*e*) *Special Methods for Addition-Polymerization Reactions.* Polymerization reactions which proceed by a chain mechanism, i.e. excluding polycondensation reactions, require, in general, more extensive measurements for the complete elucidation of their mechanisms, than those chain reactions hitherto mentioned. Amongst these measurements are the following:

(i) *The rate of monomer removal.* Even for polymers of low molecular weight, changes in the density and vapour pressure as the molecular weight is increased are usually appreciable. The rate of change of these properties during a polymerization can in such cases be used as a measure of the rate of monomer consumption, provided suitable calibration has been made. In the gas phase therefore, the rate of pressure fall in the absence of liquid monomer or the rate of fall of the meniscus in a capillary tube which serves as a reservoir for the liquid monomer would seem to be a possible way of observing the course of the reaction[19]. In fact this method is open to considerable objection, principally on the grounds that slow absorption of monomer by solid polymer may also cause disappearance of the monomer.

Liquid phase polymerizations can generally be followed dilatometrically and recording dilatometers are especially useful for radiation-induced reactions[20], but many other physical properties have also been employed, e.g. viscosity[21], optical activity[22], temperature rise due to the exothermicity of the reaction[16]. Since it is commonly necessary to separate the polymer for the purpose of molecular weight determination, the quantity of polymer formed is usually weighed. Complete separation can be attained by addition of an efficient precipitant, if necessary, followed by centrifugation. Whenever possible it is desirable to measure the amount of unchanged monomer directly and this may often be effected by either physical or chemical means. For example, in the polymerization of methyl methacrylate in aqueous solution the monomer may be estimated bromometrically[23].

(ii) *The rate of initiation of chains.* In polymerization reactions it is especially important to compare the actual average number of monomer units in the final polymer molecule (the degree of polymerization) with the number of monomer molecules reacted per chain started (the kinetic chain length). The latter is equal to the rate of monomer removal divided by the rate of initiation of the chains. If the reaction is initiated photochemically the initiation rate will be $\phi_i I_{abs}$ mole l.$^{-1}$ sec^{-1}, where I_{abs} is the absorbed light intensity in einstein l.$^{-1}$ sec^{-1} and ϕ_i is the number of polymer chains started per quantum absorbed. When the primary act is homolysis, e.g. reaction (2), the maximum

$$(2) \qquad H_2O_2 + h\nu \rightarrow 2OH$$

value of ϕ_i is 2·0 and when the primary act is an electron transfer reaction, e.g. reaction (3), and only one of the primary products can initiate a polymerization chain, the maximum value of ϕ_i is 1·0.

$$(3) \qquad Fe^{3+}OH^- + h\nu \rightarrow Fe^{2+} + OH$$

For liquid phase polymerizations ϕ_i is prevented from attaining the theoretical maximum values by the cage effect, mentioned in Chapter I. Thus for the aqueous reactions (2) and (3) ϕ_i has values only 48 per cent and 17 per cent respectively of the theoretical maxima[24]. Thermal catalysts are similarly prevented from attainment of 100 per cent efficiency; for instance at 70°C in liquid dimethyl formamide solvent only about 70 per cent of the radicals produced in reaction (4) at 70°C react with dissolved vinyl monomers.

(4) $((CH_3)_2(C.CN)_2N_2 \rightarrow 2(CH_3)_2\dot{C}CN + N_2$

Reliable methods of measurement of initiation rates are rare. In cases in which the catalyst or photosensitizer is dissociated into fragments which either react with monomer or recombine the rate of decomposition of catalyst or photosensitiser will fix an upper limit for the rate of initiation. Such cases are very infrequent and often the catalyst undergoes decomposition induced by the free radicals in the system. Two other methods have been used. MELVILLE and BAMFORD and co-workers[25] have added reagents such as *p*-benzoquinone and diphenylpicrylhydrazyl, which react rapidly with the radicals from the catalyst thereby preventing any chains from being initiated until after an inhibition period during which the inhibitor is destroyed. An example of this phenomenon is shown in Fig. VII.2. To calculate the initiation rate from the inhibitor destruction rate it is necessary to know the exact stoichiometry of the reaction of the catalyst radical with the inhibitor and to be certain that the catalyst decomposes at the same rate in the absence of the inhibitor. Generally uncertainty attaches to both these points[26]. The second method is that of isotopic labelling[26] of catalyst fragments so that if these initiate polymerization by addition to the double bond of the monomer then for each polymerization chain initiated by an isotopically labelled radical one isotopic atom will be present in the polymer. Unfortunately the all too common complexity of the radical-monomer interaction limits the utility of this method. These matters are further discussed in Chapter VII.

There are no general methods for direct measurement of initiation rates in ionic polymerization reaction which follow steady state kinetics.

(iii) *The rate of chain termination.* Polymerization reaction chains are almost always unbranched in the kinetic sense (see p. 171) and the concentration of centres under stationary state conditions is determined solely by the rates of the initiation and termination reactions. If the initiation of fresh chains is stopped, the centre concentration, and hence also the reaction rate, fall off with time according to a kinetic law determined by the order of the termination process. In photochemical reactions it is therefore theoretically possible to elucidate both the nature of the termination reaction and the magnitude of the appropriate velocity constant from a study of the decay of the reaction after extinction of the light. It is often found that such 'photo-after effects' extend over considerable periods and are readily measurable by the methods outlined in paragraph (e) (i). Unfortunately after-effects can arise from many causes other than the decay of the centres of the preceding photo-reaction. If the polymer is insoluble in the reaction medium then some of the growing polymer radicals will become occluded in polymer particles and will give rise to a prolonged after-effect (see Chapter V). The best method for determining the velocity constant of the termination step (k_t) in photo-polymerization reactions is to investigate the variation of the reaction rate with the frequency of interruption of the incident light beam by a rotating sector. When mutual termination of chains occurs, this variation enables the lifetime of the reaction chains to be determined. This quantity is equal to $(k_t \phi_i I_{abs})^{-\frac{1}{2}}$ (see Chapter IV) and hence if ϕ_i is known k_t may be found[25]. For the same reasons useful information may also be derived from the 'build-up' in a photochemical reaction which takes place after the irradiation has begun and stops with the attainment of the steady state.

Recently a direct method of measurement of the rate of chain termination has been developed by BAMFORD et al.[25] and COLLINSON et al.[27] which relies on the fact that an organic free radical can enter into one-equivalent oxidation or reduction reactions with compounds of metals of variable valency[20]. Thus ferric compounds are reduced to the ferrous state by polymer radicals in both aqueous (reaction (5)) and non-aqueous media (reaction (6)).

(5) $X(CH_2CH(CONH_2))_n \cdot + Fe_{aq}^{3+}$
$$\rightarrow X(CH_2CH(CONH_2))_{n-1}CH = CH.CONH_2$$
$$+ H_{aq}^+ + Fe_{aq}^{2+}$$

(6) $X(CH_2CH.CN)_n^{\cdot} + FeCl_3 \rightarrow X(CH_2CH.CN)_nCl + FeCl_2$

or $\rightarrow X(CH_2CH.CN)_{n-1}CH = CH.CN + HCl + FeCl_2$

When sufficient ferric compound is present for the rate of polymerization to be inversely proportional to its concentration, and provided the compound is unaffected by the initiation process, the rate of termination is equal to the rate of reduction of the ferric species. The particular advantages of the method are that the termination reaction is always free from complication and therefore stoichiometric and that spectrophotometric analytical procedures can be used which confer precision and sensitivity on the method (see also Chapter VII).

(iv) *The molecular weight of the polymer*. The products of a polymerization reaction consist of an assembly of molecules of a very wide range of molecular weights. The precise number of molecules in each narrow band of molecular weights is determined by the reaction kinetics and the percentage of monomer which has been allowed to polymerize. The exact form of the molecular weight distribution curve is of theoretical importance and is constructed as follows. The polymer formed at a given stage of the reaction is separated, by selective solution or precipitation, into as many fractions as possible, successive fractions consisting of successive ranges of molecular weights. The average molecular weight of any sample is then determined by one or a combination of the following methods.

Of the colligative properties available for the determination of the number average molecular weight $\overline{M}_n = \dfrac{\Sigma r N_r}{\Sigma N_r} \times M_1$ where r is the degree of polymerization, M_1 is the molecular weight of the monomer, and N_r the number of polymers of length (r), that most commonly used is osmotic pressure. It has been found that the van't Hoff relation is inadequate and is best replaced by a power series of the form

$$O.P. \text{ (osmotic pressure)} = c\,\frac{RT}{\overline{M}_n} + \alpha c^2 + \beta c^3 \quad . \quad \text{(II.3)}$$

where c, R, T, and $\overline{M}_n$ have their usual significance; it is therefore necessary to plot $O.P./c$ against c from measurements at several dilutions and to extrapolate this curve to infinite dilution when the intercept on $c = 0$ is $RT/\overline{M}_n$. The osmotic pressures are small and much effort has been directed to the construction of suitable osmometers and membranes. In the FUOSS-MEAD[28] osmometer a thin layer of solution is separated from a thin layer of solvent by a mechanically supported membrane of large area to increase the rate of equilibration. Because of the difficulty of preparing large membranes free from defects, smaller, simpler osmometers[29] have been devised having small membrane areas which can be operated either statically or dynamically, i.e. the rate of solvent flow is measured as a function of an externally applied pressure. The problem in all osmometry is to obtain a membrane which is truly semipermeable but which permits diffusion of the solvent at sufficiently rapid rates. Artificial (collodion, regenerated cellulose; synthetic polymer films) and natural (bacterial cellulose) membranes are commonly used.

Experimentally, viscosities are easier and quicker to measure than osmotic pressures, and it has been shown that the specific viscosity $\left(\eta_{sp} = \dfrac{\eta - \eta_0}{\eta_0} \right.$ where η_0 is the viscosity of the solvent and η of the solution of the polymer of weight concentration $c \Big)$ is related to the weight average molecular weight of the solute ($\overline{M}_w$) by equation (II.4).

$$\text{Lt} \left(\frac{\eta_{sp}}{c} \right)_{c \to 0} = k \overline{M}_w{}^{\alpha} \quad . \quad . \quad . \quad \text{(II.4)}$$

where k and α are constants characteristic of the particular solute-solvent system. These constants are determined by plotting log of the values of η_{sp}/c appropriate to dilute solutions of fractionated polymer samples against log of the value of $\overline{M}$ of the same samples in the same solvent determined osmotically. The slope and intercept of the resulting line are then respectively equal to α and $\log k$. The disadvantages of the viscosity method are, firstly, that the value of $\overline{M}_w$ in equation (II.4) is not a number average but a weight average, i.e. $(M_1 \Sigma r^2 N_r / \Sigma r N_r)^{1/\alpha}$ and secondly, that the constant α is very temperature dependent, and is conditioned by the shape and rigidity of the dissolved polymer molecules. Thus, when the polymer chains, because of high internal cohesion, are coiled into a ball and the solute is therefore spherical, α tends to zero. When the polymer is for reasons of its internal structure a rigid rod, α tends to unity. The viscosities referred to are for low rates of shear, i.e. Newtonian flow, and experimentally it is sufficient to measure them in an Ostwald-type viscometer immersed in a thermostat. At high rates of shear the long polymeric solute molecules may become oriented along the line of flow and streaming birefringence may be displayed. Measurements under these conditions can be interpreted to yield information about the shape of the dissolved polymer molecule.

Ultra-centrifugal investigations of sedimentation equilibrium and velocity, and of diffusion can also yield values of M, at least in theory. In practice these methods are unreliable for molecular weights in excess of 10^5 when the solute molecule is highly asymmetrical, as is commonly the case with vinyl polymers. The most promising method for molecular weight determination concerns measurements of the turbidity of polymer solutions[30]. It is not only of value in determining molecular weights, but when coupled with studies of depolarization or asymmetrical scattering measures the departure of the solute from spherical shape. The use of trace elements and end-group analysis has been advocated to determine molecular weights, but this is only justified when kinetic analysis permits a clear decision as to the number of trace elements or end groups which should be present in the particular polymer chain. Notwithstanding this fact and the intrinsic unreliability of the method for very high polymers, some work in this direction has already been undertaken.

(*f*) *Identification of Chain Centres.* It is always desirable to have independent evidence of the chemical nature of the chain centres. This is especially true of the considerable number of reactions in which the kinetic data can be interpreted quite adequately by several mechanisms involving different reaction centres. The methods available are almost as diverse as the various postulated centres, and the following have been selected for mention merely because they illustrate principles of potentially wide application. These principles are:

(i) Addition of a certain species which is suspected to be a chain carrier should increase the rate and shorten the induction period of the reaction, and may actually bring about the reaction under conditions where it is normally quiescent. It does not follow that any added species which causes acceleration is therefore a chain carrier or intermediate, since the added substance may be effecting the formation of the same products, but by a different mechanism from the original reaction. Thus, the observation that addition of formaldehyde shortens the induction period found in the oxidation of methane, strongly suggests but does not prove that $H \cdot CHO$ is normally an intermediate[31].

(ii) Addition of special reagents which are known to react with and destroy the chain carrying properties of a suspected chain centre, should act as retarding or inhibiting agents. This effect has often been observed. For example, molecular iodine is an effective inhibitor of free radical type polymerization by the reaction

$$(5) \qquad \underline{R} + I_2 \rightarrow RI + I(\rightarrow \tfrac{1}{2}I_2)$$

because an iodine atom cannot initiate a new chain. Another useful inhibitor which has been very widely employed is nitric oxide, which probably undergoes addition reactions ($R + NO \rightarrow ?$) with free radicals. The disadvantage of the method is that the inhibitor is rarely specific; for instance, in the two examples given, R may be a hydrocarbon radical containing any number of carbon atoms. This disadvantage can occasionally be overcome if the products of the inhibitor-centre reaction can be identified, for example the iodide RI formed in reaction (5) can readily be measured by modern chromatographic techniques either alone or in combination with radiochemical methods when radioactive iodine (i.e. containing $^{131}I_2$) is used as the scavenger. Similarly hydroxyl radicals which are one of the two chain-carriers in the photolysis of hydrogen peroxide in aqueous solution have been identified by addition of water-soluble vinyl compounds[32]. These substances react with hydroxyl radicals to form polymers with OH groups on at least one end of the chain. They therefore suppress the chain decomposition of the peroxide and OH groups linked to carbon atoms can be shown by infra-red spectroscopy to be present in the polymers formed.

Such chemically diagnostic methods acquire great importance when the kinetic data are inadequate to establish the nature of the chain centres with certainty. Two recently developed methods for the detection of oxygen atoms in combustion reactions are in this category. The first, due to GAYDON[33], involves the addition of nitric oxide to flames. Oxygen atoms which may be present react with the nitric oxide to form excited nitrogen dioxide molecules which emit characteristic bands in the green region of the spectrum. Similarly, WHITTINGHAM[34] has used the characteristic purple emission of SO_3^* formed in the reaction

(5) $$SO_2 + \underline{O} \rightarrow SO_3^* \text{ for this purpose.}$$

One of the clearest ways in which hydrocarbon free radical intermediates may be identified is by their reaction with metal mirrors. PANETH[35] showed that certain metals will react with organic free radicals to form the metal alkyls, e.g. $CH_3\cdot$ radicals with Pb to form $Pb(CH_3)_4$. The easiest way to observe this process is to pass the gas from the reaction vessel over a thin layer of the metal deposited on the inside of the exit tube. The mirror slowly disappears as the radicals react with the metal. Using this technique, RICE[36] has identified some of the radicals which act as chain centres in the pyrolysis of hydrocarbons. The susceptibility of metal mirrors to poisoning and their non-specificity detracts somewhat from the quantitative value of this method.

(iii) The most satisfactory method of identifying chain centres, and one which avoids any complications caused by inhibitors, is by absorption or emission spectroscopy whilst the reaction is in progress. It has been widely used, particularly by KONDRATJEW[37] and GAYDON[38] and their collaborators. In this way hydroxyl radicals have been shown to be present in the hydrogen-oxygen flame, and many other reactions successfully investigated. Absorption spectra are probably more easily investigated in static systems and no special technique is required. Emission spectra occasionally present experimental problems, particularly when cool flames of low emissivity are being observed, as for example in TOWNEND and TOPPS' work on the cool flame of formaldehyde[39]. The successful use of absorption spectroscopy depends on securing a sufficiently high concentration of intermediates. In this respect the recent work of NORRISH and PORTER[40] represents a major advance. The principle of this method is to initiate the reaction by a very high intensity flash of short duration produced in a discharge tube lying adjacent to and along the length of the reaction vessel. After a very brief interval, which may be as small as 10^{-5} sec., a second flash is produced at one end of the reaction vessel. This second flash produces a continuum and any absorption by intermediates is registered by a spectrograph suitably aligned at the other end of the reaction vessel.

If non-fluid systems, i.e. glasses or crystals, are irradiated the initial products of irradiation are largely immobilized and their concentrations may decay very slowly. Quite high concentrations of the intermediates may then be obtained, without the use of high intensities, which will persist and are therefore amenable to leisurely investigation and identification by visible, ultra-violet, infra-red or electron spin resonance spectroscopy[41]. This technique of *matrix isolation* of unstable intermediates though widely used in recent years and suitable for immobilization of such labile entities as electrons and hydrogen atoms, is generally applicable only to chain centres produced in the first step of a chain reaction initiated by light, radiation or a high-frequency discharge. One exception to this general rule is free-radical polymerization in which the growing polymer radical is only slowly terminated *either* because the polymer precipitates from an initially liquid system and radicals become trapped in polymer particles as, for example, in acrylonitrile polymerization, *or* because the monomer is crystalline and the polymerization takes place in the solid state, as in the cases of acrylamide and several metal acrylates.

(iv) One of the most characteristic properties of any species is its ionization potential. In principle, it is possible continually to leak away samples of a reacting mixture into a mass spectrometer where any molecular fragments may be identified by their masses. It is necessary to study appearance potentials in order to determine whether, say, a given radical ion has been produced in the ion-source merely by ionization of the radical rather than by breakdown of a molecular ion. Added to such interpretational difficulties, there are very considerable technical obstacles to be overcome in applying the method to the study of reaction intermediates. Nevertheless, ELTENTON[42] and others[43] have succeeded in investigating hydrocarbon combustion processes by this means.

REFERENCES

Section 1

1. NEWITT, D. M. and THORNES, L. S.: *J. Chem. Soc.*, 1656 (1937).
2. DAINTON, F. S. and NORRISH, R. G. W.: *Proc. Roy. Soc.*, A, **177**, 411 (1941).
3. BURNS, W. G. and DAINTON, F. S.: *Trans. Faraday Soc.*, **48**, 52 (1952).

4. BAMFORD, C. H. and DEWAR, M. J. S.: *Proc. Roy. Soc.*, **A, 197,** 356 (1949).

5. TRIFONOV, A.: *Z. phys. Chem.*, **B, 3,** 195 (1929).

6. HINSHELWOOD, C. N. and MOELWYN-HUGHES, E. A.: *Proc. Roy. Soc.*, **A, 138,** 311 (1932).

7. DAINTON, F. S. and KIMBERLEY, H. M.: *Trans. Faraday Soc.*, **46,** 629 (1950).

8. ALYEA, H. N. and HABER, F.: *Z. phys. Chem.*, **B, 10,** 193 (1930).

9. GRANT, G. H. and HINSHELWOOD, C. N.: *Proc. Roy. Soc.*, **A, 141,** 29 (1933).

10. WILLBOURN, A. H. and HINSHELWOOD, C. N.: *Proc. Roy. Soc.*, **A, 185,** 353 (1946).

Section 2

11. For experimental details see ref. 1, Chapter I.

12. PYE, D. R. and TIZARD, H.: *Phil. Mag.*, **44** (vi), 79 (1922).

13. MELVILLE, H. W.: *Proc. Roy. Soc.*, **A, 142,** 524 (1933).

14. BUCKLER, E. J. and NORRISH, R. G. W.: *ibid.*, **A, 167,** 292 (1938).

15. ICHIKAWA, T.: *Z. phys. Chem.*, **B, 10,** 299 (1930).

16. MELVILLE, H. W., MAJURY, T. G. and BURRELL, C. M.: *Proc. Roy. Soc.*, **A, 205,** 309, 323, 496 (1951); *ibid,* **207,** 285 (1951).

17. KOWALSKI, A.: *Phys. Z. der Sowjetunion*, **4,** 723 (1933).

18. FOORD, S. G.: *J. Sci. Instr.*, **11,** 126 (1934).

19. MELVILLE, H. W.: *Proc. Roy. Soc.*, **A, 163,** 511 (1937).

20. STARKWEATHER, H. W. and TAYLOR, G. B.: *J. Amer. Chem. Soc.*, **52,** 4708 (1930); COLLINSON, E., DAINTON, F. S., TAZUKE, S., SMITH, D. R. and TRUDEL, G. J.: *Discussion Faraday Soc.*, **29,** 188 (1960); COLEBOURNE, N., COLLINSON, E., CURRIE, D. J. and DAINTON, F. S.: *Trans. Faraday Soc.*, **59,** 1357 (1963).

21. BAMFORD, C. H. and DEWAR, M. J. S.: *Proc. Roy. Soc.*, **A, 192,** 309 (1948).

22. MARVEL, C. S.: *J. Amer. Chem. Soc.*, **62,** 3495 (1940).

23. BAXENDALE, J. H., EVANS, M. G., and KILHAM, J. K.: *Trans. Faraday Soc.*, **42,** 668 (1946).

24. DAINTON, F. S. and TORDOFF, M.: *Trans. Faraday Soc.*, **53,** 499, 666 (1957); DAINTON, F. S. and SISLEY, W. D.: *Trans. Faraday Soc.*, **59,** 1377 (1963).

25. BURNETT, G. M. and MELVILLE, H. W.: *Proc. Roy. Soc.*, **A, 189,** 456 (1947); BAMFORD, C. H., JENKINS, A. D. and JOHNSON, R.: *Proc. Roy. Soc.*, **A, 329,** 214 (1957).

26. See BEVINGTON, J. C.: *Radical Polymerization*, Academic Press, London (1961).

27. COLLINSON, E., DAINTON, F. S. and McNAUGHTON, G. S.: *Trans. Faraday Soc.*, **53,** 489 (1956).

28. FUOSS, R. M. and MEAD, D. J.: *J. Phys. Chem.*, **47,** 59 (1943); see

also KRIGBAUM, W. R. and FLORY, P. J.: *J. Amer. Chem. Soc.*, **75**, 1775 (1953).

29. ZIMM, B. H. and MYERSON, I.: *J. Amer. Chem. Soc.*, **68**, 911 (1946).
30. For a complete account see STACEY, K. A., *Light Scattering in Physical Chemistry*, Butterworths, London (1956).
31. FOORD, S. G. and NORRISH, R. G. W.: *Proc. Roy. Soc.*, A, **157**, 503 (1936).
32. DAINTON, F. S.: *J. Phys. Coll. Chem.*, **52**, 490 (1948).
33. GAYDON, A. G.: *Trans. Faraday Soc.*, **42**, 292 (1946).
34. WHITTINGHAM, G.: ibid, 42, **354** (1946).
35. PANETH, F. A. et al.: *Ber.*, **64**, 2702 (1931); *J. Chem. Soc.*, 366 (1935).
36. RICE, F. O.: *Trans. Faraday Soc.*, **30**, 152 (1934).
37. KONDRATJEV, V. N.: *Acta Physicochim.*, U.R.S.S., **7**, 65 (1937) and *Chemical Kinetics of Gas Reactions*, Pergamon, London (1964).
38. GAYDON, A. G.: *Spectroscopy and Combustion Theory*. Chapman and Hall, London (1948).
39. TOWNEND, D. T. A. and TOPPS, J. E. C.: *Trans. Faraday Soc.*, **42**, 345 (1946).
40. For a summary of this method see NORRISH, R. G. W. and THRUSH, B.A.: *Quart. Rev.*, **10**, 149 (1956).
41. For application of this method see MINKOFF, G. J.: *Frozen Free Radicals*, Interscience, London (1960) and BASS, A. M. and BROIDA, H. P.: *Formation and Trapping of Free Radicals*, Academic Press, London, (1960).
42. ELTENTON, G. C.: *J. Chem. Physics*, **10**, 403 (1942); *J. Phys. Coll. Chem.*, **52**, 463 (1948).
43. BARBER, M., CUTHBERT, J., FARMER, J. and LINNETT, J. W.: *Proc. Roy. Soc.*, A, **274**, 285, 293, 306 (1963).

CHAPTER III

THE CHEMICAL NATURE OF THE INDIVIDUAL STEPS

1. Propagation. The propagation process may usually be represented by equations of the type (1) and (2) (*a* or *b*).

(1) $$X + R \rightarrow Y + Pr$$

(2)
$$\begin{cases} (a) & Y + R' \rightarrow X + Pr' \\ (b) & Y \quad\quad \rightarrow X + Pr' \end{cases}$$

R and R' denote reactants, Pr and Pr' denote products or substances readily converted to products by reactions which do not involve the chain centres X and Y. These individual chain steps, whether bimolecular (1, 2*a*) or unimolecular (2*b*), should have large velocity constants at the temperature of reaction. Otherwise the chain termination processes (section 7 below) will compete successfully with the propagation reactions and the chains will be very short; in the limit, such competition may be sufficiently effective to prevent the propagation reaction from being repeated and the overall process ceases to be a chain reaction, becoming a series of consecutive reactions in which one initiation process is followed by one (or two) propagation steps, after which the reaction centres are destroyed.

A large velocity constant implies either a low energy of activation and/or a large P factor or entropy of activation. The first of these conditions is most easily satisfied for exothermic processes, since an endothermic reaction

(3) $$R + R' \rightarrow Pr + Pr' - q$$

would require at least one of the two propagation steps to be endothermic to an extent $\geqslant q/2$. Reference to Fig. I.1 shows that the minimum value of the energy of activation of any reaction is $\Delta E_0{}^\circ$ and hence the minimum value of the energy of activation of at least one of the propagation steps is $q/2$. It is not therefore surprising that all chain reactions with reasonably long chains are exothermic. Some examples are given in Table 1, from which it will be seen that iodine is a notable omission from the halogenation reactions. This is due to the fact that iodides are not very exothermic compounds, i.e. bonds involving iodine atoms are relatively weak, and correspondingly, iodine atoms are less able to displace other atoms from molecules. Hence, although the exothermic reaction

(4) $H + I_{2(g)} \rightarrow HI + I + 28$ k.cal

occurs readily, the reaction

(5) $I + H_2 \rightarrow HI + H - 39 \cdot 5$ k.cal

which is the necessary second reaction for chains to be propagated through gaseous mixtures of hydrogen and iodine, is too endothermic to occur with the requisite speed.

A corollary to the principle that the effective activation energy should be low is that the reaction centre should be either a *highly activated molecule*, or an *atom or free radical*, or an *unstable ion*. Examples of all these types are to be found in the succeeding pages.

2. Propagation Reactions in Addition Polymerization of Un-saturated Compounds. These reactions are not adequately represented by the formalized equations (1), (2*a*), and (2*b*). They differ in that the product of one propagation step is also the centre for the next, i.e. the reaction is the addition of a monomer molecule (m_1) to a chain centre (m_j^*) which already contains j monomer units, according to equation (6).

(6) $m_j^* + m_1 \rightarrow m_{j+1}^*$

The asterisk denotes that the polymeric species m_j^* and m_{j+1}^* are activated in some way which ensures further growth according to this equation. The inner nature of this reaction has been most clearly expounded by HARMAN, HULBERT, TOBOLSKY and EYRING[9]. A carbon atom in its ground state has the electronic configuration $2s^2 2p^2$; and a hydrogen atom is in a $1s$ state. Each of the two carbon atoms may then be regarded as being brought (i.e. promoted) into a 'trigonal' state of hybridization with the p_y orbitals unchanged and three equivalent orbitals constructed from the $2s, 2p_x$ and $2p_z$ orbitals. These latter are used in the formation of the C,C σ bond and, with the $1s$ orbitals of the hydrogens to form the four C—H bonds. The p_y orbitals give rise to the 'π bond' and the electrons are less localized than those in the rest of the molecule. The ground state (N) is thus a 'singlet' state and the most stable configuration is that in which all four hydrogen atoms are coplanar, i.e. either *cis* or *trans*. All

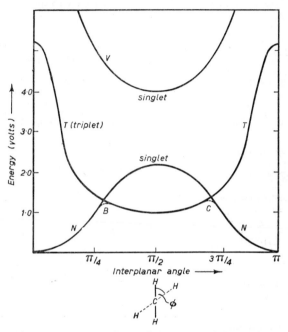

Fig. III.1. The dependence of the energy of the ethylene molecule on the interplanar angle ϕ in the ground state (N) and the first excited state (T)

other configurations have higher energy. If, for example, the two CCH_2 planes are rotated with respect to one another the potential energy increases as shown in Fig. III.1, reaching a maximum when the interplanar angle is $\pi/2$. The height of this maximum will be the value of the activation energy for isomerization of *cis* to *trans* compounds and vice versa, and there is some experimental evidence that this activation energy is about

Frequency factors and energies of activation of the propa

Overall Reaction	$\Delta E°$	Propagation Steps	A^*
$H_2 + Cl_2 \xrightarrow{h\nu} 2HCl$	-45	$Cl + H_2 \rightarrow HCl + H - 1$ $H + Cl_2 \rightarrow HCl + Cl + 46$	$10^{10.9}$ $\sim 10^{10}$
$H_2 + Br_2 \rightarrow 2HBr$	-17	$Br + H_2 \rightarrow HBr + H - 17$ $H + Br_2 \rightarrow HBr + Br + 34$	10^{11}
$CO + Cl_2 \xrightarrow{h\nu} COCl_2$	-24	$COCl + Cl_2 \rightarrow COCl_2 + Cl$	$10^{9.4}$
Polymerization of Vinyl Cpds. $m_1 \rightarrow \dfrac{1}{n} m_n$		$m_j{}^* + m_1 \rightarrow m_{j+1}{}^* + (-\Delta E°)$	
$CH_2 = C \cdot COOCH_3$ $\quad\quad \mid$ $\quad\quad CH_3$	-13	$+13$	5×10 or 5×10
$CH_2 = CH \cdot C_6H_5$	-17.5	$+17.5$	10^6 or 2.2×10
$CH_2 = CH \cdot O \cdot CO \cdot CH_3$	-21.3	$+21.3$	2.4×10 or 2.1×10
$RH + O_2 \rightarrow RO_2H + \text{minor}$ $\quad\quad\quad\quad\quad\quad\quad \text{products}$ $RH = \text{olefine containing group}$ $R = \phi CH_2-$ $R = -CH_2-CH:CH-CH-$ $R = -CH_2-C:CH-CH_2-$ $\quad (b) \quad\quad \mid \quad\quad (a)$ $\quad\quad\quad\quad CH_3 \ (c)$	-50	$RO_2 + RH \rightarrow RO_2H + R$	10^{7} 10^{7} $(a)\ 10^{7}$ $(b)\ 10^{7}$ $(c)\ 10^{7}$

$*$ Concentration ur

E k.cal	Termination Steps	$2A^*$	E k.cal	Refs.
$\cdot5 \pm 1\cdot0$ ~ 2	$2Cl + Cl_2 \rightarrow 2Cl_2$	6×10^8	?	1 2
~ 18 $1\cdot2$	$2Br + M \rightarrow Br_2 + M$	$\sim 10^{10}$ $(M = CO_2)$	0	3
3	$COCl + Cl \rightarrow CO + Cl_2$ $NOCl + Cl \rightarrow NO + Cl_2$	$10^{11\cdot6}$ 10^{10}	$0\cdot8$ $1\cdot06$	4
	$m_j^* + m_k^* \rightarrow P_{j+k}$ or $P_j + P_k$			
$6\cdot3$ or $4\cdot4$		7×10^8 or 10^8	$2\cdot8$ or 0	5 5
$6\cdot5$ or $7\cdot8$		$3\cdot10^8$ or $1\cdot3 \times 10^9$	$2\cdot8$ or $2\cdot4$	6 5
$7\cdot3$ or $4\cdot4$		2×10^{11} or $3\cdot10^9$	$5\cdot2$ 0	ref. 23, Ch. VII 7
	$2RO_2 \rightarrow$?		$\not> 5$	8
$10\cdot2$ $9\cdot7$ $8\cdot5$ $9\cdot7$ $11\cdot2$		$\sim 10^{5\cdot7}$	$\not> 5$	

$= $ mole l.$^{-1}$, time in secs.

40 k.cal. If one of the π electrons is promoted to a non-bonding orbital a triplet state (T) is reached, in which the potential energy has minima at interplanar angles of $\pi/2$ and $3\pi/2$ and maxima at 0 and π. Optical transitions between these N and T levels are 'forbidden', but transitions can take place at B and C (dotted lines) under the perturbing influence of the electrical or magnetic field of an adjacent free radical or ion. The system must have sufficient energy to be twisted into the configuration corresponding to the angle at B. This energy is about 20 k.cal, but some of this may be forthcoming from that released in incipient bond formation in the transition state. The observed energy of activation of this reaction which in the case of a free radical (R) may be written

$$(7) \qquad \underline{R} + CH_2 = CH_2 \rightarrow R - CH_2 - \underline{CH_2}$$

is therefore likely to be considerably less than 20 k.cal, which is certainly true of the vinyl compounds cited in Table II. When an ion is the attacking agent (reaction (8))

$$(8) \qquad \overset{+ \text{ or } -}{-\underline{CR_2}} + CH_2 = CR_2 \rightarrow - CR_2 - CH_2 - \overset{+ \text{ or } -}{\underline{CR_2}}$$

the energy of activation may be quite different from that for reaction (7) even though the heats of the two reactions will be identical. In the first place a very considerable ion-induced dipole interaction energy will be quite important even at quite large separations of reactants in reaction (8) and absent in reaction (7). Secondly, the relative degrees of solvation of the attacking ion and the transition state will undoubtedly influence both the frequency factor and energy of activation of reaction (8), from which one may also deduce that the rate constant of of this reaction will be markedly dependent on the nature of the solvent and especially on its polarity. The scant experimental data available tend to confirm these expectations[10] (see also Chapter VII).

The 'ionic' and 'free radical' type polymerizations may easily be distinguished. In the first place it would be expected that polymerization by the cationic mechanism would be favoured by electrophobic substituents such as alkyl groups, whereas the free radical or anionic type would be the favoured mechanism when the ethylenic hydrogen atoms are substituted by electrophilic groups such as —CN, —COR, —CO·OR. Moreover, if steric hindrance is not an important factor, unsymmetrical, i.e. a 1,1 disubstitution, should enhance this difference. This is found to be the case, and recently it has been emphasized that very few monomers can polymerize by both the radical and cationic mechanisms[10]. Secondly, ionic polymerizations should be subject to acid-base catalysis in its widest sense, and the rate of reaction be dependent on the dielectric constant of the medium. Both these predictions have been verified[10]. Thirdly, in the 'ionic' type reactions chain termination implies charge neutralization (see section 7 (a) (ii)), whereas in 'radical' reactions this step involves saturation of a free valency. Accordingly inhibitors for the latter, e.g. oxygen, do not retard cationic polymerizations; they may even act as catalysts, e.g. iodine catalyses the polymerization of vinyl ethers.

Whether it is 'ionic' or radical in character, the propagation reaction in all vinyl polymerization processes differs from other chain propagation processes in three important respects: (a) in an unsymmetrically substituted ethylene there are two possible modes of addition, so-called 'head to head' or 'head to tail', e.g. in styrene the polymer resulting from the two types contains the groups:

(9) Head to head

$$-CH_2-CH-CH-CH_2-CH_2-CH-CH-CH_2-$$
$$\underset{C_6H_5}{|}\ \underset{C_6H_5}{|}\underset{C_6H_5}{|}\ \underset{C_6H_5}{|}$$

(10) Head to tail

$$-CH_2-CH-CH_2-CH-CH_2-CH-CH_2-CH-$$
$$\underset{C_6H_5}{|}\underset{C_6H_5}{|}\underset{C_6H_5}{|}\underset{C_6H_5}{|}$$

(b) the molecular weight of the chain centre increases by constant amounts as the chain develops; and (c), by using several monomers each of which may act as m_1 in equation (4), the product formed is a polymeric pot-pourri in which the individual monomers are incorporated in proportions determined by their mole fractions in the reactant mixture and the appropriate velocity constants. (See Chapter VII.)

(c) is referred to as *copolymerization* and has often been realized. (a) and (b) are of particular interest in relation to the common assumption that in a single component system, a fixed value for the velocity constant of the propagation reaction can be used. Unsymmetrically substituted ethylenes are known to have an unsymmetrical charge distribution, the sign of which is determined by the electrophilic character, or otherwise, of the substituents. In ionic reactions head to tail union involves approach of unlike charges and is therefore inherently more probable than head to head addition, for which the reverse is true. Similar, but less obvious arguments, apply to free radical type polymerizations, and in confirmation of these conclusions there is now a considerable amount of experimental evidence that polymers formed from vinyl compounds ($CH_2 = CHX$) have the same substituent on alternate carbon atoms.

The tertiary carbon atoms in vinyl polymers are asymmetric and NATTA[11] has pointed out that the *D*- and *L*-configurations may be either randomly or regularly distributed along the polymer chain. Polymers possessing the random arrangements are called *atactic*, those in which *all* the asymmetric carbon atoms in a chain have the same configuration are called *isotactic* and those in which there is a regular alternation of *D*- and *L*-configurations are called *syndiotactic*. The relations between these are illustrated below, where the carbon atoms of the main chain are envisaged as lying in the same plane. Co-planarity of the carbon atoms is

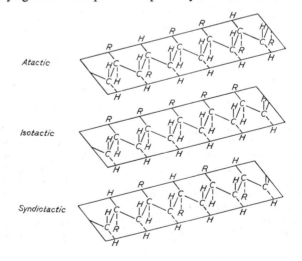

not that of lowest potential energy and an even more regular
array of the atoms in isotactic vinyl polymers is that in which the
4th, 7th, 10th, etc., asymmetric carbon atom has the same configuration as the first. The main chain is then in the form of a
helix the end-on view of which would be as shown, where the

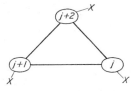

circles represent successive CH_2—CH units the C—C axes of
which are perpendicular to the plane of the paper and the X
denotes the pendant group. Whilst polymers having *stereoregular* structures of these kinds are of immense importance in
polymer chemistry because of their crystallinity and associated
physical properties their kinetic significance is in the precise
stereospecific control of the propagation step. The chemical
causes of this are not yet fully understood but it is inconceivable
that, when elucidated, they will not also give deeper comprehen-
sion of the factors controlling the rates of propagation[12].

The propagation reaction in a single component system is
therefore chemically the same as the chain develops; and after
the effect of the initiating group (see section (iii)) has been
damped out along a chain of, say, four or more carbon atoms, i.e.
when $j > 2$, it would be expected that the energy of activation
would be constant. Since the reaction is essentially a bimolecular
association process, the P factor should be less than unity (see
p. 18). The expression for the rate constant of reaction (6)
appropriate to the gas phase on the transition state theory after
making all possible simplification is

$$k = e^{\frac{-\Delta E_0^{\ddagger}}{RT}} \frac{h^5}{64\pi^5(kT)^2 m_1^{\frac{9}{2}}(I_A I_B I_C)^{\frac{1}{2}}}$$

$$\cdot \frac{\sigma_1}{g_1} \left\{ \left(\frac{m^{\ddagger}}{m_j}\right)^{\frac{3}{2}} \left[\frac{(I_A I_B I_C)^{\ddagger}}{(I_A I_B I_C)_j}\right]^{\frac{1}{2}} \frac{\prod\limits^{3nj+3n-7} (1 - e^{\frac{-h\nu}{kT}})^{-1}}{\prod\limits^{3n-6} (1 - e^{\frac{-h\nu}{kT}})^{-1} \prod\limits^{3nj-6} (1 - e^{\frac{-h\nu}{kT}})^{-1}} \right\}$$

$$\cdot \quad \cdot \quad \cdot \text{ (III.1)}$$

in which the subscript 1 refers to monomer the atomicity of which is n, and the subscript j is the number of units of monomer in the chain centre $m_j{}^*$. This expression corresponds to a much lower value of k than the simple collision theory expression; and as j increases, the term in brackets will decrease to a steady value which should be attained at quite low values of j. Such independence of the rate constant of the molecular weight of the growing polymer has been observed by MELVILLE[13] and low P factors are observed in all the propagation constants measured hitherto (see Table I).

3. **Chain Transfer.** A growing polymer chain may occasionally enter into a propagation reaction with a monomer molecule (equation (11)), in which a dead polymer is formed and the monomer is so activated to start a new chain. This could be represented by

(11) $$m_j{}^* + m_1 \rightarrow m_1{}^* + m_j$$

and is called *chain transfer to monomer* because the power of growth of the chain has been transferred. Chemically this may involve proton (in cationic chains) transfer to the monomer, or in radical chains transfer of a hydrogen atom in either direction. Transfer of activity may occur to other molecules present in the system, including saturated molecules. For example when carbon tetrachloride was used as a solvent in the catalysed polymerization of styrene, chlorine was present in the final polymer in analytically detectable amounts[14]; presumably due to the reactions

(12) $$m_j{}^* + Cl - CCl_3 \rightarrow m_j - Cl + \cdot CCl_3{}^*$$

(13) $$\cdot CCl_3{}^* + m_1 \rightarrow Cl_3C\, m_1{}^*$$

In a polymerization reaction in which no chain transfer is occurring, the average number of monomer units in a final polymer molecule (called the *average degree of polymerization* ($\bar{P}$)) will be the rate of removal of monomer divided by the rate at which chains are started (this ratio is also called the *kinetic chain length*). Chain transfer will therefore be revealed if $\bar{P}$ is found to decrease with increasing amounts of transfer agent to an extent greater than the rate decreases. In this way alkyl benzenes have been found to be very effective transfer agents for growing polystyrene radicals[15].

In the event of chain transfer occurring with either a dead or a growing polymer, then the resultant polymer will contain branched aliphatic carbon chains. That such structural branching caused by chain transfer occurs with increasing ease as the temperature is raised, may be the explanation of the observation that at low temperatures it is possible to produce a polystyrene which dissolves rapidly in benzene to give a solution of high viscosity, whereas the product formed at higher temperatures swells and dissolves slowly to give a solution of low viscosity. These physical properties are associated with long unbranched paraffinic hydrocarbon chains; and structurally branched chains respectively.

4. The Reversibility of the Propagation Step. By the Principle of Microscopic Reversibility the reverse reaction in any elementary reaction must exist. The velocity of this back reaction can be treated theoretically by the methods outlined in Chapter I. Reference to Fig. I.1 indicates that the energy of activation of the reverse reaction (E_r) is connected with the energy of activation (E_f) and increase in energy (ΔE^0) of the forward reaction by equation (III.2).

$$E_r = E_f - \Delta E^0 \qquad . \quad . \quad . \quad . \quad (III.2)$$

For exothermic reactions ΔE^0 is negative and therefore in those chain propagation reactions which are exothermic (the vast majority) the velocity of the reverse reaction is negligible in comparison with the forward process at room temperature. As the temperature is raised the constant for the reverse reaction will increase more rapidly than that for the forward reaction, and a temperature may be reached above which it is no longer justifiable to neglect the reverse reaction. As far as the propagation reaction in polymerization processes is concerned, the reverse reaction is

$$(14) \qquad\qquad m_{j+1}{}^* \rightarrow m_j{}^* + m_1$$

and may be regarded as the stepwise removal of monomer molecules from long hydrocarbon free radicals or ions. It will be seen later (Chapter VII) that the existence of this process profoundly influences the temperature dependence of the overall rate of reaction, and permits the entropy change in the polymerization to be directly evaluated.

When the chain propagation step is thermoneutral or endothermic it is rarely, if ever, justifiable to neglect the reverse process. Examples of this are:

(15) $\quad \underline{Cl} + H_2 \rightleftharpoons HCl + \underline{H}; \Delta E_0^0 = +1{\cdot}06 \text{ k.cal}$

(16) $\quad \underline{Br} + H_2 \rightleftharpoons HBr + \underline{H}; \Delta E_0^0 = +16{\cdot}7 \text{ k.cal}$

5. Initiation of Chains. Original chain centres from which the reaction chains develop are produced by reactions which are quite distinct from the propagation and branching processes. Such initial centres may be formed *in situ* or be injected into the system. In the former case, very varied means are available, and some typical examples are given below.

(*a*) *Homogeneous Initiation.* By this is meant initiation by the action of heat or radiation on either a reactant or a catalyst in a homogeneous system. We may distinguish the following categories.

(i) *Thermal decomposition of reactants.* In many thermal chain reactions the initial step is the unimolecular symmetrical fission of a covalent bond to form two atoms or radicals, e.g.

(17) $Br_2 \rightarrow \underline{2Br}$ in the thermal reaction $H_2 + Br_2 \rightarrow 2HBr$

(18) $C_2H_5OC_2H_5 \rightarrow \underline{C_2H_5} + \underline{OC_2H_5}$ in the pyrolysis of diethyl ether.

(19) $C_2Cl_6 \rightarrow \underline{C_2Cl_5} + \underline{Cl}$ in the pyrolysis of hexachlor-ethane.

Although these reactions are unimolecular, the kinetic order under the conditions of pressure obtaining in the experiment may be greater than unity (cf. p. 7 *et seq*). In reactions involving two reactants, both may be involved in a bimolecular initiation reaction, e.g. in the oxidation of phosphorus the initial act is

(20) $\qquad\qquad P_4 + O_2 \rightarrow \underline{P_4O} + \underline{O}$

and in the low temperature oxidation of paraffinic hydrocarbons the reaction may be

(21) $RH + O_2 \rightarrow RO{\cdot}OH$ (alkyl hydroperoxide) $\rightarrow \underline{RO{\cdot}} + \underline{{\cdot}OH}$

followed by dehydrogenation of the hydrocarbon RH by RO·
and ·OH to form the chain carrying radical R.

(ii) *Decomposition of reactants by radiation* is a most common
method of initiating reaction chains, e.g. chlorine atoms, which
are centres in most photochlorination reactions, are formed by
direct optical dissociation of chlorine molecules by ultraviolet
light of wavelengths shorter than 4785 Å.

$$(22) \qquad Cl_2(^1\Sigma_g{}^+) \xrightarrow{h\nu} \underline{Cl}(^2P_{\frac{1}{2}}) + \underline{Cl}(^2P_{\frac{3}{2}})$$

When the magnitude of the absorbed quantum is greater than
the dissociation energy involved, the excess energy appears as
excitational (translational, vibrational or rotational) energy of
the fragments. The reactivity of such 'hot' species may be greater
than that of the same species in thermal equilibrium with their
surroundings[16].

Although the energy requirements for diradical formation
from an ethylenic bond correspond to a light quantum in the
ultraviolet region, absorption by this chromophore does not
occur until wavelengths ∼ 1800 Å are reached. This absorption
region is of little practical value because wavelengths < 2000 Å
are strongly absorbed by quartz. The possibility exists in vinyl
compounds (CH_2CHX) that the substituent X might absorb a
quantum which, whilst sufficiently large to open the double
bond, yet corresponds to a wavelength freely transmitted by
quartz. Substituents such as RCO, HCO, C_6H_5 meet this requirement and it is possible that the photopolymerization of such
vinyl compounds induced by light in this spectral region might
be written

$$(23) \qquad CH_2{=}CH{-}X + h\nu \rightarrow \cdot CH_2{-}CH(X)\cdot$$

However theoretical arguments exist which make the formation of such diradicals less likely than the dissociation

$$(24) \qquad CH_2{=}CH{-}X + h\nu \rightarrow \underline{CH_2{=}CH}\cdot + \underline{X}\cdot$$

High energy radiation, e.g. X- and γ-rays, β-particles, α-rays,
etc., may also be used to start chains which may be either ionic
or free-radical in character. The cause of this duality is that all
high energy radiation transfers its energy to the substance which
it penetrates by ionizing molecules close to the path of fast
charged particles and electronically exciting molecules which

are a little more distant. Some of the excited molecules may subsequently dissociate into radicals and some of the ions may be neutralized by capturing an electron, in which case the molecule is highly excited and may well dissociate. Consequently ions and free radicals are always present in irradiated systems. An unambiguous example of an ionic chain reaction initiated by high energy radiation is reaction (25). THOMPSON and SCHAEFFER[17] showed that this radiation-induced chain reaction was suppressed

$$(25) \qquad H_2 + D_2 \xrightarrow{\quad\sim\sim\quad} 2HD$$

by the addition of small amounts of xenon and krypton which have ionization potentials (12·1 and 14·0 eV respectively) below that of hydrogen (15·4 eV) and can therefore react with H_2^+ or D_2^+, according to equation (26), thereby preventing the latter from initiating the ionic isotopic exchange reaction. The fact that argon, neon, and helium, having ionization potentials of 15·8, 21·5 and 24·5 eV, have little effect confirms this interpretation. In other cases, as for instance the polymerization of styrene at room temperature the free-radicals are the initiators of the

$$(26) \quad H_2^+ \text{ or } D_2^+ + Xe \text{ or } Kr \rightarrow H_2 \text{ or } D_2 + Xe^+ \text{ or } Kr^+$$

chain process[18].

(iii) *Catalysts and subsidiary catalytic reactions* may be used as sources of the initial centres. Many cases are known in which a catalyst acts by virtue of its ready splitting into active fragments at some weak bond, e.g. dibenzoyl peroxide decomposes into phenyl and benzoyloxy radicals

$$(27) \quad (C_6H_5COO)_2 \rightarrow 2\underline{C_6H_5COO}\cdot \ \rightarrow 2\underline{C_6H_5}\cdot \ + 2CO_2$$

both of which can initiate radical type polymerization. In other cases the catalyst reacts with a reactant. Thus all the chain reactions involving chlorine can be catalysed by sodium vapour which produces chlorine atoms by the reaction[19]

$$(28) \qquad Na + Cl_2 \rightarrow Na^+Cl^- + \underline{Cl}$$

In aqueous media, *electron transfer reactions* are of great importance as sources of atoms and radicals. The transfer always involves an ion and either another ion or a neutral molecule, e.g.

$$(29) \quad Cu^{++} + SO_3^= \rightarrow Cu^+ + \cdot\underline{SO_3^-} \ (+ \ H^+ \rightarrow \underline{HSO_3}\cdot)$$

$$(30) \qquad Fe^{2+} + H_2O_2 \rightarrow Fe^{3+} + OH^- + \cdot\underline{OH}$$

The second of these reactions has been very carefully investigated[20] and has a velocity constant $= 1\cdot8 \times 10^9 e^{\dfrac{-10\cdot1 \text{ k.cal}}{RT}}$ l. mole^{-1} sec^{-1}. Both these reactions can be used to initiate the polymerization of water soluble vinyl compounds. This type of initiation is sometimes referred to as *reduction activation*[21]. One of the difficulties in these systems is their sensitivity to inhibition by dissolved oxygen, but this difficulty can be completely overcome by making the oxygen the oxidizing partner in the initiating redox couple. This is achieved by using a very strongly reducing ion. Thus dilute solutions of vanadous salts are oxidized according to the equation

$$(31) \qquad V^{2+} + O_2 + H_2O \rightarrow VO^{2+} + 2\underline{OH}$$

Accordingly deaerated solutions of vanadous salts containing monomers are stable until oxygen is admitted, when polymerization *begins*[22].

When the chain centres are themselves ionic, the catalyst is an acid or base in either or both of the Lewis or Lowry-Brönsted senses. For instance in cationic polymerization the catalyst may be a proton donor of the mineral acid variety (e.g. H_2SO_4), or a proton donor formed by combination of a readily hydrolysable halide such as a Friedel-Crafts type catalyst ($AlCl_3$, $SnCl_4$, $TiCl_4$, BF_3, etc.) with a hydroxylic compound (ROH where $R\cdot = H\cdot$, $C_4H_9\cdot$, $ClCH_2CO$) usually called the cocatalyst[23], or even an unstable cation such as I^+ in equilibrium with a parent molecule $(2I_2 \rightleftharpoons I^+ + I_3^-)$[24]. In such cases the initiation reaction can often be identified by infrared spectroscopic analysis of low molecular weight fractions of the final polymer. In the case of the room temperature polymerization of isobutene by BF_3 using D_2O as cocatalyst the initiation reaction has been shown by this means to be[25]

$$(32) \qquad (CH_3)_2C\!:\!CH_2 + DOD\cdot BF_3 \rightarrow$$
$$(CH_3)_2C^+\cdot CH_2D + BF_3OD^-$$

Very recently many anionically initiated polymerization processes have been studied. The catalyst is then either a powerful electron donor, i.e. a Lewis base which initiates by transferring an electron to the monomer to form the radical ion, as in reaction (33), or is an anion or potential anion which can add to the

$$(33) \quad Na^+ C_{10}H_8^- + CH_2:CH.C_6H_5$$
$$\rightarrow C_{10}H_8 + \dot{C}H_2.\overline{C}H(C_6H_5).Na^+$$

monomer as in reactions (34) and (35). Frequently these processes involve colour changes and can then be seen to be extremely

$$(34) \quad NH_2^- + CH_2:CH.CN \rightarrow NH_2.CH_2.\overline{C}H.CN$$

$$(35) \quad LiCH_2CH_2CH_2CH_3 + CH_2:CH.C_6H_5$$
$$\rightarrow CH_3(CH_2)_4\overline{C}H(C_6H_5).Li^+$$

rapid. Although the mechanisms of some of these anionic initiation processes are very complex the polymer anion which is formed is often not terminated and persists until some specific reagent is added (see 7 (*a*) (ii) below) to destroy the active anionic end. It is then termed a *living polymer*. If the polymer anion is coloured, spectrophotometry can be used to determine the number of living polymer ends present which will be equal to the number of chains initiated.

(iv) *Decomposition of catalysts by radiation.* When the radiation is in the visible or ultraviolet region it is selectively absorbed and if the actinic light is absorbed by the catalyst only, the process is called photosensitization. The two most common types are *homolysis* and *electron transfer*, the latter being confined to liquid systems. Typical examples of the former are:

$$(36) \quad (CH_3)_2CO_{(g)} \xrightarrow{\lambda < 3200\text{Å}} \underline{CH_3} + \underline{CH_3CO}$$

$$(37) \quad H_2O_{2(aq)} \xrightarrow{\lambda < 3700\text{Å}} 2\underline{OH}$$

Theoretically photochemical electron transfer can take place from a donor of ionization potential, I_D, to an acceptor of electron affinity E_A, the magnitude of the quantum necessary being greater than $I_D - E_A$ by a quantity which depends on the interaction of the donor acceptor complex in its ground and excited states. These transfers have been particularly well studied in aqueous solutions where they frequently occur between the partners in an ion-pair complex comprising the higher valency state of a transition metal cation and a halide (Cl^-, Br^-) or pseudo halide (OH^-, N_3^-, SCN^-) anion, as illustrated in equation (38). In all these cases a free radical ($Cl\cdot$, $Br\cdot$, $HO\cdot$, $N_3\cdot$, $SCN\cdot$) is

$$(38) \qquad Fe^{3+}OH^- + h\nu \rightarrow Fe^{2+} + \cdot\underline{OH}$$

formed which can initiate a chain reaction[27]. A particularly interesting case is that of photochemical electron transfer from a reducing cation M_{aq}^{z+} (e.g. Fe^{2+}, Cr^{2+}, Eu^{2+}, $Fe(CN)_6^{4-}$) or anion A_{aq}^{y-} (e.g. I^-, SH^-, OH^-, $C_6H_5O^-$) to the water. Investigations of flash photolysis and neutral salt effects on these systems show that an aquated electron e_{aq}^- in reaction (39), is initially

$$(39) \qquad M_{aq}^{z+} \text{ or } A_{aq}^{y-} + h\nu \rightarrow M_{aq}^{(x+1)+} \text{ or } A_{aq}^{(y-1)-} + e_{aq}^-$$

formed[28] and in neutral water persists for about 100 μsec before reacting to form hydrogen according to equation (40). The

$$(40) \qquad e_{aq}^- \rightarrow H + OH_{aq}^- \text{ or } H_2 + O_{aq}^-$$

aquated electron can also be identified by performing these photochemical reactions in alkaline aqueous glasses at $-196°C$ when it is immobilized and has a typical singlet electron spin resonance signal and blue colour[29]. As the simplest free radical it can be used to initiate chain reactions such as the polymerization of water soluble vinyl compounds. In acid solution it is rapidly converted to a hydrogen atom by reaction

$$(41) \qquad e_{aq}^- + H_{aq}^+ \rightarrow H\cdot$$

(41) the rate constant of which is $2\cdot3 \times 10^{10}$ l. mole^{-1} sec^{-1}[30] and this species can also serve to initiate reaction chains.

When high energy radiations are used they are not selectively absorbed but energy is deposited in each component of a mixture according to the electron fraction which that component contributes to the total electron density. Consequently, in contrast to the photosensitizer, which need only be present in small concentration, the radiation-sensitizer must be the component in great excess if the fraction of energy absorbed by the reactant is to be sufficiently small to produce a negligible change by direct action. The entities produced, are as mentioned earlier, a mixture

of ions and free radicals. Thus in the most extensively investigated case, namely, water, the primary act is given by equation
(42). About 10^{-11} sec after the primary act has taken place,
the odd electron species present will comprise OH, e_{aq}^-, and H.

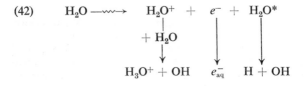

(42)

Some of these combine to form hydrogen and hydrogen peroxide,
the remainder are available to initiate chain reactions, particularly
in alkaline solution, where, for example, the hydration of
carbon monoxide to form formate,[31] the oxidation by dissolved
nitrous oxide of hydrogen, carbon monoxide or organic solutes[32]
and the isotopic exchange between oxygen and water[33] can easily
be brought about. The value of the method is that both ions and
uncharged free radicals are produced and conditions can be
chosen in which either free radical chains (as above) or ionic
chains (as in the γ-ray induced polymerization of acrylamide
dissolved in ammonia at $-64°C$)[34] are initiated.

Ultrasonic waves may also be used to generate radicals in
condensed media. The mode of action of this radiation is not
completely understood but it is known to produce effects similar
to those produced by nuclear radiations[35].

(b) *Heterogeneous Initiation*. This may well occur in many
gas phase chain reactions but the evidence is frequently neither
easy to secure nor conclusive, because any treatment of the
vessel wall designed to modify the efficiency of the initiation
reaction also alters the efficiency of any wall termination reactions. The clearest evidence is obtained when the reaction will
not proceed in the absence of certain surfaces. MELVILLE and
LUDLAM have concluded that the glow oxidation of phosphorus
vapour which may be brought about by a heated tungsten
filament at partial pressures of oxygen below the lower limit is
due to chain initiation on the filament[36]. It is tempting to regard the role of heated metal filaments used as sources for the
propagation of flame through cold explosive gas mixtures as
being of this character.

Heterogeneous initiation is not confined to gas phase reactions. Many solutions are decomposed by colloidal metals, unsaturated compounds may be reduced by gaseous hydrogen in the presence of catalysts. By using the polymerization of aqueous solutions of acrylonitrile as a test TAYLOR and PARRAVANO[37] have shown atoms or radicals to be present in several such systems including the colloidal platinum catalysed decomposition of hydrogen peroxide and formic acid, and the desorption of hydrogen from palladium. An example of heterogeneous initiation which is of considerable technical importance is provided by the catalysis by siliceous earths, such as floridin, of the ionic polymerization of olefines[38]. The initiation reaction is probably the surrender of a proton by the catalytic clay (cf. equation (32)).

(c) *Injection of Centres.* HABER and others[39] have used atomic hydrogen, obtained by blowing hydrogen gas through a tungsten arc, to initiate chains in the hydrogen oxygen reaction, and NALBANDJAN[40] has used atomic oxygen from a Woods tube for the same purpose. Because centres are generally very short lived molecular fragments the technique of injection of controlled amounts is often difficult and the results are rarely of more than qualitative significance. In some reactions the centres are of longer life and it then becomes possible to add a sample of partially reacted reagents containing reaction centres to fresh reagents which are not reacting because no chains are being initiated. Reaction chains are then propagated from the reaction centres of the first mixture throughout the second. This method was first used by SEMENOV and EMANUEL[41] to study the properties of the intermediates in the slow oxidation of hydrogen sulphide, and has recently been brilliantly adapted by MELVILLE and HICKS[42] to the synthesis of 'block' copolymers. The latter workers forced a sample of n-butyl methacrylate monomer (A) to flow from a reaction zone in which its own polymerization was photo-initiated down a capillary, during which time polymer radicals of the type $AAA(A)_n\cdot$ were formed, into a vessel containing another monomer (B). The polymeric $A_n\cdot$ radicals entering this second vessel initiated the polymerization of monomer B, thus leading to the formation of the 'block' copolymer A_nB_m.

One of the most striking methods which literally involves the placing of reaction centres into a reagent and thereby initiating a chain reaction is that devised by CHAPIRO[43]. It was remarked above that high energy radiation will cause the formation of radicals. It is also penetrating. If a solid polymer is irradiated bonds are broken throughout the solid both by scission of the main chain and by detachment of atoms or groups attached to the main chain. The free radicals thus created are prevented by the rigidity of the solid from motion and hence from mutual destruction by combination or disproportionation. When the irradiated polymer is immersed in a polymerizable liquid monomer which can diffuse into the polymer, monomer molecules can seek out and react with the free-radicals. In this way chains of polymers derived from the monomer become 'grafted' on to the original polymer either as extensions of the main chain or as branches.

6. Branching. This is the occasional production of more than one centre in a propagation step. Reactions in which this happens have been classified by SEMENOV[44] as follows.

(*a*) *Linear Branching* in which the rate of production of new centres is proportional to the first power of the concentration of those already present. This is the usual type and may be subdivided further.

(i) *Energy branching*, which occurs when the products of some highly exothermic step include a molecule sufficiently excited to dissociate a reactant molecule. This type of mechanism, first proposed in 1929 by SEMENOV[45] to account for branching in the explosive oxidation of dry carbon monoxide gas according to reaction (44), though not free from objection, is still the best available. Oxygen atoms are chain carriers in this reaction and an obvious way by which CO_2 might be formed is

$$(43) \qquad\qquad CO + \underline{O} \rightarrow CO_2{}^*$$

but this reaction is extremely exothermic and the CO_2 molecule formed will be highly excited. This excitation energy may be transformed into the observed ultraviolet and infrared emission, or if the $CO_2{}^*$ encounters an oxygen molecule the latter may be dissociated.

$$(44) \qquad\qquad CO_2{}^* + O_2 \rightarrow CO_2 + \underline{O} + \underline{O}$$

(ii) *Normal branching* merely comprises the occasional production of two or more centres from a reaction in which one centre is destroyed. Such reactions are rare because they are frequently endothermic and have a considerable energy of activation which is usually known as the *energy of branching* and is important in relation to the temperature dependence of isothermal explosion boundaries (see Chapter V). Although there is no single mechanism which provides a unique solution to the kinetics of the reaction between hydrogen and oxygen, most workers[46] in this field agree that the branching reactions are

$$(45) \qquad \underline{H} + O_2 \to \underline{HO} + \underline{O}$$

$$(46) \qquad \underline{O} + H_2 \to \underline{OH} + \underline{H}$$

with energies of activation of ~ 18 and 12 k.cal respectively.

(iii) *Continuous branching* occurs when the propagation reaction is also the branching reaction. Perhaps the best examples are the nuclear chain reactions, on which the utilization of atomic energy depends, but on a more usual scale, the oxidation of phosphorus may be taken as representative of this class[47]. Here the reaction is

$$(47) \qquad \underline{P_4O_n} + O_2 \to \underline{P_4O_{n+1}} + \underline{O} \qquad\qquad n < 10$$

An interesting distinction between continuously branched chains and the other types of branched chain is that long chains are not likely to be found in the slow reaction region outside the explosion limits. In the case of phosphorus, any reaction which does occur is too small to be detected.

(iv) *Degenerate branching* differs from the other forms of linear branching in that the primary chain is unbranched, and the additional centres are produced by side reactions of products of the primary chain. It is possible that peroxides formed in the oxidation of organic compounds in the cool flame regions fill this rôle. Thus RCH_2OOH may be formed in the primary unbranched chain by the reactions

$$(48) \qquad \underline{RCH_2\cdot} + O_2 \to \underline{RCH_2OO\cdot}$$

$$(49) \qquad \underline{RCH_2OO\cdot} + RCH_3 \to \underline{RCH_2\cdot} \mid RCH_2OOH$$

This substance may then either be dehydrated on the surface to form the appropriate aldehyde (RCHO) or break at its weakest link as follows:

$$(50) \qquad RCH_2O\cdot OH \to \underline{RCH_2O\cdot} + \underline{OH}$$

giving a new centre (OH) and the alkoxy radical which may decompose to give formaldehyde and an alkyl radical

$$(51) \qquad \underline{RCH_2O} \cdot \rightarrow H \cdot CHO + \underline{R} \cdot$$

Reaction (49) therefore constitutes a branching reaction.

(b) *Quadratic Branching* is the formation of additional centres at a rate proportional to the square of the concentration of those already present. No chain reaction exists of which it may be said unequivocally that this type of branching is operative. SEMENOV[48] has suggested that in the oxidation of carbon disulphide, sulphur monoxide molecules are formed by

$$(52) \qquad CS_2 + \underline{O} \rightarrow \underline{CS} + SO$$

$$(53) \qquad \underline{CS} + O_2 \rightarrow COS + \underline{O}$$

These are not normally chain carriers and may be converted to the final products without affecting the chain development. They might also react with oxygen

$$(54) \qquad SO + O_2 \rightarrow SO_2 + \underline{O}$$

forming an oxygen atom, in which case the chains would be degenerately branched. In addition there is the possibility that the two sulphur monoxide molecules would interact to form a fresh centre, e.g. by reactions (55) and (56):

$$(55) \qquad 2SO \rightarrow SO_2 + S$$

$$(56) \qquad S + CS_2 \rightarrow \underline{CS} + S_2$$

This would constitute quadratic branching since *two* of the original chains must interact for the creation of extra centres. On p. 119 it is shown that, unlike other systems, the value of the explosion limit depends on the rate of initiation. This test has not been applied in the CS_2/O_2 reaction but it is known that hydrogen or oxygen atoms injected into H_2/O_2 mixtures enlarge the explosion region[39],[40]. This is conceivably due to quadratic branching, but other explanations can be given of the phenomenon.

No example of branching has been drawn from polymerization reactions, although it is well known that polymers can be formed in which the long carbon chains are *structurally* branched, i.e. bifurcated, and even cross linked, so that the polymer is a three dimensional network. This omission was deliberate since there is no evidence that even the most complex structures are formed by *kinetically* branched chain reactions.

7. Termination. Termination reactions involve the destruction of one or two reaction centres and accordingly, like branching reactions, may be classified as either *linear* or *quadratic*, respectively. It is also of great importance to know whether the reaction occurs homogeneously or at the wall of the reaction vessel.

(*a*) *Linear Homogeneous Termination Reactions* may be subdivided according to the nature of the chain which is broken.

(i) If *energy chains* are involved, then termination may merely be the deactivation of the centre in a collision of the second kind; and the deactivating agent would be any molecular or atomic species in the system capable of accepting the excitation energy of the centre and subsequently degrading it to thermal energy. An established example of this type of behaviour is not easy to find because energy chains have proved to be much less common than was at one time thought.

(ii) When chains are propagated by the ionic mechanism they will be removed by a charge neutralization process, either by expulsion of the charge on the reaction centre or by addition of a charge of equal magnitude but opposite sign. This is particularly well exemplified in POLANYI and A. G. EVANS' mechanism for the termination of reaction chains in the low temperature BF_3 catalysed polymerization of isobutene[23]. It has already been mentioned (p. 63) that the real catalyst is a complex of catalyst and co-catalyst written provisionally as $ROH \cdot BF_3$ and the chain centre is a hydrocarbon chain having a carbonium ion at the growing end. The two possible termination reactions are:

(i) Charge expulsion by transfer of H^+ to the anionic fragment of catalyst.

$$(57)\ (CH_3)_3C\!-\!\left(\!CH_2\!-\!\overset{\displaystyle CH_3}{\underset{\displaystyle CH_3}{\overset{|}{\underset{|}{C}}}}\!\right)^{\!+}_{\!j} + (BF_3OR)^-$$

$$\rightarrow (CH_3)_3C\!-\!(CH_2\!-\!C(CH_3)_2)_{j-1}\!-\!CH_2\!-\!\overset{\displaystyle CH_2}{\underset{\displaystyle CH_3}{\overset{\|}{\underset{|}{C}}}} + ROH \cdot BF_3 \quad (a)$$

$$\text{or } (CH_3)_3C - (CH_2 - C(CH_3)_2)_{j-1} - CH = \overset{\overset{\displaystyle CH_3}{\displaystyle |}}{\underset{\underset{\displaystyle CH_3}{\displaystyle |}}{C}} + ROH \cdot BF_3 \qquad (b)$$

(ii) Addition of the anionic fragment of the co-catalyst.

$$(58)\ (CH_3)_3C - \left(CH_2 - \overset{\overset{\displaystyle CH_3}{\displaystyle |}}{\underset{\underset{\displaystyle CH_3}{\displaystyle |}}{C}} \right)^+_j + (BF_3OR)^-$$

$$\rightarrow (CH_3)_3C - (CH_2 - C(CH_3)_2)_{j-1} - CH_2 - \overset{\overset{\displaystyle CH_3}{\displaystyle |}}{\underset{\underset{\displaystyle CH_3}{\displaystyle |}}{C}} - OR + BF_3$$

These two mechanisms differ in one important respect which has far-reaching kinetic consequences. In reaction (i) the effective catalyst is regenerated and may start a new reaction chain; to this extent the reaction may be regarded as a chain transfer reaction with the anionic fragment of the catalyst. In reaction (ii) the anionic catalyst fragment is destroyed and since BF_3 is not the effective catalyst, this termination reaction causes the catalyst concentration to be steadily reduced. It will be noticed that the structure of one of the end-groups is entirely determined by the nature of the termination reaction. Identification of the actual structure is possible by examination of infrared absorption spectra of low molecular weight polymers. This has been carried out by DAINTON and SUTHERLAND[25] and the results exclude reaction (57 (b)) and indicate that the proton expulsion reaction (57 (a)) is most important.

When anionic polymerization occurs termination reactions can be formulated which are analogous to (57) and (58) for cationic polymerization and which involve either hydride ion (H^-) transfer from the growing anion to the gegen ions or proton transfer from the solvent to the growing anion. Frequently however the gegen ion is an alkali metal cation which is too stable to accept the hydride ion and the medium, often an organic ether, has no proton-donating capacity, i.e. is *aprotic*. Growing carbanions then remain unterminated and grow until all the monomer has been polymerized when they constitute the 'living polymers' referred to earlier and, having retained their capacity for growth, will polymerize any monomer which may subsequently be added. Addition of proton-donors, e.g. water or substances which can add to the anion to give stable products, e.g. carbon dioxide or methyl iodide, can then terminate or 'kill' the living polymers (see reactions (59), (60), and (61)).

(59) $—CH_2—\overline{C}H(C_6H_5)Na^+ + H_2O$
$$\rightarrow —CH_2—CH_2—C_6H_5 + NaOH$$

(60) $—CH_2—\overline{C}H\cdot(C_6H_5)Na^+ + CO_2$
$$\rightarrow —CH_2—CH(C_6H_5)CO\cdot O^-Na^+$$

(61) $—CH_2—\overline{C}H\cdot(C_6H_5)Na^+ + CH_3I$
$$\rightarrow —CH_2—CH(C_6H_5)CH_3 + NaI$$

Such reactions are generally stoichiometric and can therefore be used to count the number of 'living ends' present in the polymerizing system[26].

(iii) When free radicals or atoms are the chain carriers, linear chain termination reactions usually involve addition of the chain carrier to some other molecule already present in the reacting system to form a more stable entity incapable of propagating the chain. In certain low temperature oxidation processes in which the chains are carried by oxygen atoms, they are terminated by formation of

(62) $$O + O_2(+ M) \rightarrow O_3(+ M)$$

ozone in a 3-body process (equation (62)), traces of which may be detected in the products[47].

Added substances which fulfil the requirements of reacting very rapidly with the chain centre to produce a non-chain propagating substance will act as negative catalysts. Many such retarding agents are known, among which is the odd electron molecule NO which can add on to free radicals both of long life and of short life. There is still some uncertainty as to the precise way in which nitric oxide destroys chain centres. Nitric oxide is itself removed and in the case of its reaction with methyl radicals there are indications that the following sequence occurs[49]:

(63) $CH_3\cdot + NO \rightarrow CH_3NO \overset{?}{\rightarrow} [CH_2{=}NOH] \rightarrow$ decomposition

products including $HCN + H_2O$ and $CO + NH_3$.

Other retarding agents which are themselves destroyed by the reaction with the chain centre are usually stable molecules which surrender or accept an atom to satisfy the free valency of the chain centre. The portion of the retarding agent which remains will also have a free valency but for various reasons is incapable of starting a new reaction chain. The action of molecular iodine has already been cited (p. 44). Most negative catalysts are much more complex than this and surrender their atom readily to form a relatively unreactive radical which is stabilized by resonance. Consider the retarding action of *p*-hydroquinone on the photochemical decomposition of aqueous solutions of hydrogen peroxide. The chain carriers include hydroxyl radicals and it is possible that the *p*-hydroquinone exerts its effect by the reaction

(64) $HO\cdot + HO\!\!\left<\!\!\bigcirc\!\!\right>\!\!-OH \rightarrow H_2O + \cdot O\!\!\left<\!\!\bigcirc\!\!\right>\!\!-OH$ (R)

in which the semiquinone radical R would be expected to be far less reactive than say the methyl radical, and much less able to start a fresh reaction chain by decomposing hydrogen peroxide by either of the reactions (65) or (66).

(65) $\underline{R} + H_2O_2 \rightarrow ROH + \underline{HO}$

(66) $\underline{R} + H_2O_2 \rightarrow RH + \underline{HO_2}$

It would be destroyed either by further loss of a hydrogen atom to form *p*-benzoquinone or by combination of two fragments to form quinhydrone. In this reaction the inhibitor acts by surrender of a hydrogen atom or an electron. The same stable radical R could, however, be formed by transfer of a hydrogen atom from a chain centre to *p*-benzoquinone, in which case *p*-benzoquinone would be a negative catalyst. *p*-benzoquinone is indeed a strong inhibitor for many polymerization reactions, and it is notable that as the reaction proceeds the characteristic yellow colour of this compound fades and the extinction of the colour is roughly coincident with the cessation of the inhibition[50]. This action could be accounted for by the reaction

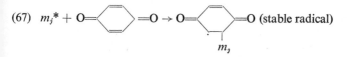

$$(67) \quad m_j^* + O=\langle\ \rangle=O \rightarrow O=\langle\ \rangle=O \text{ (stable radical)}$$
$$m_j$$

A negative catalyst which is extremely reactive towards the chain centre and is destroyed by this reaction will, when present in trace quantities, cause an inhibition period (see p. 29) but does not affect the steady rate ultimately attained after the inhibitor has been destroyed. This is the rôle of *p*-benzoquinone in the photosensitized polymerization of vinyl acetate (see p. 185). When the chain terminating agent is regenerated in some side reactions its concentration is maintained at a steady level and the retardation is permanent. The effect of nitrosyl chloride on chlorination reactions falls into this category. It terminates reaction chains by surrender of a chlorine atom, e.g.

$$(68) \qquad \underline{Cl} + NOCl \rightarrow Cl_2 + NO$$

$$(69) \qquad \underline{C_2Cl_5} + NOCl \rightarrow C_2Cl_6 + NO$$

but the nitric oxide (which may itself inhibit) is speedily reconverted to nitrosyl chloride by the excess chlorine present.

In principle, organic free radicals can both accept an electron to form a carbanion and donate an electron to form a carbonium ion, i.e. they can act both as oxidizing agents and reducing agents. Consequently compounds of transition metals which can undergo one-equivalent oxidation or reduction reactions are generally good terminating agents of free-radical chains. Examples of oxidative chain termination of growing polymer radicals have been given in equations (5) and (6) of Chapter II, where it was pointed out that these reactions are stoichiometric. The same is true of reductive chain termination, illustrated by reaction (70). There is, however, a marked mechanistic difference between these two types of reaction The rate-determining process in

$$(70) \quad X(CH_2CH(CONH_2))_n\cdot + Cr_{aq}^{2+} + H_2O$$
$$\rightarrow X(CH_2CH(CONH_2))_nH + Cr^{3+} + OH^-$$

the former is the transfer of an electron to the oxidizing compound and is rapid either if this contains a vacant d orbital, e.g. $Fe^{3+}(3d^5)$ or if the ligand, being substitution stable, has good electron conducting properties, e.g. $Fe(CN)_6^{3-}$ or $Fe(o\text{-phenan-throlene})_3^{3+}$; but is very slow if the oxidant has a complete d shell, e.g. Ag^+, $Hg^{2+}(d^{10})$ or if the ligand, being substitution stable, is also non-conducting, e.g. $Co(NH_3)_6^{3+}$. The frequency factor and energy of activation of this reaction are both small and there is no solvent isotope effect. In marked contrast the rate-determining factor in reductive termination reactions such as (70) appears to be the ease with which a hydrogen atom is transferred from the water of solvation of the reducing ion to the radical. For these reactions k_{obs}° is about 10^{11} l. mole^{-1} sec^{-1}, the energy of activation is generally greater than 10 k.cal mole^{-1}, as befits a bond breakage process, and the rate constant is related, not to the electronic configuration of the ion, but to its redox potential[51].

(b) *Linear Heterogeneous Chain Termination* most often occurs in gas reactions by adsorption of atoms and radicals at the wall, where they may combine and re-evaporate as molecules. Unless the centre is desorbed unchanged the reaction chain of which it was a part will be terminated. There is abundant evidence from studies of adsorption that atoms (in particular) may be adsorbed on surfaces and there is also no doubt that many reaction chains are terminated on surfaces, but unfortunately there is no chain reaction in which the wall termination reaction can be exactly specified. Reflection of centres from surfaces, which is kinetically equivalent to their re-evaporation unchanged, will be least likely to occur on those surfaces which are most able to facilitate the combination of the centres. TAYLOR and LAVIN[52] found that the coating of glass surfaces by potassium chloride increases the efficiency of the surface for promoting the reaction $H + OH \rightarrow H_2O$. Since H and $\cdot OH$ are chain carriers in the high temperature thermal reaction between hydrogen and oxygen it is not surprising that similar treatment of the walls of the reaction vessel enhances their chain breaking efficiency in this reaction.

Possibly the clearest example of heterogeneous termination is provided by the ionic polymerization of olefines on catalytic clays. In this case the chain centre is positively charged and can only be destroyed by neutralization of this charge by the excess negative charge of the catalyst surface which has been acquired in the initiation step. It is significant that similar heterogeneous reactions can be written for the removal of gaseous chain centres, e.g. $HO_2 + wall^- \rightarrow HO_2^- + wall$. Here 'wall' might be a metal-ion impurity in the glass. The wall may also contain impurities which will react with reducing centres such as H-atoms.

Although so little understood, the power of crystalline and metallic surfaces to stop chains, has been applied to the development of safety measures in industrial operations involving the exposure of explosive mixtures to sources of ignition. The protection afforded by dispersal of silicate or carbonate dusts when explosive charges are fired in coal mines may in part be due to the dust particles providing a large area on which the chains propagated through potentially explosive mixtures of fire damp and air can be efficiently terminated.

(*c*) *Quadratic Termination* reactions are extremely important. Heterogeneous processes in which two centres are almost simultaneously adsorbed on adjacent sites on the surface are intrinsically improbable and there is no reaction known for which this termination mechanism need be assumed. Homogeneous recombination reactions of centres are often encountered, however, and two types may be distinguished. If the centres are atoms or simple radicals then as pointed out on page 6, their recombination will probably require the presence of a third body (*M*) to withdraw all or part of the heat of formation of the newly formed molecule. Many examples of this behaviour are known, in fact the relative efficiency of the various substances when acting as 'third bodies' for the recombination of bromine atoms may be deduced from the effect of such substances on photo-bromination reactions[53]. Since the reaction of the third body is to de-energize the excited molecule which is formed, this order of efficiency ought to be similar to the order of collision cross-section for quenching of resonance radiation. Available data do indicate that the efficiency of a molecule as a quenching agent and as a third body is increased by increased atomicity or increased unsaturation (see Chapter I, ref. (5)).

If the centres combine to form a molecule with a considerable number of vibrational degrees of freedom, it is possible that the third body will not be required, e.g. $2CCl_3 \cdot \rightarrow C_2Cl_6$. This is due to the increased possibilities of delocalization of the energy of formation away from the bond formed (i.e. reverse of the process described on pp. 8 and 9) as the number of vibrational modes increases. Another factor which reduces the necessity for a third body is the tendency for radicals to undergo disproportionation reactions, simple examples of which are

(71) $$2HO_2 \rightarrow H_2O_2 + O_2$$

(72) $$\underline{COCl} + \underline{Cl} \rightarrow CO + Cl_2$$

Such dismutation processes, whilst not being recombination reactions, result in the formation of stable molecules from pairs of centres and therefore still constitute quadratic termination. They are probably of great importance in systems containing large hydrocarbon radicals, e.g. radical type polymerization processes, since it is known from studies of the photolysis of ketones in paraffin solution that paraffin radicals may react in pairs to form a paraffin and mono olefine.

(73) $$2RCH_2\text{---}CH_2 \cdot \rightarrow RCH\text{==}CH_2 + RCH_2CH_3$$

Considerations mentioned in Chapter I indicate that the dismutation reaction (73) would have a P factor approaching unity, but also an appreciable energy of activation, whereas the combination reaction (74)

(74) $$2RCH_2\text{---}CH_2 . \rightarrow RCH_2CH_2CH_2CH_2R$$

would possess both a smaller P factor and activation energy. It is therefore possible that as the temperature of a radical-type polymerization reaction is increased the mutual termination reaction might change progressively from a predominantly combination (74) reaction to a predominantly dismutation reaction (73). No unequivocal experimental evidence on this point is available.

For quadratic termination to be the dominant mode the velocity constant must be large since the concentration of centres is extremely small. Some values are given in Table II. A survey of quadratic termination reactions which have been postulated reveals that they are all considerably exothermic and that when the atomicity of the centres exceeds four, disproportionation rather than association is the rule, in agreement with the general notions of the transition state theory. Such high velocity constants prompt the question as to whether in some cases the controlling factor in the rate of quadratic termination is not the fruitfulness of collision but the rate at which the centres can diffuse together. This might well prove to be the case for large radicals in viscous media and hence, in considering polymerization reactions in the liquid phase where this effect is likely to be most marked (cf. p. 189) it should not be too readily assumed that the velocity constant of the termination reaction is constant as the reaction proceeds. The viscosity and the mean size of the growing chain will affect this velocity constant and both will vary throughout the reaction[54].

So far in this chapter most of the chain processes which can conceivably occur have been described and exemplified. Two further matters require particular emphasis. Firstly, in any one reaction under a given set of experimental conditions, it is usually true that only one of each of the initiation and termination processes given above are important; and that the experimental conditions can be varied to enhance selectively the role of the particular chain process it is wished to study. In the thermal reaction between hydrogen and bromine for example, at total pressures *ca.* 400 mm in cylindrical reaction vessels of diameter greater than 20 mm at temperatures 200–300°C; the reaction follows the scheme:

Initiation.   (75) $Br_2 \rightarrow 2\overline{Br}$: Thermal dissociation homogeneously in the gas phase

Propagation.   (76) $\overline{Br} + H_2 \rightleftharpoons HBr + \overline{H}$ ⎱ straight unbranched
            (77) $\overline{H} + Br_2 \rightarrow HBr + \overline{Br}$ ⎰   chains

Branching.   None

Termination. (78) $2\overline{Br} + M \rightarrow Br_2 + M$: Recombination of atoms. M may be *any* other species.

Secondly the chain centres have their quota of translational energy and will diffuse like any other molecular species in the system. As a result, if reaction chains are removed, but not generated at the wall, their concentration adjacent to the wall will be small and will increase to a maximum value at the centre of the reaction vessel. It is therefore at the centre (central axis

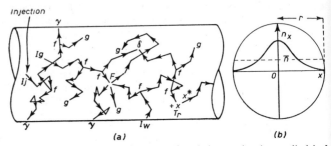

Fig. III.2. The spatial development of a chain reaction in a cylindrical reaction vessel of radius r. (a) elevation; (b) cross section

(a) Chain centres are imagined to follow the direction of the arrows from creation to destruction. *Propagation* is denoted by an angle unmarked by any symbol. It should be remembered that the actual path of a centre between successive propagation steps is not straight, but is the usual re-entrant diffusion path. *Chain transfer* with the agent X occurs at the angle marked Tr. *Initiation* homogeneously by photochemical, radiochemical, or thermal reactions of reactants or catalysts is denoted by Ig; heterogeneous initiation by Iw and introduction of a centre from an external source by Ij. *Linear branching* by the energy, radical, continuous or degenerate mechanisms is summarized by the bifurcation of lines at points marked f; and *quadratic branching* by the interaction of two lines at F. Homogeneous and heterogeneous *linear termination* are symbolized by cessation of the lines at points marked g and γ respectively. *Quadratic* or *mutual termination* is indicated by the stopping of two independent chains at δ.

(b) The radial distribution of the centres when wall termination is occurring. n_x is the concentration of the centres at the distance x perpendicularly from the central axis O. The region of most intense reaction (n_x a maximum) is the axis. $\bar{n}$ is the average concentration of the chain centres.

in cylindrical vessels) of the reaction vessel where the greatest reaction rates are to be found and where in the case of branching chain reactions there is the greatest proneness to ignition.

Diagrammatic Summary. In Fig. III.2 above an attempt has been made to depict the development of reaction chains through a reaction vessel, and the legend summarizes the classification used in this chapter.

REFERENCES

1. RODEBUSH, W. H. and KLINGELHOEFFER, W. C.: *J. Amer. Chem. Soc.*, **55**, 130 (1933); BACHER, E. and BONHOFFER, K. F.: *Z. Phys. Chem.*, A, **119**, 385 (1926); TAMURA, M.: *Rev. Phys. Chem. Japan*, **11**, 1 (1937); ASHMORE, P. G. and CHANMUGAM, J., *Trans. Faraday Soc.*, **49**, 254 (1953).

2. BOOTH, M. H. and LINNETT, J. W.: *Nature*, **199**, 1181 (1963).

3. BODENSTEIN, M. and LÜTKEMEYER, H.: ibid, **114**, 208 (1925); KISTIAKOWSKY, G. B. and VAN ARTSDALEN, E. R., *J. Chem. Phys.*, **12**, 469 (1944).

4. Ref. 3, Chapter II.

5. MATHESON, M. S., AUER, E. E., BEVILACQUA, E. B., and HART, E. J.,: *J. Amer. Chem. Soc.*, **71**, 502 (1949); **73**, 1700 (1951). MELVILLE, H. W. and MACKAY, M. H.: *Trans. Faraday Soc.*, **45**, 323 (1949).

6. Ref. 21, Chapter II.

7. BARTLETT, P. D. and SWAIN, C. G.: *J. Amer. Chem. Soc.*, **68**, 2381 (1946).

8. BATEMAN, L. and GEE, G.: *Proc. Roy. Soc.*, A, **195**, 376, 391 (1948).

9. HARMAN, R. A., HULBERT, H. M., TOBOLSKY, A. V., and EYRING, H.: *Ann. N.Y. Acad. Sci.*, **44**, 371 (1943).

10. See for example p. 113 et seq; *The Chemistry of Cationic Polymerization*, Ed. PLESCH, P. H., Pergamon, London (1963).

11. NATTA, G.: *J. Polymer Sci.*, **16**, 143 (1955); **48**, 219 (1960).

12. For a discussion of causes see COOPER, W., in *Progress in High Polymers*, **1**, 281, Heywood, London (1961).

13. Ref. 25, Chapter II.

14. BREITENBACH, J. W. and MASCHIN, A.: *Z. phys. Chem.*, A, 187, 175 (1940).

15. MAYO, F. R.: *J. Amer. Chem. Soc.*, **65**, 2324 (1943).

16. OGG, R. A. and WILLIAMS, R. R.: *J. Chem. Phys.*, **13**, 586 (1945) and HARRIS, G. M. and WILLARD, J. E.: *J. Amer. Chem. Soc.*, **76**, 4678 (1954).

17. THOMPSON, S. O. and SCHAEFFER, O. A.: *J. Amer. Chem. Soc.*, **80**, 553 (1958).

18. For other examples of free-radical as well as ionic chain polymerization induced by high energy radiation see CHAPIRO, A.: *Radiation Chemistry of Polymeric Systems*, Interscience, New York (1962).

19. Ref. 14, Chapter I.

20. BAXENDALE, J. H., EVANS, M. G. and PARK, G. S.: *Trans. Faraday Soc.*, **42**, 155 (1946).

21. BACON, R. G. R.: ibid, **42**, 140 (1946).

22. DAINTON, F. S. and JAMES, D. G. L.: *Trans. Faraday Soc.*, **54**, 649 (1958).

23. EVANS, A. G. and POLANYI, M.: *J. Chem. Soc.*, **252** (1947); see also PLESCH[10].

24. ELEY, D. D. and RICHARDS, A. W.: *Trans. Faraday Soc.*, **45**, 425 (1949).

25. DAINTON, F. S. and SUTHERLAND, G. B. B. M.: *J. Polymer Sci.*, **4**, 37 (1949).

26. SZWARC, M.: *Nature*, **178**, 1168 (1956); LEVY, M. and SZWARC, M.: *J. Amer. Chem. Soc.*, **82**, 521 (1960).

27. EVANS, M. G., SANTAPPA, M., and URI, N.: *J. Polymer Sci.*, **7**, 243 (1951). See also reference 24 of Chapter II.

28. MATHESON, M. S., MULAC, W. A. and RABANI, J.: *J. Phys. Chem.*, **67**, 2613 (1963).

29. SCHULTE-FROHLINDE, D. and EIBEN, K.: *Z. Naturforsch.*, **17a**, 445 (1962), **18a**, 99 (1963); ERSOV, B. G., PIKAEV, A. K., GLAZUNOV, P. J. and SPITSYN, V. J.: *Doklady*, **149**, 363 (1963).

30. GORDON, S., HART, E. J., MATHESON, M. S., RABANI, J. and THOMAS, J. K.: *Disc. Faraday Soc.*, **36**, 193 (1963); KEENE, J. P., ibid 304, (1963).

31. RAEF, Y. and SWALLOW, A. J., *Trans. Faraday Soc.*, **59**, 1631 (1963).

32. DAINTON, F. S., GIBBS, A. R., SMITHIES, D. and WALKER, D. C., to be published.

33. GORDON, S., HART, E. J. and HUTCHINSON, D. A.: *J. Chim. Physique*, **52**, 570 (1955).

34. DAINTON, F. S., SMITHIES, D., SKWARSKI, T. and WEZRANOWSKI, E., *Trans. Faraday Soc.*, **60**, 1068 (1964).

35. E.g. MILLER, N.: *Trans. Faraday Soc.*, **46**, 546 (1950); PRUD'-HOMME, R. O. and GRABAR, P.: *J. Chim. Physique*, **46**, 323 (1949).

36. MELVILLE, H. W. and LUDAM, E. B.: *Proc. Roy. Soc.*, A, **135**, 315 (1932).

37. PARRAVANO, G. S.: *J. Amer. Chem. Soc.*, **72**, 3856 (1950).

38. See ref. 10, page 223.

39. HABER, F. and OPPENHEIMER, F.: *Z. phys. Chem.*, B, **16**, 443 (1932).

40. NALBANDJAN, A., DUBOWITSKI, F., and SEMENOV, N.: *Trans. Faraday Soc.*, **29**, 606 (1933).

41. SEMENOV, N.: *J. Chem. Phys.*, **7**, 683 (1939).

42. HICKS, J. A. and MELVILLE, H. W.: *Nature*, **171**, 300 (1953).

43. CHAPIRO, A. in ref. 18.

44. SEMENOV, N., *Chemical Kinetics and Chain Reactions*, Oxford (1935).

45. SEMENOV, N.: *Chem. Rev.*, **6**, 347 (1929).

46. See ref. 10 Chapter II; HINSHELWOOD, C. N.: *Proc. Roy. Soc.*, A, **188**, 1 (1947). SEMENOV, N.: *C.R. Acad. Sci.*, *U.R.S.S.* **43**, 342; **44**, 62, 241 (1944); LEWIS, B. and VON ELBE, G.: *Combustion, Flames, and Explosions of Gases*, Academic Press, New York (1962);

47. Ref. 7, Chapter II.

48. SEMENOV, N.: *J. Chem. Phys.*, **7**, 683 (1939).
49. COE, C. S. and DOUMANI, T. F.: *J. Amer. Chem. Soc.*, **70**, 1516 (1948); CHILTON, H. T. J. and GOWENLOCK, B. J.: *J. Chem. Soc.*, 3232 (1953).
50. Ref. 25, Chapter II.
51. COLLINSON, E., DAINTON, F. S., MILE, B., TAZUKÉ, S. and SMITH, D. R.: *Nature*, **198**, 26 (1963); also ref. 20 Chapter II.
52. TAYLOR, H. S. and LAVIN, G. I.: *J. Amer. Chem. Soc.*, **52**, 1910 (1930).
53. RITCHIE, M.: *Proc. Roy. Soc.*, A, **146**, 828 (1934); HILFERDING, K. and STEINER, W.: *Z. Phys. Chem.*, B, **30**, 399 (1935); PALMER, H. B. and HORNIG, D. F.: *J. Chem. Phys.*, **26**, 98 (1957); BRITTON, D., *J. Phys. Chem.*, **64**, 742 (1960).
54. NORRISH, R. G. W. and SMITH, R. R.: *Nature*, **150**, 336 (1942).

CHAPTER IV

THE MATHEMATICAL TREATMENT
OF CHAIN REACTIONS

A. Introductory and the Principle of Stationary States with Simple Applications

Introductory. There are two approaches to the problem of the mathematical representation of chain reactions. In the first method, only the steady state conditions are considered, whilst the second method which was originally developed by the Russian School takes account of non-steady state conditions. Both methods lead to the same expressions for the dependence of the steady state rate and explosion limits on such variables as the temperature, vessel shape and condition, foreign gas concentration, etc., but only the second method gives a satisfactory account of rate-time curves, induction periods, and after-effects. Since both methods are in common use, both will be given; the steady state method in outline and the other in greater detail.

The Steady-State Method: The Principle of Stationary States. Except for those reactions in which the chains are very short and in which the termination step results in product formation, the rate of formation of each product is determined solely by the velocity of the appropriate propagation reaction. For the case in which there are *two* chain centres X and Y reacting according to equations (1), (2a), or (2b) of Chapter III, we can write

$$\frac{d[Pr]}{dt} = k_1[X][R] \quad \text{and} \quad \frac{d[Pr']}{dt} = k_{2a}[Y][R'] \text{ or } k_{2b}[Y] \quad \text{(IV.1)}$$

In general, if there are l propagation reactions involving l different centres which result in product formation there will be l equations of the form of one of these in (IV.1). Since the different products $Pr, Pr', Pr'', \ldots$ which may emerge from these reactions will be formed in a constant ratio to one another which will be determined by the form of the chemical equation which defines the overall stoichiometry it follows that there will be $l - 1$ equations of the form (IV.2) which define the relative concentrations of the chain centres during reactions. Two important conclusions may be drawn. Firstly, however complex the dependence of

$$\frac{[X]}{[Y]} = \frac{k_{2a}[R']}{k_1[R]} \quad \text{or} \quad \frac{k_{2b}}{k_1[R]} \quad \cdots \quad \text{(IV.2)}$$

the concentration of any individual chain centre on time or any experimental variable, the concentration of all the other centres will vary in a similar manner because the relative concentrations of all the centres depends only on the magnitude of the reactant concentrations which bear a fixed ratio to one another which is determined by the experimenter's choice of conditions, and the rate constants of the appropriate reactions. Secondly, if the overall reaction rate, $d[Pr]/dt$ or $d[Pr']/dt$ or . . . , is found to be constant under the conditions of the experiment and when the concentration of reactants is maintained constant, the concentration of each chain centre will be invariant, i.e. there will be l equations of the form (IV.3)

$$\frac{d[X]}{dt} = 0 \quad \cdots \quad \text{(IV.3)}$$

This is called the *steady state* or *stationary state* condition. If, on the other hand, the overall reaction is continually accelerating or decelerating the concentration of each of the centres must likewise be increasing or decreasing in proportion and *non-steady state* or *non-stationary state* conditions are said to prevail.

The general procedure for obtaining a relationship between the steady state rate and the reactant concentration which is based on a postulated reaction mechanism will now be evident. For each of l centres an equation corresponding to (IV.3) is written down, and the l simultaneous equations solved to give expressions for the concentration of each centre, $[X]$, $[Y]$, etc. Finally, substitution of these expressions in the appropriate equations (IV.1) will give the desired rate equation. For a chain reaction in which quadratic branching and termination are absent one of the equations (IV.3) can usually be put in the form

$$\frac{d[X]}{dt} = I + F[X] + k_{2a}[Y][R'] \quad \text{(or } k_{2b}[Y])$$
$$- k_1[X][R] - G[X] - W[X] = 0 \quad \text{(IV.4)}$$

where I is the rate of initial formation of X, $F[\underline{X}]$ is the expression for the rate of formation of additional $\overline{X}$ centres in linear branching processes, and $W[\underline{X}]$ and $G[\underline{X}]$ are the rates of removal of this centre at the wall and in the gas phase respectively. If the chains are long the third and fourth terms on the right-hand side of equation (IV.4) will be equal and, incidentally, each will be much larger than any of the other terms, so that this equation reduces to

$$\frac{d[\underline{X}]}{dt} = I + F[\underline{X}] - G[\underline{X}] - W[\underline{X}] = 0 \qquad . \text{ (IV.5)}$$

therefore

$$[\underline{X}] = I/(G + W - F) \quad . \quad . \quad . \quad . \quad . \text{ (IV.6)}$$

and

$$\frac{d[Pr]}{dt} = \frac{k_1 I[R]}{G + W - F} = \frac{I}{\bar{t}(G + W - F)}. \quad . \text{ (IV.7)}$$

where $\bar{t} = (k_1[R])^{-1}$ is $1.443 \times$ the average half-life* of the centre X in the propagation reaction, $X + R \to Pr + Y$, i.e. it is a measure of the average time which centre X exists between its formation in one propagation step and its disappearance in the next. Equation (IV.7) indicates that a steady state is possible provided $(G + W) > F$, and that the explosion boundary is the locus of all the combinations of experimental variables for which $G + W = F$. The average number of product molecules formed in a chain, called the *kinetic chain length* (k.c.l.) = reaction rate $\div$ initiation rate = $[(G + W - F)\bar{t}]^{-1}$ and the average lifetime of a chain between creation and destruction $\tau = \bar{t} \times$ k.c.l. $= (G + W - F)^{-1}$.

In contrast with this result, if the principal mode of chain termination is by a recombination reaction such as $X + \overline{X} + M \to X_2 + M$ (velocity constant $= k_t$) and the chains are unbranched, we have, when the stationary state is attained,

$$\frac{d[\underline{X}]}{dt} = I - k_t M[\underline{X}]^2 = 0 . \quad . \quad . \quad . \quad . \quad . \text{ (IV.8)}$$

and $\dfrac{d[Pr]}{dt} = k_1[R] \left[\dfrac{I}{k_t[M]} \right]^{\frac{1}{2}} = \dfrac{1}{\bar{t}} \left[\dfrac{I}{k_t[M]} \right]^{\frac{1}{2}} \quad . \quad . \quad . \quad . \text{ (IV.9)}$

* For a discussion of the terms half-life and lifetime see Appendix 1.

and the rate expression includes rate constants and concentrations to the half power. The average lifetime (τ) between creation and destruction is now $= (Ik_t[M])^{-\frac{1}{2}}$ and is longer the smaller the rate of initiation.

As an illustration of the detailed application of the principle of stationary states we will consider the photosynthesis of hydrogen chloride[1]. This is a typical chain reaction. It has a high quantum yield, an induction period, is very susceptible to negative catalysis, is sensitive to vessel dimensions, and has a complicated rate equation. Chains are initiated by photo-dissociation of chlorine molecules according to

(1) $$\underline{Cl}_2 + h\nu \rightarrow \underline{Cl} + \underline{Cl}$$

at a rate $= \phi_1 I_{abs}$, where I_{abs} is the number of quanta absorbed per second per unit volume and ϕ_1 the quantum efficiency of this primary act in units of chlorine atoms per absorbed quantum. Chains are propagated by the steps

(2) $$\underline{Cl} + H_2 \rightarrow HCl + \underline{H} - 1 \text{ k.cal}$$

(3) $$\underline{H} + Cl_2 \rightarrow HCl + \underline{Cl} + 46 \text{ k.cal}$$

(4) $$\underline{H} + HCl \rightarrow H_2 + \underline{Cl} + 1 \text{ k.cal}$$

Reactions (2) and (3) result in formation of HCl, i.e. product, reaction (3) accounting for almost all the heat evolved in the reaction which is manifested in the pressure rise called the Draper effect. Reaction (4) is the reverse of reaction (2) and whilst it is not a chain termination process is retarding in the sense that product molecules, i.e. HCl are converted to a reactant i.e. H_2 (cf. p. 60). The near thermoneutrality of reactions (2) and (4) indicates that their respective energies of activation are about equal and therefore, if reaction (2) is assumed, reaction (4) must also be included in the mechanism. There is no evidence for branching at room temperature and no branching reaction need be considered, i.e. $F[X] = 0$. At total pressures greater than 30 mm and in the absence of any negative catalyst the predominant chain termination reaction is expected to be the recombination of the chlorine atoms, which is presumably

(5) $$\underline{Cl} + \underline{Cl} + M \rightarrow Cl_2 + M$$

but at very low total pressures, *ca.* 10–20 mm this reaction is negligible compared with wall termination of the chains which could be written

(6) $\qquad$ $\underline{Cl}$ + wall → destruction

(7) $\qquad$ $\underline{H}$ + wall → destruction

Under all conditions the rate of formation of hydrogen chloride is

$$\frac{d[HCl]}{dt} = k_2[\underline{Cl}][H_2] + k_3[\underline{H}][Cl_2] - k_4[\underline{H}][HCl] \quad . \quad (IV.10)$$

but the appropriate stationary state equations depend on the pressure. Considering first the high pressure region

$$\frac{d[\underline{Cl}]}{dt} = \phi_1 I_{abs} - k_2[\underline{Cl}][H_2] + k_3[\underline{H}][Cl_2] + k_4[\underline{H}][HCl] -$$
$$k_5[\underline{Cl}]^2[M] = 0$$

$$\frac{d[\underline{H}]}{dt} = k_2[\underline{Cl}][H_2] - k_3[\underline{H}][Cl_2] - k_4[\underline{H}][HCl] = 0$$

Whence

$$\frac{d[\underline{Cl}]}{dt} = \phi_1 I_{abs} - k_5[M][\underline{Cl}]^2 = 0 \quad \text{(cf. equation (IV.8))}$$

Therefore $\qquad$ $[\underline{Cl}] = \left[\dfrac{\phi_1 I_{abs}}{k_5[M]}\right]^{\frac{1}{2}}$

and

$$[\underline{H}] = \frac{k_2[H_2]\left[\dfrac{\phi_1 I_{abs}}{k_5[M]}\right]^{\frac{1}{2}}}{k_3[Cl_2] + k_4[HCl]}$$

and the theoretical expression for the rate is

$$\frac{d[HCl]}{dt} = \frac{2k_2 k_3[H_2][Cl_2]}{k_3[Cl_2] + k_4[HCl]} \cdot \left[\frac{\phi_1 I_{abs}}{k_5[M]}\right]^{\frac{1}{2}} \quad \text{(cf. equation (IV.9))}$$

The quantum yield γ = HCl molecules formed per quantum absorbed is therefore

$$\gamma = \frac{2k_2 k_3[H_2][Cl_2]}{k_3[Cl_2] + k_4[HCl]}\left[\frac{\phi_1}{k_5[M]I_{abs}}\right]^{\frac{1}{2}} \quad . \quad . \quad . \quad . \quad (IV.11)$$

and the chain length

$$= \frac{\gamma}{\phi_1} = \frac{2k_2k_3[H_2][Cl_2]}{k_3[Cl_2] + k_4[HCl]}[\phi_1 k_5[M]I_{abs}]^{-\frac{1}{2}} . \quad . \quad (IV.12)$$

The expression for the quantum yield γ is identical with that found experimentally by NORRISH and RITCHIE[2], with the exception of the term $[M]^{-\frac{1}{2}}$. These authors did not detect any effect of total pressure in this sense, and it must be concluded that reaction (5) either does not involve a third body or is not the true chain termination reaction. It has been suggested[3] that the homogeneous reaction (5) is insufficiently fast at room temperature and an alternative reaction which has been proposed[4] is

(8) $$Cl + Cl_3 \rightarrow 2Cl_2 \text{ with } Cl + Cl_2 \rightleftharpoons Cl_3$$

which does not require a third body. At temperatures below about $-100°C$, reaction (4), which has an energy of activation of about 6 kcal mole^{-1}, becomes unimportant, i.e. $k_3[Cl_2] \gg k_4[HCl]$ and, making this substitution, equation (IV.11) becomes

$$\gamma = 2k_2[H_2](\phi_1/k_5[M]I_{abs})^{\frac{1}{2}} \quad . \quad . \quad (IV.13)$$

which, apart from the term $[M]^{-\frac{1}{2}}$ is identical with that observed experimentally by POTTS and ROLLEFSON[5].

In the low pressure region where the chains are terminated at the walls we have

$$\frac{d[Cl]}{dt} = \phi_1 I_{abs} - k_2[Cl][H_2] + k_3[H][Cl_2] + k_4[H][HCl] \\ - k_6[Cl] = 0$$

$$\frac{d[H]}{dt} = k_2[Cl][H_2] - k_3[H][Cl_2] - k_4[H][HCl] - k_7[H] = 0$$

Whence, solving for $[Cl]$ and $[H]$ and substituting the values in equation (10),

$$\frac{d[HCl]}{dt} = \frac{\phi_1 k_2[H_2]I_{abs}(2k_3[Cl_2] + k_7)}{k_7k_2[H_2] + k_3k_6[Cl_2] + k_4k_6[HCl] + k_6k_7}$$

(cf. equation (IV.7) when $F = 0$)

Both k_6 and k_7 represent rates of diffusion and will be inversely proportional to the time taken to diffuse the average distance to the wall. Let this distance be Δ, then by the Einstein–Schmoluchowsky equation, k_6 and k_7 will be proportional to $\left(\dfrac{\Delta^2}{2D}\right)^{-1}$ where D is the appropriate diffusion coefficient. This average distance Δ will be proportional to the vessel diameter d and we can therefore write $k_6 = k_6'/d^2$ and $k_7 = k_7'/d^2$. Allowing for this fact we conclude that at low pressures the rate should be proportional to the square of the vessel diameter. This expectation was very elegantly confirmed by TRIFONOV[6]. Unfortunately he did not test the dependence of the rate on light intensity and partial pressures of hydrogen and chlorine under these conditions.

The photosynthesis of hydrogen chloride was chosen to illustrate the way in which the stationary state method is applied partly because it is the reaction from the study of which the concept of chain reactions was first developed by BODENSTEIN and his colleagues. Even though some fifty years have elapsed since the first quantitative experiments on this reaction were carried out some features of the mechanism are still uncertain, surely, a salutary comment on the progress of this branch of chemical kinetics!

REFERENCES

1. For accounts of this reaction see LEIGHTON, P. and NOYES, W. A.: *The Photochemistry of Gases*, p. 265, Reinhold, New York (1941); TROTMAN-DICKENSON, A. F.: *Gas Kinetics*, p. 181, Butterworths, London (1955).
2. NORRISH, R. G. W. and RITCHIE, M.: *Proc. Roy. Soc.*, A, **140**, 112 (1933).
3. BENSON, S. W.: *J. Chem. Phys.*, **20**, 1605 (1952).
4. ROLLEFSON, G. K. and EYRING, H.: *J. Amer. Chem. Soc.*, **54**, 170 (1932).
5. POTTS, J. C. and ROLLEFSON, G. K.: *J. Amer. Chem. Soc.*, **57**, 1027 (1935).
6. Ref. 5, Chapter II.

APPENDIX I

Note on the Use of the Terms Half-life and Average Lifetimes

The half-life and average lifetimes of a species in a chemically reacting system require careful definition. The half-life is defined as the time for the concentration of the species to diminish to half the value which it had at time zero. When the species is disappearing in a single first order process, i.e. $dx/dt = -kx$, then $t_{\frac{1}{2}} = \ln 2/k = 0.693/k$ and when it is simultaneously disappearing by m first order processes having rate constants k', k'', k''', ..., the *actual* half life, $t_{\frac{1}{2}} = 0.693/\sum\limits^{m}(k' + k'' + k''' \ldots)$, and is related to the half-lives $t_{\frac{1}{2}}'$, $t_{\frac{1}{2}}''$, $t_{\frac{1}{2}}'''$, . . . for disappearance in each one of the processes considered separately by the equation; $t_{\frac{1}{2}}^{-1} = \sum\limits^{m}(^1/t_{\frac{1}{2}}' + {}^1/t_{\frac{1}{2}}'' \ldots)$. When the species is disappearing by interaction with another species of the same kind, $\underline{X} + \underline{X} \rightarrow X_2$, and the kinetics of the process is defined by the equation

$$- d[\underline{X}]/dt = k_a[\underline{X}]^2$$

the *actual* half-life $t_{\frac{1}{2}} = k_a[\underline{X}]_0)^{-1}$, where $[\underline{X}]_0$ is the concentration of $\underline{X}$ at time zero. In chain reactions a chain carrier may take part simultaneously in a variety of unimolecular (e.g. $\underline{X}$ + wall), pseudo-unimolecular (e.g. $\underline{X}$ + retarder, $[\underline{X}] \ll [\text{retarder}]$) and bimolecular (e.g. $\underline{X} + \underline{X}$) reactions in which it is destroyed. If the rate constants of these reactions are k_1, k_2, and k_3 the decay equation is

$$- d[\underline{X}]/dt = [\underline{X}](k_1 + k_2[\text{retarder}] + k_3[\underline{X}]) = [\underline{X}]0.693/t_{\frac{1}{2}}$$

where $t_{\frac{1}{2}}$, the *actual* half-life, depends on [retarder] and $[\underline{X}]$ and the 'contribution' to this half-life from the bimolecular process is 69.3 per cent of the half-life of $\underline{X}$ if this were decaying from an initial concentration $= [\underline{X}]$ solely by the bimolecular reaction. For many purposes it is more convenient to refer to the average lifetime $\bar{t}$, as the reciprocal of the unimolecular or pseudo-unimolecular rate constant. This quantity is $1.443 \times$ actual half-life for a unimolecular or pseudo-unimolecular process and is the time for $[\underline{X}]$ to diminish to $[\underline{X}]/e$, but for the bimolecular process it is also the true half-life, i.e. the time for $[\underline{X}]$ to fall to $[\underline{X}]/2$.

APPENDIX II

Facility in the use of the stationary state method is best gained by working out rate expressions from reaction mechanisms. Below are given some mechanisms to which the reader may apply this method.

1. Gaseous Photochlorination

A mechanism for the gaseous photochlorination of a substance A (= CO or olefine) to form the adduct ACl_2 involves the steps:

Initiation   (1) $Cl_2 + h\nu \rightarrow 2\underline{Cl}$

Propagation $\begin{cases} (2) & Cl + A \rightarrow \underline{ACl} \\ (3) & \underline{ACl} + Cl_2 \rightarrow ACl_2 + \underline{Cl} \end{cases}$

Mutual
Termination $\begin{cases} (4) & 2\underline{ACl} \rightarrow A + ACl_2 \\ (5) & \underline{ACl} + \underline{Cl} \rightarrow A + Cl_2 \\ (6) & 2\underline{Cl} + M \rightarrow Cl_2 + M \end{cases}$

Deduce the rate expression (*a*) when (4), (5), or (6) is the predominant chain termination step, (*b*) when the reaction $\underline{ACl} \rightarrow A + \underline{Cl}$ occurs and is faster than reaction (3) and reaction (5) is the main termination step, (*c*) when NOCl is added and destroys $\underline{Cl}$ and $\underline{ACl}$ radicals in bimolecular reactions.

2. Decomposition of Aqueous Hydrogen Peroxide

(*a*) *By Ultra-violet Light.* The reaction steps for acid solution are

Initiation   (1) $H_2O_2 + h\nu \rightarrow \phi_{OH}\underline{OH}$

Propagation $\begin{cases} (2) & \underline{OH} + H_2O_2 \rightarrow H_2O + \underline{HO_2} \\ (3) & \underline{HO_2} + H_2O_2 \rightarrow H_2O + O_2 + \underline{OH} \end{cases}$

Termination   (4) $2\underline{HO_2} \rightarrow H_2O_2 + O_2$

Deduce the rate expression.

(*b*) *By Added Ferrous Salts.* Other possible reactions are

(5) $Fe^{2+} + H_2O_2 \rightarrow Fe^{3+} + \underline{OH} + OH^-$

(6) $\underline{OH} + Fe^{2+} \rightarrow Fe^{3+} + OH^-$

(7) $\underline{HO_2} + Fe^{2+} \rightarrow Fe^{3+} + HO_2^- (+ H^+ \rightarrow H_2O_2)$

(8) $\underline{HO_2} + Fe^{3+} \rightarrow H^+ + O_2 + Fe^{2+}$

Given that at pH $\simeq 1$, $k_8 \simeq 0.1 k_7$, $k_2 \simeq 10^{-2} k_6$ consider the following:

(i) The stoichiometry and the dependence of the rate on $[H_2O_2]_0$ and $[Fe^{2+}]_0$ when $[Fe^{2+}]_0 \gg [H_2O_2]_0$.

(ii) The rate of oxidation of ferrous ion and the stationary ferrous ion concentration which is attained when $[Fe^{2+}]_0 \ll [H_2O_2]_0$.

3. Polymerization of Acrylamide in Aqueous Solution

Acrylamide ($m_1 = CH_2:CH.CO.NH_2$) undergoes free-radical polymerization when dissolved in water.

(a) Given that the primary acts in the γ-irradiation of water at pH 1 can be represented by (1)

(1) $\qquad 4.5H_2O \xrightarrow{} 3.7H + 2.9OH + 0.8H_2O_2 + 0.45H_2$

per 100 eV of energy absorbed and in the irradiation of hydrogen peroxide by 2537 Å light by (2), deduce expressions for the rates

(2) $\qquad\qquad H_2O_2 + h\nu \rightarrow 0.9OH$

and degrees of polymerization for the γ-ray initiated and H_2O_2-photosensitized polymerizations of acrylamide in dilute aqueous solution.

(b) When ferric ions are present in the solution they react with the polymer radicals according to equation (3). Consider how k_3 may be measured.

(3) $\qquad\qquad m_j + Fe^{3+} \rightarrow P_j + H^+ + Fe^{2+}$

(c) When the species $Fe^{3+}OH_{aq}^-$ absorbs 3130 Å light reaction (4) occurs

(4) $\qquad\qquad Fe^{3+}OH_{aq}^- + h\nu \rightarrow 0.18Fe^{2+} + 0.18OH$

Consider the kinetics of the ferric ion photosensitized polymerization of acrylamide in aqueous solution.

(d) Argentous ions are inert to polymer radicals but are rapidly reduced by hydrogen atoms according to equation (5). Consider the effect of added argentous salts on the rate of polymerization

(5) $\qquad\qquad H\cdot + Ag^+ \rightarrow H^+ + Ag$

and how this may be used to obtain the relative reactivity of argentous ions and acrylamide towards hydrogen atoms.

4. Pyrolysis of Ethane

This proceeds by the mechanism

(1) $$C_2H_6 \rightarrow 2CH_3$$

(2) $$CH_3 + C_2H_6 \rightarrow CH_4 + C_2H_5$$

(3) $$C_2H_5 \rightarrow C_2H_4 + H$$

(4) $$H + C_2H_6 \rightarrow H_2 + C_2H_5$$

(5) $$2C_2H_5 \rightarrow C_4H_{10}$$

Obtain expressions for the rates of production of H_2, CH_4, and C_2H_4 and consider the significance of the observation that the order of reaction with respect to ethane concentration increases above unity as the pressure is reduced and that in this low pressure region the presence of an inert gas accelerates the reaction.

When nitric oxide is added in increasing amounts the rate falls to a limiting value. Deduce the expression for this limiting rate on the assumption that nitric oxide causes the following reactions to replace reactions (1), (2), and (5).

(6) $$C_2H_6 + NO \rightarrow C_2H_5 + HNO$$

(7) $$H + NO \rightarrow HNO$$

(8) $$HNO \rightarrow H + NO$$

(9) $$HNO + C_2H_5 \rightarrow C_2H_6 + NO$$

CHAPTER V

THE MATHEMATICAL TREATMENT
OF CHAIN REACTIONS

B. General Mathematical Treatment including Non-steady State Conditions

EQUATION (IV.1) is valid whether or not a stationary state exists and hence, under isothermal conditions, the variation of the reaction rate with time will depend on the way in which $[X]$ and $[R]$ alter. The reactant concentration must always decrease as the reaction proceeds and *acceleration* of the reaction can only be due to an increase of $[X]$. In general, the fate of a reaction, i.e. whether it is to be explosively rapid or attain a speed which is to be steady for an appreciable part of the reaction, is determined by the conditions which obtain initially and therefore before $[R]$ has undergone much decrease. A useful approach to the discussion of the time dependence of chain processes is, therefore, to consider the way in which the concentration of centres would vary with time, the reactant concentration being presumed constant. Although more than one chain centre may be involved in the propagation of the chains, and the concentration of each will differ, these concentrations will bear a constant ratio to one another not only during steady state conditions but also when the reaction rate is increasing or decreasing. For the purposes of investigating the time dependence of the rate it therefore suffices to consider in a general way how an average centre concentration which we will call n varies.

The rates of the three processes of *initiation*, *branching*, and *termination* are the sole arbiters of the fate of n. Let θ represent the total rate of initial formation of centres, assumed to be uniform and homogeneous, fn be the rate of linear branching, Fn^2 the rate of quadratic branching, gn the rate of linear termination in the gas phase, and δn^2 the rate of mutual destruction of centres. The centres may also be destroyed at the wall of the reaction vessel. Usually this process is efficient and the rate of chain termination due to this process is proportional to the rate of diffusion to the wall. When each centre takes part in a propagation reaction it produces a new centre and it is therefore legitimate to consider the same centre to be diffusing provided a suitably weighted mean value of the diffusion coefficients is used. However, wall termination will cause a spatial variation of the value of n from zero in the gas layer immediately adjacent to the vessel wall to a maximum at the point most remote from the wall (cf. Fig. III.2). Rigorous mathematical representation of the effect of wall termination is therefore only possible if the shape of the vessel has some elements of symmetry which permit the specification of a co-ordinate for the concentration gradient— in short—if a proper diffusion equation can be set up. This has been done by many authors, notably BURSIAN and SOROKIN[4], and a full discussion is given in SEMENOV's book[1]. In the simplest case of a reaction vessel of two parallel plane walls of infinite area we may write

$$\frac{dn_x}{dt} = \theta + (f - g)n_x + (F - \delta)n_x^2 + \bar{D}\frac{\partial^2 n_x}{\partial x^2} \quad . \quad . \quad (V.1)$$

where $\bar{D}$ is the mean coefficient of diffusion of the centres through the particular gas mixture and n_x is the concentration of the centres at a distance x from the median plane of the vessel. In the case of a spherical vessel this equation would of course be

$$\frac{dn_x}{dt} = \theta + (f - g)n_x + (F - \delta)n_x^2 + \bar{D}\frac{1}{x^2}\cdot\frac{\partial(x^2\partial n_x/\partial x)}{\partial x} \quad (V.2)$$

where x is now the distance from the centre.

The analytical solution of these equations is only possible for certain limiting conditions, e.g. for the stationary state and when the term in n_x^2 is omitted. This limitation is not so restrictive as would appear, since, as stated on p. 79, the experimental conditions are often such that only one type of termination or branching may be operative. Before discussing these cases in detail an important general conclusion may be anticipated, viz. provided the centres are not generated at the wall, the rate of wall termination may be taken, as a first approximation, as proportional to $\bar{D}/d^2$ where d is the diameter of a long cylindrical vessel or of a spherical reaction vessel.

(a) Unbranched Chains Linearly Terminated

Case (1): *Straight chains initiated homogeneously and terminated at the wall.* An example of this behaviour is the hydrogen chlorine reaction at low pressures in narrow tubes of short length. For sufficiently short tubes and low pressures of chlorine with a large incident light intensity the chlorine atoms, formed by the optical dissociation of chlorine molecules, may be considered to be generated at the same rate throughout the reaction vessel. The chains are unbranched and the principal mode of stopping is by adsorption of atoms at the vessel walls. The appropriate equation is

$$\frac{\mathrm{d}\boldsymbol{n}_x}{\mathrm{d}t} = \theta + \bar{D}\frac{\partial^2 \boldsymbol{n}_x}{\partial x^2} \quad . \quad . \quad . \quad . \quad (V.3)$$

and it is evident that a stationary state is soon reached. When the reaction is enclosed between two infinite planes a distance d apart, integration of this equation when $d\boldsymbol{n}_x/\mathrm{d}t = 0$ leads to a value for the total number of centres in a volume 1 sq cm cross section extending perpendicularly from wall to wall, of $\dfrac{\theta d^3}{12\bar{D}}$ and hence the overall average concentration per unit volume of the reaction vessel $= \bar{n} = \dfrac{\theta d^2}{12\bar{D}}$. Whence, if the average lifetime of a centre between successive propagation reactions is $\bar{t}$ (cf. p. 86), the reaction rate $\dfrac{\mathrm{d}[Pr]}{\mathrm{d}t} = \dfrac{\bar{n}}{\bar{t}} = \dfrac{\theta d^2}{12\bar{D}\bar{t}}$ and the average kinetic chain length = number of product molecules formed on the average from each initial centre $= \dfrac{\mathrm{d}[Pr]}{\mathrm{d}t}\bigg/\theta = \dfrac{d^2}{12\bar{D}\bar{t}} = d^2/4\bar{z}\lambda^2$

where $\bar{z}$ is the average number of collisions undergone by a centre in time $\bar{t}$, and λ is the mean free path.

In the particular example cited, TRIFONOV[2] has shown that equimolar mixtures of hydrogen and chlorine at total pressures about 10 mm react at a rate strictly proportional to d^2.

This dependence of the steady rate on the square of the diameter is readily seen from the Schmoluchowski diffusion relation, which states that the number of collisions undergone by a particle diffusing a distance $\bar{\Delta}$ is $3\pi\bar{\Delta}^2/4\lambda^2$. Hence the average number of collisions undergone by chain centres in reaching the walls is $\pi d^2/16\lambda^2$. The kinetic chain length will be this number divided by the number ($\bar{z}$) of collisions undergone in time $\bar{t}$ and hence the chain length is $\pi d^2/16\bar{z}\lambda^2$, a result similar to that obtained by the exact method.

The effect of pressure on chain reactions involving wall termination is twofold. Firstly the average time between propagation steps will be reduced since $\bar{t} = (k_1[R])^{-1}$ (cf. Chapter IV), and secondly the diffusion constant D will be sensitive to pressure. Although the precise relation between $\bar{D}$ and composition is unknown, it is likely that $\bar{D} = \bar{D}_0/p$ for mixtures of constant composition. The two effects reinforce one another and it would be expected that for a constant rate of initiation, the rate of a chain reaction of this type would be proportional to p^2 as well as d^2. No clear example of this effect can be cited.

Case (2): *Straight chains initiated and terminated at the wall.* This is a case for which it is not possible to give a definite example; for although there are a number of cases in which it is suspected that chains start at the wall and are propagated into the gas phase, e.g. the oxidation of phosphorus vapour catalysed by a hot tungsten wire, studied by MELVILLE and LUDLAM[3]; there is none of which it can be said with certainty that the chains are terminated solely at the walls of the vessel from which they also start. Nevertheless this problem must be stated for the sake of completeness. In the case of the parallel plane-sided vessel, it is readily shown that the velocity $= 3\theta d/\bar{z}\lambda$, i.e. the chain length is now proportional to the first power of the diameter. The alternative approach employing the Schmoluchowski equation leads to the same result.

The difference between cases (1) and (2) is most clearly seen as follows. The average concentration of centres is equal to the ratio of the initiation and surface termination rates. The latter term is proportional to d^{-2} for spherical vessels. In case (1), the rate of initiation expressed as the average number of chains started per unit volume is independent of d. In case (2) the total number of chains started will be proportional to d^2 and the number per unit volume of the whole vessel will be proportional to d^2/d^3. The average centre concentration and average rate is therefore proportional to the first power of the diameter.

Case (3): *Straight chains initiated homogeneously and terminated homogeneously.* This case occurs quite frequently, e.g. (*a*) when some specific retarding agent is employed, or (*b*) when oxygen atoms are involved at low temperatures. In the latter case chain termination is often by means of the reaction $O + O_2 + (M) \rightarrow O_3 + (M)$. The fundamental equation is

$$\frac{dn}{dt} = \theta - gn \quad . \quad . \quad . \quad . \quad \text{(V.4)}$$

and the concentration of centres is uniform over the whole reaction vessel*, attaining a steady value of θ/g. Correspondingly the steady reaction rate is $\theta/g\bar{\imath}$ and the average chain length is $1/g\bar{\imath}$. In such cases the coefficient of g is proportional either to the concentration of retarding agent (case (*a*)) or to the square of the total pressure (case (*b*)).

Case (3) leads to interesting results when, as may sometimes happen, atoms or free radicals which start the reaction chain are also capable of stopping it. Let [Z] be the instantaneous concentration of such chain starting and stopping entities and k_i and k_t' the velocity constants for the initiating and terminating reactions which may be written

$$Z + R \xrightarrow{k_i} \text{initial centres}$$

$$Z + \text{chain} \xrightarrow{k_t'} \text{termination}$$

Equation (4) becomes

$$\frac{dn}{dt} = k_i[Z][R] - k_t'[Z]n$$

and the steady reaction rate $= \dfrac{k_i[R]}{k_t'\bar{\imath}}$ and is thus independent of the value of [Z] and of the rate of production of Z initially.

Case (4): *Straight chains initiated on the walls and terminated in the gas phase.* In this case the initiation rate, averaged over the whole volume of the reaction vessel would, as in case (2), be inversely proportional to the diameter. It would therefore be expected that the reaction velocity would decrease with increase of diameter, and since no gaseous chain reaction has this

---

* Whenever there is no wall initiation or termination and the rate of initiation, θ, is uniform throughout the volume, the concentration of centres will be uniform, i.e. $n_x = \bar{n}$. For simplicity we shall write the concentration of centres as n in these cases.

property, it must be concluded that no reactions conform to this mechanism.

Cases (5) *and* (6): *Straight chains subject to simultaneous homogeneous and wall termination.* The equation is now

$$\frac{\mathrm{d}n_x}{\mathrm{d}t} = \theta - gn_x + \bar{D}\frac{\partial^2 n_x}{\partial x^2} \qquad . \quad . \quad . \quad (V.5)$$

and experimental systems could readily be devised which would correspond to this expression. For instance mixtures of 5 mm H_2 + 5 mm Cl_2 + 10 mm O_2 in cylindrical reaction vessels of diameter 10 mm correctly illuminated would contain chains initiated homogeneously, some of them being stopped by diffusion of centres to the wall and some by interaction of centres with oxygen. A stationary state would be produced, and BURSIAN and SOROKIN[4] have shown that the volume average of the centre concentration is given by

$$\bar{n} = \frac{\theta}{g}\left\{1 - \frac{\tanh\left(\mathrm{d}\sqrt{\frac{g}{4\bar{D}}}\right)}{\mathrm{d}\sqrt{\frac{g}{4\bar{D}}}}\right\} \qquad . \quad . \quad . \quad (V.6)$$

This expression leads to the values of $\bar{n} = \theta/g$ and $\theta d^2/12\bar{D}$ for the extreme cases of negligible wall and negligible gas phase termination corresponding to cases (3) and (1) respectively. The intermediate case where both types of termination are appreciable has never been tested experimentally, nor has the more complex case in which the chains are initiated at the walls.

The Approach to the Steady State. All the cases (1) to (6) thus far discussed have the one common feature that the average concentration of centres ($\bar{n}$) attains a steady value. In those cases ((3) and (4)) which involve gas phase termination only, the way in which the centre concentration builds up from zero to the steady value is obtained by integration of equation (V.4).

$$\bar{n} = \frac{\theta}{g}(1 - \mathrm{e}^{-gt}) \qquad . \quad . \quad . \quad . \quad (V.7)$$

whence the rate expression becomes

$$\frac{\mathrm{d}[Pr]}{\mathrm{d}t} = \frac{\theta}{g\bar{t}}(1 - \mathrm{e}^{-gt})$$

and the amount of product formed is given by

$$[Pr] = \int_0^t \frac{\theta}{g\bar{t}} (1 - e^{-gt})\, dt = \frac{\theta}{g\bar{t}}\left\{t + \frac{e^{-gt}}{g} - \frac{1}{g}\right\} \quad . \quad (V.8)$$

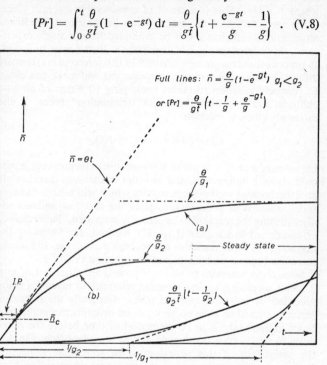

Fig. V.1. Growth of centre concentration ($\bar{n}$) with time (t) in a reaction proceeding by straight chains undergoing linear termination. Curve (a) termination coefficient g_1. Curve (b) termination coefficient g_2, $g_2 > g_1$. *I.P.* denotes induction period defined by equation (V.10).

In Fig. V.1 the variation of $\bar{n}$ and $[Pr]$ with t is indicated, and it will be seen that when $t \gg 1/g$ the reaction proceeds at the steady rate $\theta/g\bar{t}$. The amount of product formed during the steady state increases linearly with time according to the equation

$$[Pr] = \frac{\theta}{g\bar{t}}\left\{t - \frac{1}{g}\right\} \quad . \quad . \quad . \quad . \quad (V.9)$$

and if this curve is extrapolated backwards it cuts the time axis
where $t = 1/g$. This is a result of considerable interest, since,
if the early stages of the reaction can be measured, the linear
termination coefficient g can be evaluated from a single experiment. It follows that if θ is also known, then $\bar{\imath}$ may be found.
In practice the accurate measurement of this intercept is extremely
difficult because g is so large. An example will make this clear.
In photochlorination reactions containing 10^{-2} mm of nitrosyl
chloride and in which the major termination process is the
extremely efficient reaction

$$Cl + NOCl \rightarrow Cl_2 + NO,$$

the value of g at 27°C is about 1000 sec^{-1}[(5)]. The intercept is thus
only about 1 millisecond, and in order to measure it accurately
an experimental method is necessary which will enable the very
small amounts of product formed in the first few milliseconds
after starting the reaction to be precisely estimated. Nevertheless,
as mentioned in Chapter II (p. 37), methods for following the
first stages of rapid reactions are becoming available, and it may
therefore become possible to exploit equation (V.9).

Since chain reactions of all kinds possess an initial rate of zero
it is not surprising to find repeated reference to reactions being
preceded by induction periods (*I.P.*). Generally the induction
periods referred to have no very precise or uniform significance.
Some authors take it to be the period of time before the maximum or steady state is achieved, but as is evident from Fig. V.1
the assessment of this period must be somewhat subjective.
Others take it to be the period of time before which the reaction
becomes perceptible, in which case its magnitude is a function
of the measuring devices employed. For example if the minimum
perceptible luminosity accompanying reaction is the criterion,
the induction period is given by (V.10).

$$I.P. = -\frac{1}{g} \ln \left(1 - \frac{n_c g}{\theta} \right) \quad . \quad . \quad . \quad . \quad (V.10)$$

where n_c is the concentration of centres corresponding to the
rate at which the light emission is just detectable, and if this rate
is small $I.P. \simeq n_c/\theta$. On the other hand it is commonly the case
that the induction period corresponds to the presence of a

minimum detectable amount of product $[Pr]_c$, e.g. a given pressure change or degree of turbidity, etc. The induction period is then the value of t in equation (V.8) when $[Pr] = [Pr]_{cr}$, and if g is large, or the measuring device crude, then the *I.P.* $\simeq g\bar{\imath}[Pr]_c/\theta$. Quantitative deductions from such *I.P.* data are obviously impossible.

At the steady state, when $t \gg 1/g$, the value of the reaction rate deduced from equation (V.7) is $\theta/g\bar{\imath}$. This result is equivalent to that (equation (V.11)) which would be obtained by using the stationary state method

i.e.
$$\frac{\mathrm{d}[Pr]}{\mathrm{d}t} = \frac{k_1 I[R]}{G} = \frac{I}{G\bar{\imath}} \quad . \quad . \quad . \text{ (V.11)}$$

since $I = \theta$, $W = F = 0$, $G = g$.

When the chains are terminated at the wall as well as in the gas phase the increase of the chain centre population with time is obtained by integration of equation (5) and leads to a value for $\bar{n}$ which is the sum of a complex series. Despite this complexity the general trend of the chain centre population with time can be described and related to the cases when surface termination is absent. In the initial phase $\dfrac{\mathrm{d}\bar{n}}{\mathrm{d}t} \simeq \theta$ and as before $\bar{n} = \theta t$. In the steady state region we must consider whether gas or wall termination is dominant. If the gas termination is the more important, e.g. in large vessels, then as in the previous section $n = \dfrac{\theta}{g}$; but when the wall termination predominates, e.g. in small vessels, $\bar{n} \simeq \dfrac{\theta d^2}{\Gamma \bar{D}}$ where Γ is a numerical constant determined by the shape and condition of the reaction vessel. When both modes of termination are comparable in magnitude $\bar{n}$ is approximately equal to $\dfrac{\theta}{\dfrac{\Gamma \bar{D}}{d^2} + g}$. It is a useful *approximation* to write equation (12) instead of (5)

$$\frac{\mathrm{d}\bar{n}}{\mathrm{d}t} = \theta - \left(g + \frac{\Gamma \bar{D}}{d^2}\right)\bar{n} \quad . \quad . \quad . \quad . \text{ (V.12)}$$

and hence

$$\frac{\mathrm{d}[Pr]}{\mathrm{d}t} = \frac{\theta}{\left(g + \dfrac{\Gamma \bar{D}}{d^2}\right)\bar{t}} \cdot \left(1 - \mathrm{e}^{-\left(g + \frac{\Gamma \bar{D}}{d^2}\right)t}\right) . \quad . \text{ (V.13)}$$

The corresponding induction periods would then be obtained by substituting $\left(g + \dfrac{\Gamma \bar{D}}{d^2}\right)$ for g in equation (10).

(b) **Branched Chains Linearly Terminated.** The introduction of another factor controlling chain growth greatly increases the number of possible cases which would require discussion in a comprehensive survey. In practice, all the new features introduced when linear branching is included in the possible fates of the chain are most usefully discussed under one heading.

Case (7): *Linearly branched chains terminated singly.* The appropriate equation is now

$$\frac{\mathrm{d}n_x}{\mathrm{d}t} = \theta + (f - g)n_x + D\frac{\partial^2 n_x}{\partial x^2} . \quad . \quad . \text{ (V.14)}$$

and when $g > f$ this reduces to case (5) or (6). This is to be expected because, when $g > f$, more chains are terminated in the gas phase than branch, and the net effect of the branching therefore appears as a decrease of the value of g in equations (3) to (13).

This situation probably obtains in the slow reaction region just above the upper limit in the region of the tip of explosion peninsulae. Here the branching of the chains is held in check partly by gas phase removal, but at the low total pressures obtaining, partly by surface termination.

If $f > g$, or if there is no appreciable termination of the centres in the gas phase, the condition for a stationary state derived from equation (V.14) is that $f < \left(g + \dfrac{\pi^2 \bar{D}}{d^2}\right)$ and the value of the stationary state concentration is given by[4]

$$\bar{n} = \frac{\theta}{f - g}\left\{\frac{\tan\left(\dfrac{(f - g)d^2}{4\bar{D}}\right)^{\frac{1}{2}}}{\left(\dfrac{(f - g)d^2}{4\bar{D}}\right)^{\frac{1}{2}}} - 1\right\} . \quad . \text{ (V.15)}$$

If, instead of using the diffusion equation (14), it had been assumed that the probability of termination at the wall of a chain situated anywhere in the reaction vessel is $\dfrac{\pi^2 \bar{D}}{d^2}$, the results obtained would not have been very different from that given by equation (14). Thus the condition for a stationary state would have been the same, namely $f < g + \dfrac{\pi^2 D}{d^2}$; the values of the stationary concentrations of centres given by

$$\bar{n} = \frac{\theta}{-\left(f - g - \dfrac{\pi^2 \bar{D}}{d^2} \right)}$$

are of the same order (although larger) and show the same trend as d is varied as do the values given by equation (15); and the growth of the chain centre population with time follows a similar course to the full line of Fig. V.1.

An entirely different situation arises when $f > g + \dfrac{\pi^2 \bar{D}}{d^2}$. In this case the branching rate exceeds the termination rate and the chains will multiply indefinitely provided the reactant concentration can be maintained. It is convenient to define a net branching factor $\phi = f - (g + \pi^2 \bar{D}/d^2)$ and the development of the concentration of centres with time is then given by

$$\frac{\mathrm{d}\bar{n}}{\mathrm{d}t} = \theta + \phi\bar{n} \quad . \quad . \quad . \quad . \quad \text{(V.16)}$$

i.e.

$$\bar{n} = \frac{\theta}{\phi}(\mathrm{e}^{\phi t} - 1) \quad . \quad . \quad . \quad \text{(V.17)}^*$$

and is shown in the full line of Fig. V.2.

Since the reaction rate $= \bar{n}/\bar{\iota}$ we have

$$\frac{\mathrm{d}[Pr]}{\mathrm{d}t} = \frac{\bar{n}}{\bar{\iota}} = \frac{\theta}{\phi\bar{\iota}}(\mathrm{e}^{\phi t} - 1) \quad . \quad . \quad . \quad \text{(V.18)}$$

* The deduction of the exact relation for $\bar{n} = f(t)$ is given by BURSIAN and SOROKIN[4] and the relation obtained differs from equation (17) only in a constant multiplicand on the R.H.S. which is slightly less than unity.

and when $e^{\phi t} \gg 1$ this becomes

$$\frac{d[Pr]}{dt} = \frac{\theta}{\phi \bar{t}} \cdot e^{\phi t}. \quad \ldots \ldots \quad (V.19)$$

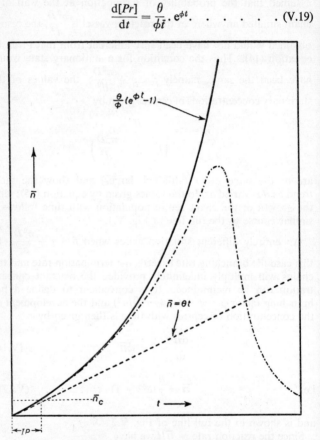

Fig. V.2. Growth of centre concentration ($\bar{n}$) with time (t) in a linearly branched and terminated reaction. *I.P.* denotes induction period defined by equation (V.22).

We have thus the possibility, when $f - g - \dfrac{\pi^2 D}{d^2} = \phi$ is positive, of an indefinitely accelerated reaction, even under isothermal

conditions. Actually most branching chain reactions are exothermic and therefore their temperatures rise and the reaction
tends to become self-accelerating on this account also. Moreover
the attainment of such rapid reaction rates occurs so quickly the
reactants are speedily consumed and the decay of their concentration has a retarding effect on the rate. The overall effect of
these factors causes the actual $\bar{n}/t$ curve to follow the line
— . — . — in the figure. The rate-time curve will have a similar
shape typical of an explosion (see curve 2 of Fig. II.3, p. 28).

The amount of product formed after a given time is a measurable quantity and can easily be shown to be from equation (19)

$$[Pr] = \frac{\theta}{\phi^2 \bar{t}} \cdot e^{\phi t} \qquad \ldots \qquad \text{(V.20)}$$

and

$$\ln [Pr] = \ln \frac{\theta}{\phi^2 \bar{t}} + \phi t \qquad \ldots \qquad \text{(V.21)}$$

and hence in the initial stages of a gaseous explosion which
involves a pressure change, we should anticipate that $\log \Delta p$,
where Δp is the pressure change at time t, plotted against t would
give a straight line of slope equal to the net branching factor.
This relation has received most elegant experimental verification
by KOWALSKI[6] in the case of the explosion of $2H_2 + O_2$ mixtures
at 520 and 485°C just above the lower limit. The reaction was
very (explosively) rapid and KOWALSKI followed the pressure
changes by the distortion of a suitably time-based membrane
manometer of very low inertia. The $\Delta p/t$ curves are shown in Fig.
V.3 (a), the corresponding $\dfrac{d(\Delta p)}{dt} \bigg/ t$, i.e. rate-time curves in Fig.
V.3 (b) and the $\log (\Delta p)/t$ curves in Fig. V.3 (c).

The close conformity of these results to the theoretical predictions indicates that in this particular case of the hydrogen
oxygen explosion just above the lower limit, no appreciable
temperature rise is involved and that the explosion is due solely
to the rate of the branching of reaction chains exceeding their
rate of removal under isothermal conditions. A further point of
interest in this work is that the time after admitting the gas until
the first appreciable deflection of the manometer membrane
occurs, and which presumably corresponds to a certain pressure

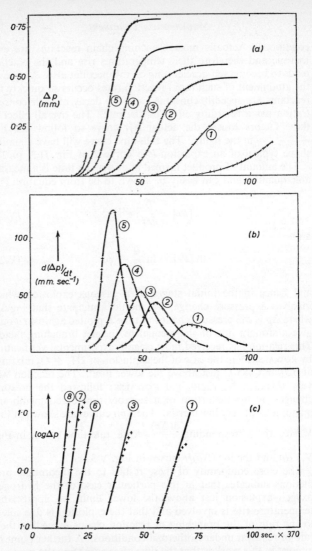

Fig. V.3. The initial stages of the low pressure explosion in stoichiometric mixtures of hydrogen and oxygen. Curves (a) and (b) refer to 485°C and initial pressures of 6·1, 6·4, 6·8, 7·1, 7·4 mm for curves (1) to (5) respectively. Curves (c) refer to 485°C experiments (1), (3) and (6); the remaining curves to 520°C.

Adapted from ref. 33, Chapter III, pp. 223-4

change, increases steadily as ϕ decreases. At 485°C the corresponding values are:

ϕ	175	156	148	119	106	100	63
I.P. (sec $\times$ 370)	18	21	24	28	32	55	72
P (mm)	8·2	7·8	7·4	7·1	6·8	6·1	5·8
$\phi \times I.P.$	3·15	3·03	3·55	3·33	3·39	5·5	4·53

Assuming that equation (19) describes the growth of the chains fairly well over the induction period, the value of the latter is*

$$I.P. = \frac{1}{\phi}\left\{\ln [Pr]_{\text{crit}} - \ln \frac{\theta}{\theta^2 \bar{\iota}}\right\}. \quad . \quad . \quad . \text{(V.22)}$$

and if $[Pr]_{\text{crit}} \gg \theta/\phi^2 \bar{\iota}$ the induction period should be inversely proportional to ϕ. As the figures in the table show, this is only roughly correct. Nevertheless the change of the reciprocal of the induction period with any parameter may in practice provide a useful qualitative guide to the way in which the net branching factor alters with the same parameter.

We may summarize the discussion of chain reactions which do not involve interaction of pairs of centres (cases (1) to (7)) as follows. The growth of the average chain centre concentration ($\bar{n}$) with time from its zero value at the instant of admixture of the reactants is given by

$$\frac{d\bar{n}}{dt} = \theta + \phi\bar{n}$$

where θ is the rate of initiation of chains, ϕ is the net branching factor and may be written in a first approximation as $= f - g - \dfrac{\Gamma \bar{D}}{d^2}$, in which f is the coefficient of linear branching, g is the coefficient for homogeneous chain termination, and $\Gamma \bar{D}/d^2$ is the coefficient for wall termination. $\bar{D}$ is the average coefficient of diffusion of the reaction centres, d the vessel diameter and Γ is a constant characteristic of the vessel shape

---

* Using the more exact relation obtained by integration of (18) the expression for the induction period becomes

$$[Pr]_{\text{crit}} = \frac{\theta}{\phi t}\left\{\frac{e^{\phi(IP)} - 1}{\phi} - IP\right\}$$

and condition. When branching is either not occurring or is held in check by each or both of the termination processes, ϕ is negative, and $\bar{n}$ increases to a steady value of $\dfrac{\theta}{-\phi}$ in such a way that its instantaneous value is given by $\dfrac{\theta}{-\phi}(1 - e^{\phi t})$. The reaction is never explosive and is first detected after an induction period which is largely determined by θ, being smaller the greater the value of θ. The intercept on the time axis, of the linear portion of the $[Pr]$ vs. t curve when extrapolated back is equal to $-\phi^{-1}$. When ϕ is positive the reaction is capable of continual acceleration under conditions of constant temperature and constant reactant concentration according to the relation

$$\frac{d[Pr]}{dt} = \frac{\theta}{\phi \bar{t}}(e^{\phi t} - 1) \simeq \frac{\theta}{\phi \bar{t}} e^{\phi t} \quad . \quad \text{(V.17, 19)}$$

where $\bar{t}$ is the average lifetime of the chain centre between stages of the propagation process. The induction period is now approximately inversely proportional to the net branching factor ϕ and only to a lesser degree dependent on θ.

In a particular reaction ϕ may vary continuously from positive to negative values and vice versa as some experimental parameter such as temperature, pressure, vessel diameter or reactant ratio is varied; but the curve of reaction velocity against this variable will show a discontinuity corresponding to explosive (non-steady state) rates for positive values of ϕ and slow non-explosive reactions for negative values of ϕ. This is the interpretation on the chain theory of sharp explosion boundaries, the precise value of which may be obtained by equating ϕ to zero. In passing it is important to notice that changes of θ—the initiation rate— alter the induction period and steady reaction rate but would be expected to have *no* effect on the explosion boundary. These points are discussed in greater detail in Chapter VI.

(c) Interactions between Growing Chains: Quadratic Termination:

Case (8): *Straight chains terminated in pairs.* There are a large number of chain reactions, notably thermal and photo-halogenation processes, in which unbranched chains are propagated and the recombination of atoms and radicals is almost the sole termination process. In addition, in many of the radical type polymerizations of vinyl compounds, the growing polymer radicals which constitute the chain centres are terminated by interaction in pairs. The chain development is then described by

$$\frac{\mathrm{d}n}{\mathrm{d}t} = \theta - \delta n^2 \quad . \quad . \quad . \quad . \quad (V.23)$$

where δ is the velocity constant of the termination reaction which may involve a third body (see p. 77, Chapter III). The concentration of centres grows according to

$$n = \sqrt{\frac{\overline{\theta}}{\delta}} \cdot \frac{e^{2t\sqrt{\theta\delta}} - 1}{e^{2t\sqrt{\theta\delta}} + 1} \quad . \quad . \quad . \quad (V.24)$$

approaching the limiting value of $\left(\dfrac{\theta}{\delta}\right)^{\frac{1}{2}}$ asymptotically. There is thus no possibility of explosion and in the initial stages of reaction the time taken to form $[Pr]_{\mathrm{crit}}$, i.e. the induction period τ will increase with δ but decrease with increase in θ. An important feature of such chain reactions is the appearance of half integral powers in the rate expression; in particular it will be noted that the steady reaction rate is now proportional to the square root of the rate of initiation. When the initiation is a photochemical formation of centres the rate will therefore be proportional to $(\phi_i I_{\mathrm{abs}})^{\frac{1}{2}}$. In the radical type vinyl polymerization referred to above the initiation is often due to first order decomposition of a catalyst (see p. 177) and accordingly the rate of disappearance of monomer is found to be proportional to the square root of the catalyst concentration. A second important feature of chain processes conforming to this behaviour is that the chain length, defined as $\dfrac{\mathrm{d}[Pr]/\mathrm{d}t}{\theta}$ is $(t\sqrt{\theta\delta})^{-1}$, i.e. unlike the cases in which linear termination of the chains only is occurring, the chain length is dependent on the initiation rate. In the two examples cited the chain length is inversely proportional to the square root of I_{abs} and catalyst concentration respectively.

Equation (V.24) may be written in the form

$$n = (\theta/\delta)^{\frac{1}{2}} \tanh (t\sqrt{\theta\delta})$$

and hence by integration we obtain

$$[Pr] = (1/\delta \bar{t}) \ln \cosh (t\sqrt{\theta\delta}) \qquad . \quad . \text{(V.25)}$$

In Fig. V.4, both n and $[Pr]$ have been plotted against time and it will be noticed that when the steady state has been attained

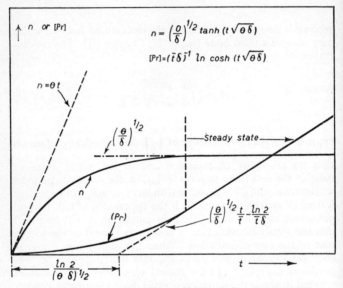

Fig. V.4. The variation with time of (a) the chain centre concentration (n) and (b) the amount of product formed $[Pr]$ in a reaction proceeding by straight chains undergoing quadratic termination.

$[Pr]$ increases linearly with t. The equation of this line is obtained by putting $t\sqrt{\theta\delta} \gg 1$ (the condition for the steady state), when $\cosh (t\sqrt{\theta\delta}) = e^{t\sqrt{\theta\delta}}/2$ and hence

$$[Pr] = \sqrt{\frac{\theta}{\delta}} \cdot \frac{t}{\bar{t}} - \frac{\ln 2}{\delta \bar{t}} \qquad . \quad . \quad . \quad . \text{(V.26)}$$

A comparison of the slope, $(\sqrt{\theta}/\bar{t}\sqrt{\delta})$, and intercept on the time axis, $(\ln 2/\sqrt{\theta\delta})$, of the observed $[Pr]$ vs. t line after the steady rate has been reached, will thus enable δ and $\bar{t}$ to be determined provided the rate of initiation (θ) is also known. In many chain reactions the value of δ lies in the range 10^6 to 10^{10} l.mole^{-1} sec^{-1} and therefore intercept values of the order of 10 secs are to be expected for some values of the initiation rate lying between 10^{-8} and 10^{-14} moles litre^{-1} sec^{-1}. The experimental conditions of photochemically initiated chain reactions can usually be adjusted to meet this requirement, and since the time zero can also be precisely determined in such reactions, they are suitable systems for the application of this method. Recently, BURNETT[7] has investigated the initial stages of the photopolymerization of styrene and treated the results in this way. The values of δ and $\bar{\imath}$ so obtained were in accord with the values determined by other methods.

Case (9): *Straight chains terminated linearly and quadratically.* It quite frequently happens that a reaction may be subject to chain termination simultaneously by two different mechanisms, one proceeding at a rate proportional to the concentration of centres and the other showing a second order dependence on the chain centre concentration. The former linear termination may occur either on the vessel surface or homogeneously. For example the reaction chains in the photochlorination of ethylene are extremely long and undergo ready mutual termination. In narrow vessels they may also be terminated at the walls and in addition they are subject to ready termination by retarding agents, indeed, this susceptibility to negative catalysis constitutes an acute experimental embarrassment. The equations appropriate to these two conditions are, respectively,

$$\frac{\mathrm{d}n_x}{\mathrm{d}t} = \theta - \delta n_x^2 + D \frac{\partial^2 n_x}{\partial x^2} \quad . \quad . \quad . \quad . \quad \text{(V.27)}$$

and

$$\frac{\mathrm{d}n}{\mathrm{d}t} = \theta - \delta n^2 - gn \quad . \quad . \quad . \quad . \quad \text{(V.28)}$$

where $\theta = \phi_1 I_{\mathrm{abs}}$. Initially the reaction rate will increase at a rate principally determined by the light intensity, as may be seen from equation (V.29) which is obtained by integrating (V.28).

$$\frac{\mathrm{d}[Pr]}{\mathrm{d}t} = \frac{n}{\bar{\imath}}$$

$$= \frac{2\theta}{\bar{\imath}} \left\{ \frac{\mathrm{e}^{(g^2 + 4\delta\theta)^{\frac{1}{2}}t} - 1}{[(g^2 + 4\delta\theta)^{\frac{1}{2}} - g] + [(g^2 + 4\delta\theta)^{\frac{1}{2}} + g]\mathrm{e}^{(g^2 + 4\delta\theta)^{\frac{1}{2}}t}} \right\} \quad \text{(V.29)}$$

and will ultimately attain the steady value given by

$$\frac{d[Pr]}{dt} = \frac{n}{\bar{t}} = \frac{-g + \sqrt{g^2 + 4\delta\theta}}{2\delta\bar{t}} \quad . \quad . \quad \text{(V.30)}$$

and which, unlike case (8), will be dependent on the intensity raised to a power between 0·5 and 1·0. This exponent will decrease as the light intensity is increased.

Equation (V.27) has not been integrated, but an exact solution for the steady state conditions can be obtained[9] and leads to a conclusion similar to that obtained by using the approximation $\bar{D} \dfrac{\partial^2 n_x}{\partial x^2} = -\dfrac{\Gamma \bar{D}}{d^2} \bar{n}$. This conclusion is that the intensity exponent will lie between 0·5 and 1·0 and will increase as the vessel diameter or the light intensity is diminished. Conversely, to decrease this exponent, i.e. to minimize the influence of wall termination, large vessels, high light intensities and high reactant pressures should be employed.

When the experimental conditions for a reaction in which the chains are simultaneously terminated linearly and quadratically cannot be adjusted sufficiently to make either gn or δn^2 negligibly small it is possible to assess the relative magnitude of these terms for a given value of θ from measurements of the dependence of the overall rate of reaction on the rate of initiation[8]. Suppose that the reaction rate at an initiation rate θ is $n/\bar{t}$ and that at a larger initiation rate $y\theta$ ($y > 1$) the reaction rate is $n'/\bar{t}$. The measured initiation rate exponent, x, is then given by

$$n/n' = (\theta/y\theta)^x = y^{-x} = \frac{\sqrt{1 + \beta} - 1}{\sqrt{1 + y\beta} - 1} \quad . \quad . \quad \text{(V.31)}$$

where $\beta = 4\delta\theta/g^2$, and the corresponding fractions λ and λ' of chains which are linearly terminated will be $gn/(gn + \delta n^2 = \theta)$ and $gn'/(gn' + \delta n'^2 = y\theta)$, i.e.

$$\left. \begin{array}{l} \lambda = 2(\sqrt{1 + \beta} - 1)/\beta \\ \lambda' = 2(\sqrt{1 + y\beta} - 1)/y\beta \end{array} \right\} \quad . \quad . \quad . \quad \text{(V.32)}$$

and

These equations may be rearranged to give equations (V.33), which are formulae

$$\lambda = \frac{y^{1-x} - y^x}{1 - y^x} \quad \text{and} \quad \lambda' = \frac{1 - y^{2x-1}}{1 - y^x} \quad . \quad . \quad \text{(V.33)}$$

enabling λ and λ' to be calculated from the chosen value of y and the measured value of x. It will be evident that $\lambda' < \lambda$ if $y > 1$, i.e. that as the rate of initiation is increased the fraction of chains terminated linearly will diminish. Thus if a doubling of the light intensity in a photochemically initiated chain reaction which follows this pattern causes the rate to increase by 68 per cent then $x = 0{\cdot}75$ and the fraction of chains terminated linearly at the lower intensity is 72 per cent, whilst the fraction at the higher intensity is 61 per cent.

In these mixed termination systems the lifetime, τ_g, of those chains which are linearly terminated is equal to g^{-1} and the lifetime, τ_δ, of those chains which are quadratically terminated is equal to $(\delta n)^{-1}$. Since $g/\delta n$ is the ratio of the fraction of chains which are linearly terminated to the fraction which is quadratically terminated we may write

$$g/\delta n = \lambda/(1 - \lambda) = \tau_\delta/\tau_g \qquad . \qquad . \text{ (V.34)}$$

The average lifetime, τ, of all the chains in a chain reaction has been defined (see Chapter IV) as $\bar{t} = k.c.l. = \bar{t} \times n/\bar{t}\theta$, which, since $\theta = gn + \delta n^2$ in this system, leads to

$$\tau^{-1} = (g + \delta n) = \tau_g^{-1} + \tau_\delta^{-1} \qquad . \qquad . \text{ (V.35)}$$

and

$$\tau_g = \lambda\tau \quad \text{and} \quad \tau_\delta = (1 - \lambda)\tau \qquad . \qquad . \text{ (V.36)}$$

Equations (36) are important because they indicate that if τ_δ can be measured (see case (13) below) for a photochemical chain reaction in which the intensity exponent x lies between 0·5 and 1·0 then τ_g and hence the linear termination coefficient, g, can be measured. This situation is especially common in free radical addition polymerization reactions.

Case (10): *Branched chains terminated in pairs.* If the chains are branched linearly and terminated quadratically the appropriate equation is

$$\frac{\mathrm{d}n}{\mathrm{d}t} = \theta + fn - \delta n^2 \qquad . \quad . \quad . \quad . \text{ (V.37)}$$

and hence, no matter how large f may be, the reaction rate must always ultimately attain a stationary value given by

$$\frac{\mathrm{d}[Pr]}{\mathrm{d}t} = \frac{f + \sqrt{f^2 + 4\delta\theta}}{2\delta\bar{t}} \qquad . \quad . \quad . \quad . \text{ (V.38)}$$

and if $f^2 \gg 4\delta\theta$, i.e. a very low initiation rate

$$\frac{d[Pr]}{dt} = f/\delta\bar{\imath} \quad . \quad . \quad . \quad . \quad . \quad . \quad \text{(V.39)}$$

In this case therefore the steady reaction rate is entirely independent of the number of chains starting, so that theoretically, provided the reaction is once started the initiation process can be stopped without any effect on the rate. Every time a chain centre is destroyed it is, on the average, replaced by one formed in the branching process, and the chains are therefore apparently of infinite length. The way in which the rate varies with time is of interest. In all the other cases discussed in which the rate finally becomes steady, the rate time curve was shown to be concave to the time axis over its whole range. Integration of (37) leads to

$$\frac{d[Pr]}{dt} = \frac{2\theta(e^{(f^2+4\delta\theta)^{\frac{1}{2}}t}-1)}{\bar{\imath}\{f + (f^2 + 4\delta\theta)^{\frac{1}{2}} - (f - (f^2 + 4\delta\theta)^{\frac{1}{2}})e^{(f^2+4\delta\theta)^{\frac{1}{2}}t}\}}$$

$$. \quad . \quad \text{(V.40)}$$

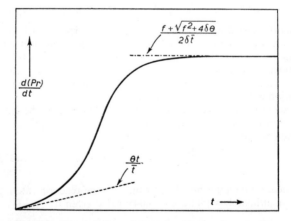

Fig. V.5. The variation of the rate with time in a reaction proceeding by linearly branched chains undergoing quadratic termination.

and if $f^2 \gg 4\delta\theta$, this leads to an exponential increase of rate with time in the early stages of the reaction according to equation (41)

$$\frac{d[Pr]}{dt} = \frac{\theta}{ft}(e^{ft} - 1) \quad . \quad . \quad . \quad . \quad (V.41)$$

which, it will be noted, is identical in form to equation (V.18), and represents a rate-time curve convex to t axis $\left(\dfrac{d^2[Pr]}{dt^2} \text{ is positive}\right)$. In the later stages of the reaction when e^{-ft} is very small and provided $f^2 \gg 4\delta\theta$ equation (40) becomes

$$\frac{d[Pr]}{dt} = \frac{f}{\delta t}\left\{1 - \frac{f^2}{\delta\theta}e^{-ft}\right\} \quad . \quad . \quad . \quad (V.42)$$

corresponding to a curve concave to the t axis. The overall picture is represented in Fig. V.5. The magnitude of the induction period will largely depend on whether $[Pr]_{crit}$ is formed whilst the rate is still following equation (41), in which case

$$I.P. = \frac{1}{f}\left[\ln[Pr]_{crit} + \ln\frac{\theta}{f^2 t}\right]$$

similar to equation (22).

It is quite possible, and indeed probable, that mutual termination is not the only mode, but that the linear branching is partly held in check by linear termination in the gas phase and on the walls. The equations (37) to (42) and discussion concerning them will apply to such a reaction provided ϕ (the net branching factor) is written for f.

Case (11): *Quadratically branched chains.* If quadratic branching is occurring, but the rate of branching of the chains by this mechanism is exceeded by their rate of termination in pairs, i.e. $F < \delta$; the discussion of the previous section (case (9)) applies, except that in all the formulae $(\delta - F)$ should be substituted for δ. When $F > \delta$ it is convenient to define the net quadratic branching factor $\phi' = F - \delta$ and the equation for the development of the chains is now

$$\frac{dn}{dt} = \theta + \phi n + \phi' n^2 \quad . \quad . \quad . \quad . \quad (V.43)$$

In the special case of $\phi = 0$, explosion is possible for all positive values of ϕ', and for all negative values the situation corresponds to that described in case (8). Explosion will, of course, occur for all cases in which ϕ and ϕ' are both positive, n increasing according to

$$n = \alpha \left\{ 1 + \frac{\dfrac{\alpha}{\beta} - 1}{e^{(\beta - \alpha)\phi' t} - \dfrac{\alpha}{\beta}} \right\} \quad . \quad . \quad . \quad . \quad \text{(V.44)}$$

where

$$\alpha = \tfrac{1}{2} \left\{ \sqrt{\left(\frac{\phi}{\phi'}\right)^2 - \frac{4\theta}{\phi'}} - \frac{\phi}{\phi'} \right\}$$

and

$$\beta = -\tfrac{1}{2} \left(\sqrt{\left(\frac{\phi}{\phi'}\right)^2 - \frac{4\theta}{\phi'}} + \frac{\phi}{\phi'} \right)$$

However, in addition to the possibility of ignition when ϕ is positive, it may also occur when ϕ is negative so long as $4\theta\phi' \geqslant \phi^2$, when the development of the centres with time is as shown in Fig. V.6. This conclusion is important because in such

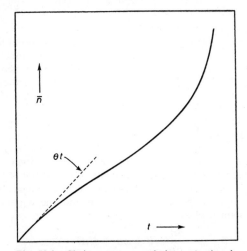

Fig. V.6. Chain centre growth in a reaction in which quadratic branching exceeds the quadratic termination, but the linear termination exceeds the linear branching and $4\theta\phi^1 > \phi^2$ (Equation V.38).

systems there exists the possibility that an increase in the rate of initial generation of centres may convert a slow reaction into an explosion. The H_2-O_2 system is one in which artificial 'boosting' of the centre concentration lowers the ignition temperature[10], but as later discussion will show, it does not necessarily follow that quadratic branching is a feature of this reaction.

(d) After-effects and Intermittent Initiation in Unbranched Chain Reactions

Case (12): *Reaction following cessation of initiation.* In the preceding paragraphs it has been repeatedly implied that once started a reaction chain will take a time (τ) to develop which is equal to the product of $\bar{t}$ and the kinetic chain length. It follows that if the initiation process is abruptly stopped, a finite time, which may be appreciable, will elapse before the concentration of centres and the reaction rate have become negligible. In photo- or radiation-chemically initiated reactions in which external sources are employed such 'after-effects' must always occur. A related effect is due to the fact that the reaction chains will diffuse a distance $= (2\bar{D}\tau)^{\frac{1}{2}}$ during their lifetime. In gaseous systems where $\bar{D}$ may be as large as $10^{-1}\,\mathrm{cm^2\,sec^{-1}}$ such diffusion distances may be as much as 3 mm. If therefore a reaction vessel is not entirely 'filled with light' an appreciable proportion of a photochemical reaction may take place just outside the illuminated zone. Since there has been little experimental investigation of this effect we shall confine this discussion to 'after-effects' in fully illuminated systems.

The amount of reaction which will have taken place in a time t after the irradiation has ceased will be $\dfrac{1}{\bar{t}}\displaystyle\int_0^t n\,\mathrm{d}t$, bearing in mind that when $t = 0$, n has the value, denoted by n_0, appropriate to the photochemical reaction at the moment of light extinction. This value may or may not be the steady state value depending on whether the preceding period of illumination was sufficiently long for this to be established. The two most important cases are (a) when the termination reaction is homogeneous and linear and (b) when the termination reaction is homogeneous and quadratic, and the appropriate equations are

(a) $$\frac{\mathrm{d}n}{\mathrm{d}t} = -gn \quad \therefore \quad n = n_0\,\mathrm{e}^{-gt} \qquad . \qquad . \qquad . \quad (V.45)$$

and
$$[Pr] = \frac{n_0}{g\bar{t}}(1 - e^{-gt}). \quad . \quad . \quad . \quad \text{(V.46)}$$

(b) $$\frac{dn}{dt} = -\delta n^2 \quad \therefore \quad n = n_0/(1 + n_0\delta t) \quad . \quad . \quad \text{(V.47)}$$

and
$$[Pr] = [\ln(1 + n_0\delta t)]/\delta\bar{t} \quad . \quad . \quad . \quad \text{(V.48)}$$

In principle these equations may readily be exploited to yield the values of g, $\bar{t}$, and δ. Thus, if the rate of the post-irradiation reaction decreases exponentially with time, the value of g will be $(\ln 2)/t_{\frac{1}{2}}$ where $t_{\frac{1}{2}}$ is the time taken for the rate to fall to 50 per cent of its initial value. Alternatively $\ln (d[Pr]/dt)$ may be plotted against t when a straight line of slope $= -g$ will be obtained. We therefore have two methods for finding the coefficient of linear termination (g), one based on a study of the early stages of the reaction (equation (V.9)) and the other method discussed above, based on the after-effect. Neither of these methods requires a knowledge of the rate of initiation (θ). In contrast the coefficient of mutual termination (δ) cannot be determined from either the early stages of reaction (equation (V.26)) or the after-effect without an independent determination of θ. This is readily seen in relation to the after-effect either by inspection of equation (V.48) or by inverting both sides of equation (V.47) and multiplying by $\bar{t}$ when we obtain

$$\frac{\bar{t}}{n} = \frac{\bar{t}}{n_0} + \delta\bar{t} \cdot t \quad . \quad . \quad . \quad . \quad \text{(V.49)}$$

The slope of the line obtained by plotting the reciprocal of the rate of the post-irradiation reaction against time is thus equal to $\delta\bar{t}$. BURNETT[7] has pointed out that when the after-effect follows a period of illumination during which steady state conditions have been obtained, $n_0 = (\theta/\delta)^{\frac{1}{2}}$ and hence the time taken for the rate to drop to half the steady state value $(t_{\frac{1}{2}})$ is given by

$$\frac{\bar{t}}{(\theta/\delta)^{\frac{1}{2}}} = \delta\bar{t} \cdot t_{\frac{1}{2}}$$

i.e.
$$t_{\frac{1}{2}} = (\theta\delta)^{-\frac{1}{2}} \quad . \quad . \quad . \quad . \quad . \quad \text{(V.50)}$$

and is thus equal to the lifetime, τ, of the chains in the steady state.
  In practice the application of these conclusions is somewhat

restricted by the large values of $\delta\theta$ and g, and the consequent smallness of $t_{\frac{1}{2}}$, combined with the experimental difficulties of following such rapid and small changes as are involved. Nevertheless, modern techniques are being developed which even now permit the non-stationary states to be investigated in certain addition polymerization reactions[10]. It may also be recalled that amongst the earliest evidence for the existence of chain reactions is the observation by WEIGERT and KELLERMAN[11] in 1923 that equimolar mixtures of hydrogen and chlorine illuminated by an intense spark discharge of about 1 microsecond duration continue to react for at least 10 milliseconds later.

Case (13): *Intermittent initiation: determination of* δ, $\bar{\iota}$, *and* g. Whilst it is experimentally difficult to investigate a single after-effect or a single period of approach to the stationary state it is relatively easy to obtain these phenomena in rapid succession over a prolonged period of time, and to measure accurately the *average* rate of reaction under these conditions. The experimental methods are simple. In photochemical reactions a circular disc with one or more segments removed is rotated at known rates about an axis parallel to the light beam so that the plane of rotation cuts the light beam at the point of narrowest cross-section of the latter, and such that the beam is close to the edge of the sector. This arrangement ensures that the intermittency pattern, although inevitably trapezoidal, is as near a 'square-wave' as possible, and that 'penumbra' errors are thereby minimized. In reactions induced by highly penetrating radiation (e.g. γ-rays) the sector must be thick and constructed of material of high stopping power. Such sectors involve problems of careful dynamical balancing and often have large penumbra errors but have nevertheless been used[12]. Alternative methods by which time-intermittency in radiation chemical systems may be achieved are either to attach a small reaction cell to a rotating arm so that the cell moves repeatedly across a collimated beam of large diameter or to arrange for a small source to be rapidly and successively inserted into, and withdrawn a considerable distance from, a well in the centre of the reaction vessel[13].

The average rate of reaction ($\bar{R}$) under conditions of intermittent irradiation is given by

$$\bar{R} = \frac{Pr_l + Pr_d}{t_l + t_d} = \frac{1}{\bar{\iota}(t_l + t_d)}\left[\int_0^{t_l} \mathbf{n}\,\mathrm{d}t + \int_0^{t_d} \mathbf{n}\,\mathrm{d}t\right]. \quad (V.51)$$

where Pr_l is the amount of product formed during the period of illumination t_l, and Pr_d the amount of product formed during the dark period t_d.

When both t_l and t_d are large compared with the lifetime of the chains, the stationary state value of n $(= n_s)$ is reached quite early in and will be maintained throughout the remainder of the light period. When the initiation ceases n rapidly decays from the value n_s, and is almost zero for most of the dark period. This behaviour is depicted in curve (*a*) of Fig. V.7; and obviously

$$\bar{R} = \frac{t_l}{t_l + t_d} \cdot \frac{n_s}{\bar{t}} = \frac{t_l}{t_l + t_d} R_0 \quad . \quad . \quad . \text{(V.52)}$$

where R_0 is the value of the reaction rate with the sector removed. The effect of the slow moving sector is thus equivalent to that which would be produced by illumination with the full intensity for $100t_l/(t_l + t_d)$ per cent of the total duration of the experiment. On the other hand when t_l and t_d are both small compared with the lifetime of the chains the chain centre concentration never attains the stationary state concentration n_s, but merely reaches a value $n_l < n_s$. When the light is turned off, n falls from n_l to a lower value n_d which, since $t_l \ll \tau$, is finite. For the first few rotations of the sector the increase in centre concentration during the illumination period exceeds the decrease occurring during darkness, but later these two quantities become equal and a quasi-stationary state exists. This behaviour is depicted in curve (*b*) of Fig. V.7. As the 'flashing time' t_l becomes shorter n_l and n_d approach more closely and the rate of removal of centres may be regarded as constant (either $gn_l = gn_d$ or $\delta n_l^2 = \delta n_d^2$) throughout the whole of a cycle of length $t_l + t_d$. However, only during the period t_l is the reaction receiving new centres at the rate θ, and the reaction will therefore behave as if it were continually receiving new centres at the rate $\theta t_l/(t_l + t_d)$. The reaction rate thus becomes

$$\bar{R} = \left(\frac{t_l}{t_l + t_d}\right)^x \cdot \frac{n_s}{\bar{t}} = \left(\frac{t_l}{t_l + t_d}\right)^x \cdot R_0 \quad . \quad . \text{(V.53)}$$

where x is the intensity exponent of the reaction under steady illumination. It will be seen that the exponent x is absent from equation (V.52) and therefore, for all photochemical chain reactions in which the rate of reaction is not directly proportional

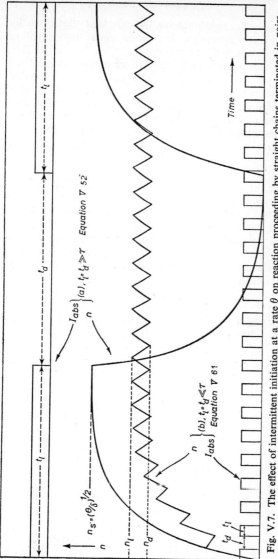

Fig. V.7. The effect of intermittent initiation at a rate θ on reaction proceeding by straight chains terminated in pairs. Case (a) $t_l = t_d \gg \tau$; case (b) $t_l = t_d \ll \tau$. Notation explained in the text.

to the absorbed light intensity, the measured rate of reaction for a given sector opening at low sector speeds ($t_l \gg \tau$) will not be the same as at high sector speeds ($t_l \ll \tau$). In practice the cases with which we are most likely to be concerned are those for which $\frac{1}{2} \leqslant x < 1$ and hence the apparent rate of reaction will decrease as the sector speed is decreased. The experimental curve of $\bar{R}$ vs. flashing time t_l then depends on τ and x, and both these quantities can be determined from one sector curve. In the case where $x > \frac{1}{2}$ due to the simultaneous termination of the chains linearly and quadratically, then, as deduced on p. 115,

$$\tau^{-1} = \tau_g^{-1} + \tau_\delta^{-1} \qquad . \qquad . \qquad . \text{(V.35)}$$

and the experimental curve of $\bar{R}$ vs. t_l permits both termination lifetimes and hence both termination coefficients to be measured.

Space does not permit the detailed derivation of the mathematical relations between $\bar{R}$, and t_l, t_d, τ, x, and θ. In what follows we outline the method and state the results leaving the reader to work out the intermediate steps. The essence of the calculation is to apply equation (V.51), using the appropriate expressions for n in the first and second integrals, the limits for these integrals being determined by the quasi-stationary state condition, i.e. $n = n_d$, $t = 0$; $n = n_l$, $t = t_l$ for the light period, and $n = n_l$, $t = 0$; $n = n_d$, $t = t_d$ for the dark period. Thus for case (5), i.e. exclusively linear termination

$$Pr_l = \frac{1}{\bar{t}} \int_0^{t_l} \left\{ \frac{\theta}{g}(1 - e^{gt}) + n_d e^{-gt} \right\} dt \qquad . \qquad . \text{(V.54)}$$

(cf. equation (V.8))

$$Pr_d = \frac{1}{\bar{t}} \int_0^{t_d} n_l e^{-gt} dt. \qquad . \qquad . \qquad . \qquad . \text{(V.55)}$$

(cf. equations (V.41), (V.42))

and $\quad n_l = \frac{\theta}{g}(1 - e^{-gt_l})/(e^{gt_d} - e^{-gt_l}); \; n_d = n_l e^{-gt_d}$

whence $\qquad \bar{R} = \dfrac{Pr_l + Pr_d}{t_l + t_d} = \dfrac{t_l}{t_l + t_d} \dfrac{\theta}{g\bar{t}} \qquad . \qquad . \qquad . \text{(V.56)}$

When quadratic termination is the only mode (case (8)), $x = \frac{1}{2}$, (see section c above) the appropriate equations are:

$$Pr_l = \frac{1}{\bar{t}} \int_0^{t_l} \left(\frac{\theta}{\delta}\right)^{\frac{1}{2}} . \tanh(\beta + t\sqrt{\theta\delta}) \, dt \qquad . \qquad . \text{(V.57)}$$

(cf. equation (V.24))

where
$$\beta = \frac{1}{2} \ln \left\{ \frac{(\theta/\delta)^{\frac{1}{2}} + n_d}{(\theta/\delta)^{\frac{1}{2}} - n_d} \right\}$$

$$Pr_d = \frac{1}{\bar{t}} \int_0^{t_d} \left\{ \frac{n_l}{1 + \delta t \, n_l} \right\} dt \quad . \quad . \quad . \quad \text{(V.58)}$$
$$\text{(cf.equation (V.47))}$$

Whence

$$\bar{R} = \frac{1}{\delta \bar{t}(t_l + t_d)} \ln \left\{ \frac{\cosh (\beta + t_l \sqrt{\delta\theta})}{\cosh \beta} + \ln (1 + \delta t_d n_l) \right\} \quad \text{(V.59)}$$

To make effective use of (V.59) we also require n_l and n_d. These values may be obtained by rewriting the terms inside the integral in the form of the times taken (respectively t_l and t_d) for the chain centre concentration to grow and decay through the amount $n_l - n_d$. Whence

$$\frac{1}{2\sqrt{\theta\delta}} \ln \left(\frac{(\theta/\delta)^{\frac{1}{2}} + n_l}{(\theta/\delta)^{\frac{1}{2}} - n_l} \cdot \frac{(\theta/\delta)^{\frac{1}{2}} - n_d}{(\theta/\delta)^{\frac{1}{2}} + n_d} \right) = \frac{1}{\delta} \left(\frac{1}{n_d} - \frac{1}{n_l} \right) \frac{t}{t_d} \quad \text{(V.60)}$$

and equation (V.59) becomes[14]

$$\bar{R} = \frac{1}{f\bar{t}} \left(\frac{\theta}{\delta} \right)^{\frac{1}{2}} \left\{ 1 + \frac{1}{b} \ln \left(1 + \frac{(f-1)b}{1 + n_s/n_d} \right) \right\} \quad . \quad \text{(V.61)}$$

where $b = t_l/\tau_\delta$

$$f = (t_l + t_d)/t_l = \text{the reciprocal sector opening}$$

and

$$\frac{n_s}{n_d} = \frac{(f-1)b \tanh b}{2[(f-1)b + \tanh b]}$$
$$\times \left\{ 1 + \left(1 + \frac{4}{(f-1)b \tanh b} + \frac{4}{(f-1)^2 b^2} \right) \right\} \quad \text{(V.62)}$$

These equations indicate that $\bar{R} \cdot (\theta/\delta)^{-\frac{1}{2}} \bar{t}$, which is the ratio of the rate of reaction under intermittent illumination to the rate under continuous illumination with light of the same intensity is a function of the sector opening ($t_l/(t_l + t_d)$) and the absolute value of t_l. For a given sector opening this ratio can be expressed as a function of a single parameter b, equal to the ratio of the time of one flash to the lifetime, τ_δ, of the reaction chains under continuous illumination. The most convenient way to apply this result is to construct, on transparent graph paper, the curve of $\bar{R}\bar{t}(\theta/\delta)^{-\frac{1}{2}}$ vs. $\log_{10} b$ for each of the sector openings to be used experimentally, e.g. 45°, 90°, and 180°. This curve may then be slid horizontally over the experimental $\bar{R}/R_0$ vs. $\log_{10} t_l$ curve with the abscissae superimposed, until the best fit of the theoretical curve and experimental points is obtained. The value of τ_δ is given by the value of antilog$_{10} t_l$ over which $\log_{10} b = 0$ falls. A typical example is given in Fig. V.8.

This method has been very widely employed and it can be extended to include simultaneous thermal and photochemical initiation[15]. The expression (V.52) requires modification to allow for 'penumbra' errors (i.e. trapezoidal rather than square light pulses) which are generally not serious, and also for non-uniform values of θ throughout the reaction vessel for systems in which the light extinction is considerable[16]. In 1942 RICE[17] discussed the case of a photochemically initiated chain reaction, terminated linearly and quadratically, and gave the result in a parametric form not readily applicable to specific examples. Recently this case has been reviewed by BURNETT and WRIGHT[18] who have shown how both lifetimes ($\tau_g = g^{-1}$ and $\tau_\delta = (\theta\delta)^{-\frac{1}{2}}$) may speedily be obtained from a single sector curve even when chains are also being initiated thermally as well as photochemically.

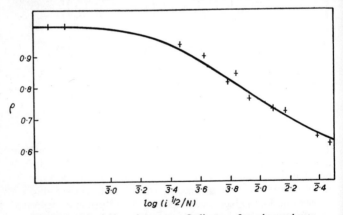

Fig. V.8. A typical section curve. Ordinate $= 2 \times$ observed rate with 90° sector (i.e. $f = 4$) divided by rate in continuous light. Abscissa $= \log_{10} (I^{\frac{1}{2}} \times t_l \text{ (min)})$. Full line denotes theoretical curve corrected for appreciable extinction (ref. 16). Experimental points are for an equimolar mixture of pure CO and Cl_2, total pressure $= 600$ mm Hg at 25°C (see ref. 3, Chapter II).

Trans. Faraday Soc. **48**, 47 (1952)

In practice the errors introduced into the values of τ_δ and τ_g by applying the formula (V.62), which is strictly valid only for the case (8) in which exclusively quadratic termination is occurring, to the experimental data for a reaction in which both types of termination are operative are generally smaller than experimental errors of measurement for intensity exponents $\leqslant 0.6$, i.e. for values of $\lambda < \sim 30$ per cent. In general the assumption leads to values of g which are larger than the true values and values of δ which are smaller than the true values[19].

In principle, similar information about quadratically terminated reaction chains could be obtained from experiments in which the rate of initiation is arranged to be spatially discontinuous. We may imagine a chain reaction photochemically initiated by equally spaced, narrow, parallel beams of light of uniform intensity entering the system and subject to quadratic termination only. When the width of each beam and the distance between beams both greatly exceed the distance which a reaction chain can travel between initiation and termination, i.e. $(2D\tau)^{\frac{1}{2}}$, the average reaction rate for the whole system will be proportional to $a_1 I_{abs}^{\frac{1}{2}}$, where a_1 is that fraction of the cross-sectional area of the system transverse to the direction of the light beams which is illuminated. However, when the beam width and inter-beam distance are both proportionately reduced so that each becomes much less than $(2D\tau)^{\frac{1}{2}}$, chains initiated in one illuminated volume will intermingle with, and be destroyed by, chains from neighbouring illuminated columns and the average reaction rate will tend to that appropriate to illumination of the whole system with an intensity $a_1 I_{abs}$, i.e. the rate will be proportional to $(a_1 I_{abs})^{\frac{1}{2}}$. Consequently a graph of the rate against log (beam diameter) will resemble that for the case of temporal discontinuity shown in Fig. V.8[20]. Although fairly precise values of the diffusion coefficient, D, of chain centres through gas mixtures can be calculated and therefore $\tau = (\theta\delta)^{-\frac{1}{2}}$ can in principle be measured by this method, in practice, spatially discontinuous illumination of gases by light always causes temperature gradients to be established and the resultant convection currents cause rapid mixing of the gases in the illuminated and dark zones. This convective mixing is likely to be less serious in liquids, particularly if the light beams are vertical, but here the disadvantage is that diffusion constants in liquids are about 10^{-4} of their values in gases and therefore, for the same values of θ and δ, the size of the light beams and their separation for this effect to be perceptible in liquids will be about 1 per cent of the size and separation necessary in the gas phase. For these reasons the method has never been deliberately applied to chain reactions either in the gas or liquid phases.* However, the somewhat analogous situation of the effect of beam size on the stationary state concentration of iodine atoms produced in a 10^{-4} M iodine solution in hexane illuminated by multiple, parallel, vertical light beams has been studied by NOYES and SALMON[21]. Here the reactions are:

$$I_2 + h\nu \rightarrow 1 \cdot 32I$$
$$2I \rightarrow I_2$$

so that the equation corresponding to equation (V.23) is

$$d[I]/dt = 1 \cdot 32 I_{abs} - \delta[I]^2$$

By using the fact that atomic iodine exchanges with isotopically labelled *trans*-diiodo ethylene the iodine concentration which, if there were a chain reaction with iodine atoms as the chain centres would correspond to n, could be measured. The results were broadly confirmatory of the theory and there is therefore little doubt that space-intermittency effects in chain reactions could be detected.

(e) 'Instantaneous' Initiation

In all the cases previously discussed it has been assumed that the rate of initiation is either constant at the value θ or, as in case (12), suddenly drops to zero. There is a significant and increasing number of reactions in which the rate of initiation is fast compared with the rate of propagation. In all these processes a fixed number of chains of concentration n_0, is initiated in a short space of time and the chains continue to propagate after the initiation is complete. This situation is achieved experimentally either by using a short pulse of light or ionizing radiation to create the initial centres or by addition of the centres as such or by addition of a given amount of a catalyst which reacts very rapidly to give an equivalent number of centres (see Chapter III, reaction 5 (iii)). When the chains are unbranched a stationary state can ensue only if there are no termination processes and this is discussed under section (*f*) below. In all other cases the number

* This is no longer true. Davies and North[26] have recently used space intermittency to measure the mean diffusion coefficients of growing poly methyl methacrylate radicals.

of centres decays with time according to either equation (V.45) or equation (V.47) and these cases will now be discussed.

Case (14): *Non-stationary states in instantaneously initiated, unbranched chain reactions in which either linear or quadratic terminations occur.* The only fully investigated examples of this situation refer to cationic polymerization in which no quadratic termination takes place. Thus in the mineral acid catalysed polymerization of styrene in ethylene dichloride the reaction steps are:

Fast Initiation $\quad$ $HA + CH_2:CH.C_6H_5$
$$\rightarrow CH_3.\overset{+}{C}H(C_6H_5).A^-$$

Propagation $\quad$ $H(CH_2.CH(C_6H_5))_j^+.A^- + CH_2:CH.C_6H_5$
$$\rightarrow H(CH_2CH(C_6H_5))_{j+1}^+A^-$$

Termination $\quad$ $H(CH_2.CH(C_6H_5))_j^+.A^-$
$$\rightarrow H(CH_2.CH(C_6H_5))_jA$$

Equation (V.45) describes this situation where $n_0 = [HA]_0$ = the concentration of mineral acid added initially. If $[m_1]$, the concentration of styrene, could be maintained at a constant value then the concentration of monomer converted to polymer at time t denoted by $-\Delta[m_1]$ is obtained from equation (V.46) and is given by

$$-\Delta[m_1] = \frac{[HA]_0 k_p[m_1]}{g}(1 - e^{-gt}) \quad . \quad . \text{ (V.63)}$$

where k_p is the rate constant of the propagation reaction. However, it is much easier in practice to add the acid to the styrene solution and allow the monomer to be used up. The equations for the decay of monomer concentration from its initial value $[m_1]_0$ are then

$$- d[m_1]/dt = [HA]_0 k_p[m_1]e^{-gt} \quad . \quad . \text{ (V.64)}$$

and therefore

$$\ln\frac{[m_1]_0}{[m_1]} - \frac{[HA]_0 k_p}{g}(1 - e^{-gt}) \quad . \quad . \text{ (V.65)}$$

and they indicate that not only the rate but also the *extent* of this reaction are dependent on the initial catalyst concentration. The extent of reaction may be defined as the fractional amount of styrene used at infinite time, i.e. $([m_1]_0 - [m_1]_\infty)/[m_1]_0$ and will have the value given by equation (V.66) which indicates that if $[HA]_0$ is less than $0.693g/k_p$ the extent of reaction will be less

$$\frac{[m_1]_0 - [m_1]_\infty}{[m_1]_0} = 1 - e^{g/k_p[HA]_0} \qquad . \qquad . \qquad \text{(V.66)}$$

than 50 per cent. The value of this kind of system is that it permits direct measurement of k_p and g from a single experiment which will yield a conversion-time curve and this was first realized and exploited by PEPPER[22]. The limitation to the method is the size of g. If this exceeds about $10^{-1}\,\text{sec}^{-1}$ the polymerization will be too limited to measure with the requisite precision.

When quadratic termination is the sole mode the pertinent equations are (V.47) and (V.48) and if n_0 is known δ and k_p can, in principle, be determined. Since this method has not yet been adequately exploited it will not be further discussed.

(*f*) Non-terminated Chains: 'Living' Polymers

In Chapter III an example was given of anionic polymerization in which the chain centres are not destroyed unless a reagent is added specifically to achieve this. Two cases may be distinguished according as the initiation rate is much slower or much faster than the propagation rate.

Case (15): *Non-terminated, instantaneously initiated, unbranched chains.* If n_0 centres are introduced into the system and none are destroyed their number will remain at this level. The rate of reaction will then be $n_0/\bar{t}$ and will remain steady at this value provided the reactant concentration is not depleted. As mentioned above (case (14)) it is much more convenient experimentally to add the initiating centres to a solution of the reagent. The reaction rate then decreases as the reaction proceeds due solely to the diminution in the concentration of the reagent. The relevant equations are

$$-\,\text{d}[R]/\text{d}t = k_p[R]n_0 \quad \text{hence } \ln\left([R]/[R_0]\right) = -\,k_p n_0 t \quad \text{(V.67)}$$

so that, if n_0 is known, k_p can be directly measured and this method has been applied many times to anionic polymerization processes[23]. In these reactions each polymerization chain is initiated at the same time and grows at the same rate, and, therefore, if there is no chain transfer, each polymer chain will contain the same number of units. This monodispersity of the polymer has been experimentally verified. There are two features of these reactions which call for special comment. Firstly, since the capacity for growth of the polymer chains is retained, i.e. they are unterminated, addition of more monomer will merely cause each polymer chain to grow to greater length at the same rate and, if the added monomer differs from that originally used, a *block copolymer* consisting of a sequence of connected units of the first monomer chemically bonded to a sequence of units of the second monomer, will be produced. Secondly, although anionic initiation may be carried out by addition of an anion to the monomer (cf. equations (34) and (35) of Chapter III), it is often achieved by transfer of an electron from a donor, as illustrated in equation (33) of Chapter III. In the latter case the growing chain centres will have a free radical at one end and an anion at the other, e.g. in the case where styrene is the monomer the structure will be $\cdot CH_2CH(C_6H_5)(CH_2 . CH(C_6H_5))_{j-2}CH_2\bar{C}H(C_6H_5)$. The free radical portions will interact with one another in pairs. If free radical ends disproportionate then the number average degree of polymerization will equal the kinetic chain length, i.e. $\overline{DP}_n = k.c.l.$ $= [m_1]_0/n_0$ when all the monomer has reacted. On the other hand, if the free radical ends combine, each polymer chain will be twice as long, i.e. $\overline{DP}_n = 2 \times k.c.l. = 2[m_1]_0/n_0$ and this is the usual state of affairs.

Case (16): *Non-terminated, slowly initiated, unbranched chains.* In this case the centre concentration will grow steadily and will have the value θt at time t. A stationary state can therefore never be reached and the rate of reaction $= \theta t/\bar{t} = k_p[R]\theta t$ should increase steadily with time provided $[R]$ is kept constant. A more probable situation would be that in which the reactant concentration is not maintained but allowed to decrease from an initial value $= [R]_0$. If the initiation process is independent of reactant concentration the relevant equations are

$$- d[R]/dt = k_p[R]\theta t \quad \text{and} \quad \ln ([R]/[R]_0) = - k_p\theta t^2/2 \quad \text{(V.68)}$$

so that as in the previous case k_p can be found directly if θ is known.

(*g*) Temporarily Terminated Chains

When the chain carriers are complex molecular species the possibility may arise that they may be converted into a form which cannot take part in a propagation reaction until a subsequent step has taken place. The chain centre thus enters an inactive phase from which it may emerge after the lapse of a period of time which is many multiples of $\bar{t}$, the average time interval between propagation steps. This phenomenon has been identified in the free-radical polymerization of several monomers and may have either a chemical or a physical origin. Consider the polymerization in an aqueous medium of the two monomers acrylamide and acrylonitrile as examples of these two cases.

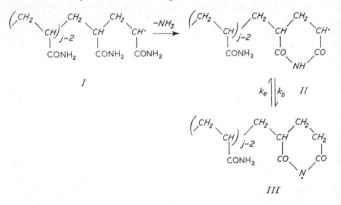

I

$k_e \Big\Uparrow\Big\Downarrow k_b$ *II*

III

Polyacrylamide is water-soluble but is known to undergo a slow loss of ammonia from adjacent amide groups. If this deamination involves the amide groups adjacent to the radical end then the polyacrylamide radical I, which is the propagating chain centre is converted to II, which has the tautomeric form III. The radical III is a substituted glutarimidyl radical, expected to be 'stabilized by resonance' and therefore much less active than either II or I. Suppose further that III is incapable of reacting with fresh acrylamide in the propagation step or of interacting with another type III radical to undergo quadratic termination or even of reacting with a retarder such as added ferric salts, whereas radical II can enter all these reactions with substantially the same speed as radical I. The kinetic situation is thus one in which normal centres in concentration n, have a finite probability denoted by a first order rate constant k_b, of changing into an inactive non-propagating form of concentration n_b, which can change back unimolecularly into the active form at a rate $= k_e n_b$. The relevant kinetic equations are thus

$$\mathrm{d}n/\mathrm{d}t = \theta - k_b n + k_e n_b - \text{either } gn \text{ or } \delta n^2 \quad \text{(V.69)}$$

and $\quad \mathrm{d}n_b/\mathrm{d}t = k_b n - k_e n_b$ . . . (V.70)

and the life history of a chain for which $k_e \simeq k_b < g$ or $\sqrt{\theta\delta}$ may then be depicted as follows. After initiation at time zero, the

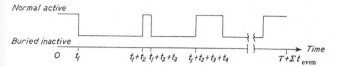

active phase continues to time t_1 when the centre tautomerizes to the inactive state in which it remains for time t_2, from which it emerges for a time t_3, etc., and so on until a time $\sum t_{\mathrm{odd}} + \sum t_{\mathrm{even}}$ has elapsed when it is terminated either linearly or quadratically. The total period in the active state is $\sum t_{\mathrm{odd}}$ which must be the kinetic lifetime $\tau =$ either g^{-1} or $(\theta\delta)^{-\frac{1}{2}}$ depending on the mode of termination, and the total time spent in the inactive phase is $\sum t_{\mathrm{even}}$. The number of active phases in the kinetic lifetime $= k_b/(g$ or $(\theta\delta)^{-\frac{1}{2}})$, and, if this is much less than unity, virtually all of the normal centres will be terminated and none will become buried. If also, radical III is stable, then $k_b \gg k_e$.

When the chains are linearly terminated, i.e. $\delta = 0$, the solution to equations (V.69) and (V.70) is given by

$$n = \frac{\theta}{g}\left\{1 - \frac{k_b e^{-k_e t}}{g + k_b} - \frac{g e^{-gt}}{g + k_b}\right\} \quad . \quad . \quad (V.71)$$

and this corresponds to an initial non-stationary state in which the chain carrier concentration is built-up at a rate determined primarily by the two rate constants k_e and g. If these are sufficiently different the form of this build-up will have two phases, OA and AB, as shown in Fig. V.9, in the second phase of which, AB, the concentration of buried centres slowly rises to its steady value. At the steady state $n_b = k_b \theta / k_e g$ and $n = \theta/g$ so that the reaction rate under the steady-state will show a dependence on the rate of initiation identical with that of case (2) in which no temporary chain termination takes place. Equations (V.69) and (V.70) also lead to the conclusion that if initiation is suddenly stopped the concentration of centres will decay in two stages, CD and DE, according to equation (V.72) as shown in Fig. V.9.

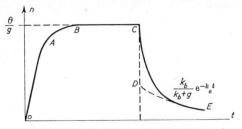

Fig. V.9. Slow build-up and decay of centres in an unbranched
temporarily terminated chain reaction.

In the first stage the active centres diminish rapidly by the
normal termination

$$n = \frac{\theta}{g} \left\{ \frac{k_b e^{-k_e t}}{g + k_b} + \frac{g e^{-gt}}{g + k_b} \right\} \qquad . \quad . \quad . \text{ (V.72)}$$

process leaving almost $k_b \theta / k_e g$ buried centres to emerge slowly
into the active phase. In short, during the protracted build up,
AB, a reservoir of buried centres is accumulated which, after the
main initiation process has been stopped acts as a slow source from
which active radicals emerge.

A photochemically initiated chain reaction falling into this
kinetic pattern should show a slow increase in rate after the
illumination has begun and a prolonged 'after-effect' after the
illumination stops in which the rate decays exponentially with
time. These phenomena are exactly those observed in the photopolymerization of acrylamide in aqueous solution when the
chains are terminated oxidatively by the ferric ion[24].

In accordance with expectation similar 'pre' and 'post-effects'
are manifested in the photopolymerization of aqueous acrylamide
when the chains are quadratically terminated, i.e. in the absence
of a retarding agent. Although analytical solutions to the
pertinent equations cannot be obtained it is readily shown (*a*)
that at the steady state $n = \sqrt{\theta/\delta}$ and $n_b = \sqrt{\theta/\delta} . k_b/k_e$ and (*b*)
that when $k_b > \sqrt{\theta\delta} \gg k_e$ there will be a very prolonged post-
effect[24].

Polyacrylonitrile is insoluble in water and consequently when
aqueous solutions of acrylonitrile are polymerized the hydro-
phobic polymer chains will tend to coil up and aggregate with

other polymer chains to form suspended polymer particles. If a growing polymer radical becomes part of a polymer particle before it is terminated then it is withdrawn from the aqueous disperse medium, which contains most of the monomer molecules, and can only react with monomer molecules which become attached to and which penetrate the polymer particles. Since polyacrylonitrile is insoluble in the monomer the adsorption of the latter on polymer particle will be weak and the rate of growth of the polymer radicals occluded in polymer particles will be very much slower than that of the short chain polyacrylonitrile radicals in the aqueous phase. Thus by a process of physical 'burial' in a polymer particle a fraction of the polymer radicals will have been terminated in the kinetic sense that their capacity for rapid propagation has been drastically reduced. Although this may lead to complex kinetic situations which are not very fruitfully described in mathematical terms one consequence is obvious, namely, that when chain initiation is stopped in the aqueous phase the soluble radicals will rapidly disappear by their normal heterogeneous termination reactions but the occluded radicals will persist. If the adsorbed monomer molecules can penetrate the particle and so 'find' the radical ends a long-lived but slow after-effect should be, and in fact is, observed[25].

REFERENCES

1. Ref. 44, Chapter III.
2. Ref. 5, Chapter II.
3. Ref. 36, Chapter III.
4. BURSIAN, V. and SOROKIN, V.: *Z. Phys. Chem.*, **B, 12**, 247 (1931).
5. Ref. 3, Chapter II.
6. Ref. 17, Chapter II.
7. BURNETT, G. M.: *Trans. Faraday Soc.*, **46**, 772 (1950).
8. DAINTON, F. S. and JAMES, D. G. L.: *J. Polymer Sci.*, **39**, 299 (1959), and also ASHMORE, P. G., private communication.
9. NOYES, R. M.: *J. Amer. Chem. Soc.*, **73**, 3039 (1951).
10. Refs. 39 and 40, Chapter III.
11. WEIGERT, F. and KELLERMANN, K.: *Z. Phys. Chem.*, **107**, 1 (1923).
12. HIMMEL, R. W., FREEMAN, G. R. and SPINKS, J. W. T.: *Science*, **119**, 159 (1954); COLEBOURNE, N., COLLINSON, E., CURRIE, D. J. and DAINTON, F. S., *Trans. Faraday Soc.*, **59**, 1357 (1963).
13. HART, E. J. and MATHESON, M. S.: *Disc. Faraday Soc.*, **12**, 169 (1952); DAINTON, F. S. and ROWBOTTAM, J.: *Nature*, **169**, 370 (1952), *Trans. Faraday Soc.*, **49**, 1160 (1953).

14. LEIGHTON, P. and NOYES; W. A.: *The Photochemistry of Gases.* Reinhold, New York, 1941, p. 205.
15. BATEMAN, L. and GEE, G.: *Proc. Roy. Soc.*, A, **195,** 391 (1948).
16. BURNS, W. G. and DAINTON, F. S.: *Trans. Faraday Soc.*, **46,** 411 (1950).
17. RICE, O. K.: *J. Chem. Physics*, **10,** 440 (1942).
18. BURNETT, G. M. and WRIGHT, W. W., *Proc. Roy. Soc.*, A, **221,** 37 (1954).
19. BENGOUGH, W. I.: *Trans. Faraday Soc.*, **58,** 716 (1962).
20. NOYES, R. M.: *J. Amer. Chem. Soc.*, **81,** 566 (1959).
21. NOYES, R. M. and SALMON, G. A., *J. Amer. Chem. Soc.*, **84,** 672 (1962).
22. HAYES, M. J. and PEPPER, D. C.: *Proc. Chem. Soc.*, **228** (1958); BURTON, R. E. and PEPPER, D. C.: *Proc. Roy. Soc.*, A, **263,** 63 (1961); ALBERT, A. and PEPPER, D. C.: *Proc. Roy. Soc.*, A, **263,** 75, (1961).
23. Ref. 26, Chapter III.
24. DAINTON, F. S. and TORDOFF, M.: *Trans. Faraday Soc.*, **53,** 499, 666 (1957).
25. DAINTON, F. S., EATON, R. S., JAMES, D. G. L. and SEAMAN, P. H.: *J. Polymer Sci.*, **34,** 209 (1959).
26. DAVIES, P. D. and NORTH, A. M.: *Proc. Chem. Soc.*, **141** (1964).

CHAPTER VI

SPONTANEOUSLY EXPLOSIVE REACTIONS

ONE of the obvious distinguishing features of certain chain reactions which was mentioned in Chapter II is that of spontaneous explosion, and in this chapter we shall discuss spontaneously explosive reactions in a little more detail. By an explosive reaction is meant one that is continually accelerated at a rate such that most of the reaction is completed within a very short time. It may be accompanied by the emission of light, by the momentary attainment of very high temperatures and by rapid pressure changes in the gas which may give rise to the formation of a shock wave. Explosions can be induced to spread through cold gas mixtures lying in certain composition ranges from a suitable igniting source such as a hot wire, an electric spark, an explosive charge or a subsidiary flame. We shall not be concerned with such systems but only with those reactions which explode without the aid of such initiators. Such explosions may be due to either or both of the following causes: (i) the exothermicity of the reaction and (ii) its chain character. Explosions due solely to the capacity of the reaction to accelerate by self heating, are called *thermal* explosions; whilst those in which the sole condition for explosion is that the rate of the branching of the chains exceeds their rate of removal are called *chain-isothermal* explosions. Since nearly all chain reactions are exothermic (see section (i), Chapter III), a chain reaction which explodes for the second reason will be self heating and will eventually undergo auto-acceleration for both reasons. When this exothermic nature also influences the onset of the explosion, so that both the heat of reaction and the coefficients of chain branching and termination appear in the condition for explosion, then the explosion is said to be *chain-thermal* in character.

In addition to the exothermicity there is a second factor which may modify the course of the reaction. When the branching only slightly exceeds the termination rate, the consumption of reactants in the early stages of the reaction may so decrease the branching rate that the reaction velocity rises to a maximum value less than that normally recognized as explosive. Such incipient explosions which die away are termed *degenerate* explosions.

In this chapter we shall consider only those reactions which give rise to chain-isothermal explosions, dealing firstly with a hypothetical generalized explosive reaction and secondly with some actual branching chain oxidation reactions.

The reaction mechanisms here presented should not be regarded as either unique or final. They have been chosen primarily to illustrate the varied kinetic problems with which the theorist in this field is faced and a type of approach which could be adopted in attempting to solve them. To categorize all the experimental findings and to consider their implications for the mechanisms of each of the three reactions discussed, is far beyond the scope and purpose of this Chapter. In recent years there has been a revival of activity in this field and the interested reader is advised to consult in the first instance, reference 1.

1. A Hypothetical Reaction. Consider a reaction in which the rate of chain branching is proportional to the total pressure of the reactants, the energy of activation of the branching reaction being B k.cal, and in which the chains are initiated homogeneously in the gas phase and terminated linearly both at the surface and in the gas phase, the rate of the gas phase linear* termination being proportional to the square of the total pressure. This reaction mechanism might be written:

Initiation (gas).   (1) $R \rightarrow X$

Propagation.   (2) $R + X \rightarrow Pr + Y$; $Y +$ etc.

Branching.   (3) $X + R \rightarrow 2X$ or $2Y$ or $X + Y$,
                                 Energy of Activation $= B$

Linear Termination (gas). (4) $X + R + R' \rightarrow$ destruction of X
           (wall). $X +$ wall $\rightarrow$ destruction of X

---

* We may omit quadratic termination, since as proved in Chapter V, case 10, linearly branched quadratically terminated reactions cannot lead to non-stationary states under isothermal conditions.

and corresponds to case (7) of Chapter V, i.e. the approximate equation for a spherical or cylindrical reaction vessel is

$$\frac{d\bar{n}}{dt} = \theta + (f - g)\bar{n} - \frac{\Gamma\bar{D}}{d^2}\,\bar{n} \quad . \quad . \quad . \text{(VI.1)}$$

where $f = k_3 p$; $g = k_4 p^2$, and $\bar{D} = \bar{D}_0/p$. $\bar{D}_0$ is here the average value of the diffusion constant at unit pressure, Γ depends on the shape of the reaction vessel and the efficiency of the wall in destroying centres which reach it, and k_3 and k_4 are velocity constants in reciprocal pressure-time units. The net branching factor ϕ is given by

$$\phi = k_3 p - k_4 p^2 - \frac{\Gamma\bar{D}_0}{p d^2} \quad . \quad . \quad . \quad . \text{(VI.2)}$$

The last two terms on the right-hand side of this equation are unlikely to be very temperature dependent since they both refer to termination processes. In contrast the coefficient of the first term will increase with temperature according to the Arrhenius Law $k_3 = k_3^\circ\, e^{\frac{-B}{RT}}$. Now the condition for chain isothermal explosion (see Chapter V, case 7) is that ϕ is positive and the equation for the explosion boundary is obtained by putting ϕ equal to zero, i.e.

$$k_3 p - k_4 p^2 - \frac{\Gamma\bar{D}_0}{p d^2} = 0 \quad . \quad . \quad . \text{(VI.3)}$$

This cubic equation always has one negative root, which is of no practical significance and provided k_3 is sufficiently large will also have two positive roots, corresponding to two pressures P_l and P_u respectively between which ϕ has positive values. We thus immediately see that as the temperature is raised a reaction may change from one in which steady state conditions obtain at all pressures, to one in which the steady state can prevail only at pressures less than P_l and greater than P_u, and which is explosive at pressures within these limits. The chemical significance of the way in which this arises may perhaps be most clearly seen by plotting each of the terms in equation (VI.2) as a function of p (as in Fig. VI.1) at a temperature for which ϕ may have positive values. The following phenomena would be expected for such a reaction.

(1) The reaction would be preceded by a true period of induction, which, whether it was determined by the minimum detectable *amount* of reaction (equation (V.22)) or by the minimum detectable *rate* (equation (V.10)), would decrease to a minimum

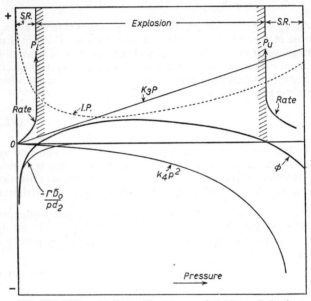

Fig. VI.1. The variation with pressure of the Rate, Induction Period (*I.P.*) and Net Branching Factor (ϕ) of a hypothetical linearly branched chain reaction subject to linear termination at the wall and in the gas phase.

value and then increase as the pressure was increased, provided there was no large change in the rate of initiation.

(2) The initial form of the product *vs.* time curves in the explosion region would be exponential (equation (V.21)) and outside the explosion region would be summarized by equation (V.8) provided we write $-\phi$ for g.

(3) Although the rate of slow reaction and the induction period (*I.P.*) would be profoundly altered by an increase in the rate of initiation, the former being increased and the latter diminished, the explosion limits would be unaltered.

(4) Since the rate of wall termination is very small in the region of the upper limit (P_u) the equation for the latter may be written

$$k_3 P_u = k_4 P_u^2$$

i.e. $\qquad P_u = k_3/k_4 = k_3^\circ \, \mathrm{e}^{\frac{-B}{RT}} / k_4^\circ \, \mathrm{e}^{\frac{-E_4}{RT}} \quad . \quad . \quad .$ (VI.4)

from which it is seen that this limit is likely to be unaffected by change of vessel dimension or surface condition but will increase with temperature provided $B > E_4$. If, as is sometimes the case, one of the reactants participating in the termination reaction (5) is merely acting as a third body, a role which can be occupied by any species present, then (a) E_4 is likely to be very small and hence $RT^2 \, \mathrm{d}(\ln P_u)/\mathrm{d}T$ may be equated to the energy of activation of the branching reaction, and (b) the effect of foreign non-reactant gases (M) on the upper limit will be described by the equation

$$P_u = k_3/k_4^R - \frac{1}{k_4^R} \Sigma k_4^M P_M \quad . \quad . \quad .$$ (VI.5)

where the termination velocity constants are dependent on the nature of the compound whose formula is written as a superscript. These constants are a function of the collision rate and the efficacy as a third body of the compound to which they refer. Thus when nitrogen is added to the system the appropriate equation would be

$$P_u = k_3/k_4^R - k_4^{N_2} P_{N_2}/k_4^R$$

The upper limit should therefore be reduced by an amount proportional to the amount of the added foreign gas, and the slopes of the curves obtained by plotting P_u against P_M should provide information as to the relative efficiencies of various substances as 'third bodies' (cf. equation (II.2)).

(5) At very low pressures the rate of wall termination greatly exceeds the rate of linear gas phase termination. The equation for the lower limit P_l is therefore

$$P_l = \left(\frac{\Gamma \bar{D}_0}{k_3^\circ d^2}\right)^{\frac{1}{2}} \mathrm{e}^{\frac{+B}{2RT}} . \quad . \quad . \quad . \quad .$$ (VI.6)

This equation predicts that the lower limit should be inversely proportional to the diameter of the vessel, should decrease as the temperature is raised, and should be very sensitive to the presence of wall coatings which modify the efficacy of the wall in chain termination. Added non-reactant gases will depress the lower limit by impeding the diffusion of chain centres to the wall. The present state of knowledge of diffusion in mixed gases does not permit precise prediction of this effect, but if we may write $\bar{D}^{-1} = \Sigma \bar{D}_{0M}^{-1} P_M$* then equation (VI.6) becomes

$$P_l = \frac{\Gamma \, e^{\frac{B}{RT}}}{k_3{}^\circ d^2} \, (\bar{D}_{0R}^{-1} P_l + \Sigma \bar{D}_{0M}^{-1} \cdot P_M)^{-1} \quad . \quad . \text{ (VI.7)}$$

This equation summarizes an effect of added non-reactant gases on the lower limit and on the temperature coefficient of this limit which is in agreement with observation in those systems which have been examined.

It was mentioned above that Γ depends on the efficiency, ε, of the wall in destroying those centres which reach it. ε can vary over a very wide range depending on any special treatment or coating applied to the surface of the reaction vessel and may have very different values for different chain centres. Equations VI.1, 2, 3, 6, and 7 apply only when ε is so large that a concentration gradient of chain centres is set up (as illustrated in Fig. III.2 (*b*)) which controls the rate at which the centres can reach the walls. When $\varepsilon \ll 1$ this concentration gradient will no longer exist throughout the reaction vessel and over most of the reaction vessel $n_x = \bar{n}$. Consequently the rate of chain termination under these circumstances will merely depend on the velocity of the chain centres and their mean distance from the wall so that equation VI.1 becomes

$$\frac{dn}{dt} = \theta + (f - g)n - \alpha n/d$$

and the lower limit will have the value $\alpha \cdot e^{B/RT}/k_3{}^\circ d$ and be much less sensitive to the presence of foreign gases but more dependent on temperature.

(6) Outside the explosion region the steady state reaction rate will be given by

$$\frac{d[Pr]}{dt} = \theta \bigg/ \bar{t} \left(\frac{\Gamma \bar{D}_0}{pd^2} + k_4 p^2 - k_3{}^\circ p e^{\frac{-B}{RT}} \right) \quad . \quad . \text{ (VI.8)}$$

---

* This is equivalent to assuming that the time for diffusion of the centre through a given distance in a given gas mixture is equal to the sum of the times required if each gas were present alone.

indicating that this rate will be markedly increased by an increase of vessel diameter or by added foreign gas at low pressures, whereas at high pressures the rate may decrease with pressure and be substantially independent of vessel shape and size. At all pressures the rate will increase with temperature.

(7) The effects of adding positive and negative catalysts to this reaction are interesting. Positive catalysts include those substances which increase the rate of initiation, those which increase the rate of branching and those which may perform both these functions. All these substances will cause a decrease in the induction period and an increase in the rate of the slow reaction, which is equal to $-\theta/\phi\bar{\imath}$, by increasing θ or f or both. Compounds in the first category will not affect the explosion limits, but substances which increase the branching rate in addition to accelerating the slow reaction and reducing the induction periods will cause the explosion limits to be widened. It quite frequently happens that only very small amounts of these latter substances, which are called explosion sensitizers, produce considerable enhancement of f with a consequential effect on the explosion limits which is dramatically large. Moreover, since the sensitizer is operative because it provides a new and easier branching mechanism which will have an energy of activation differing from B, the temperature coefficients of the limits and the slow reaction rate may be profoundly modified.

Negative catalysts usually have this property because they are effective chain terminating agents, and we must therefore add reaction (6) to our hypothetical reaction sequence.

Termination by retarder (6) $\underline{X}$ + Ret. → destruction of X.

The net branching factor then becomes

$$\phi = k_3 p - k_4 p^2 - \frac{\Gamma \bar{D}_0}{pd^2} - k_6 p_{ret} \quad . \quad . \quad . \text{(VI.9)}$$

and it is evident that such negative catalysts will increase the induction period, retard the slow reaction and cause the explosion region to contract. From the experimental curves of P_l *vs.* P_{ret} and P_u *vs.* P_{ret} estimates of k_6 may be made.

There are some nitrogenous substances including NO_2, NOCl, CCl_3NO_2, $C(NO_2)_4$ and ammonia, which are remarkable in that they, or some decomposition or oxidation product, can function both as chain branching catalysts and as chain terminating agents. The precise dependence of the catalysis of chain branching on the concentration of these sensitizers is complex, but at low pressures of sensitizers the net branching factor increases with sensitizer concentration, whilst at higher sensitizer concentration the net branching factor decreases (Fig. VI.2). Consequently there exist regions of composition and temperature for which the explosive reaction is confined between two critical concentrations of sensitizer and between two limiting pressures of reactants. These sensitizer and total pressure limits may be so related as to give rise to the pressure dependence summarized in Fig. VI.2 and a closed zone of explosion depicted in Fig. VI.3.

In the preceding paragraphs of this section it has been shown how a large number of diverse phenomena might be displayed by a linearly branched chain reaction. All the phenomena described have been observed in one system or another. It now remains to inquire a little more closely into actual chemical reactions to discover exactly what combinations of simple reactions may determine the overall kinetics. There is no lack of examples. The gaseous oxidations of many compounds of the non-metals including hydrogen, hydrocarbons, carbon monoxide, carbon disulphide, hydrogen sulphide, phosphorus and the phosphines, arsenic and the arsines, ammonia, hydrazine, amines, alcohols and in fact almost all volatile compounds of carbon containing hydrogen all possess ignition temperatures and show, to a greater or less degree, the phenomena described above. There is a vast literature on this subject to which an introduction is to be found in the books cited in reference 1 at the end of this chapter. In the remainder of this chapter a few selected reactions will be discussed.

2. The Oxidation of Hydrogen. (*a*) *The observed kinetics.* The synthesis of water vapour is accompanied by a very large decrease in free energy, but the homogeneous gas reaction proceeds only slowly at temperatures less than 400°C. Above this temperature the reaction displays many features characteristic of a branched chain reaction, some of which are summarized below. The reaction is spontaneously explosive and the boundary to this explosion region is indicated in Fig. VI.4 from which it is seen that at temperatures between approximately 400 and

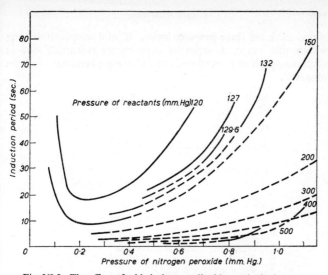

Fig. VI.2. The effect of added nitrogen dioxide on the hydrogen-oxygen reaction at a temperature at which the pure reagents react unmeasurably slowly. Full line indicates that the period of induction is succeeded by a slow reaction. Broken line indicates that explosion occurs at the end of the induction period.

Proc. Roy. Soc. **A, 177,** 393 (1941), Fig. 4, p. 401

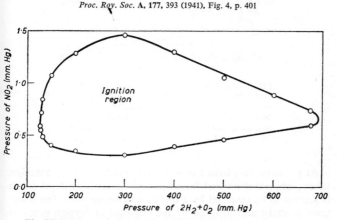

Fig. VI.3. The explosion boundary of a stoichiometric hydrogen-oxygen mixture containing nitrogen dioxide. $T = 364°C$ KCl coated narrow reaction vessel.

Proc. Roy. Soc. **A, 177,** 393, (1941), Fig. 2, p. 400

600°C there are three pressure limits. If, at a temperature lying within this range, a series of experiments is carried out at successively greater pressures, the following phenomena will be observed.

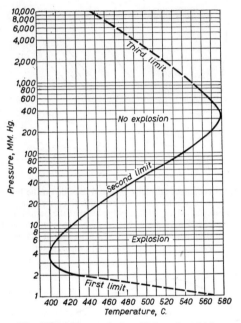

Fig. VI.4. The explosion limits of stoichiometric hydrogen-oxygen mixtures at various temperatures. Taken from Lewis and von Elbe.[1] Note (a) that first limit = P_l, second limit = P_u and third limit = π; (b) pressure scale is logarithmic; (c) KCl coated vessel 7·4 cm internal diameter.

At pressures less than the first limit (P_l) a very slow reaction takes place which has not been examined in any detail but which is known to be retarded by a decrease of vessel size. The lower limit is sharp and lowered by the addition of foreign gases or by an increase of vessel dimensions, being approximately inversely proportional to the diameter. It is also profoundly influenced by the condition of the vessel surface and decreases as the temperature is increased according to the relation, $P_l = P_i^{\circ} \exp(E/RT)$, where the values of E obtained by different investigators lie in the range 9 to 14 k.cal. In silica vessels the composition of the gas at the explosion limit in the absence of added non-reactant gases always satisfies the equation $P_{H_2}P_{O_2}$ = constant. At pressures slightly in excess of P_l the pressure-time curves are in keeping with a reaction proceeding according to the generalized scheme outlined in case (7) of Chapter V (see Fig. V.3). As expected, the net branching factor evidently increases steadily with increasing pressure from a value zero at the lower limit. As the explosion zone is penetrated the auto-acceleration becomes too rapid to measure. Further increase of pressure must cause ϕ to pass through a maximum value and decrease because an upper limit, P_u, is ultimately attained at which the reaction ceases to be explosive.

The upper limit increases rapidly with increasing temperature according to the equation $P_u = P_u^{\circ} \exp(-E/RT)$, where values of E are generally reported as being in the range 20 to 26 k.cal., i.e. about twice the value for the corresponding Arrhenius term for the lower limit. Except in boric acid coated vessels the mixture composition at the upper limit obeys the relation

$$P_{H_2} + \alpha P_{O_2} + \beta P_M = \text{constant}$$

so that added non-reactant gases, M, depress the limit. Water is much more effective than any other gas, except possibly nitrous oxide, though reactive gases such as aldehydes and hydrocarbons, which can react with specific chain carriers often have very marked effects on this limit. A surprising property of this limit which would not be expected from the discussion of Chapter V and which will be referred to again, is that the value of the limit is affected by the diameter and surface condition of the vessel. This effect is most marked at the lower end of the temperature range, where a 25 per cent decrease in vessel diameter when this is less than about 5 cm may cause about 10 per cent reduction in P_u and heavy coatings of potassium chloride produce a marked fall in the upper limit.

The slow reaction between the upper limit and the third limit (π) has received much attention. Immediately above P_u the rate passes through a minimum which is not easily detected and then increases very rapidly as the reactant pressure is increased.

Early investigators reported that the order of this reaction with respect to hydrogen was 3 and for oxygen between 1 and 2. More recent work indicates that the kinetics are considerably more complicated than this and are only satisfactorily reproducible in heavily coated vessels. The effect of added non-reactant gases is of interest. Just above the upper limit they cause a diminution of the rate by enhancing the gas phase termination rate but, at higher reagent partial pressures, the inert gases, carbon dioxide and water* cause an acceleration of the reaction and the reaction becomes more sensitive to the vessel dimensions, increasing in rate by an amount which is roughly proportional to the inverse square of the diameter. In this region the reaction is markedly retarded by surface coatings, particularly those of alkali-metal chlorides, and the energy of activation, though variable, is extremely high, many values in the region of 110 k.cal mole^{-1} having been reported. Hydrogen peroxide is also produced in small yield. At high pressures very high reaction rates exceeding 1 mm pressure change per second may be observed, and as the pressure is raised still farther an initially rapid but measurable reaction may terminate in explosion. There is thus a range of pressures in which explosion is observed, preceded by a rapid reaction of decreasing duration but increasing velocity as the initial reactant pressure is increased. The third explosion limit is located within this range, the precise value being difficult to select. The value of the limit corresponding most nearly to the initial reactant composition will be that which takes place immediately after admission of the reactants before appreciable reaction has taken place. However, since the gases cannot be premixed, oxygen is added to the hydrogen already in the reaction vessel and time must be allowed for some mixing and for dissipation of any heat generated during adiabatic compression accompanying the oxygen addition. The choice of this time is arbitrary and therefore introduces a personal element into the values of the third limit cited by various authors, which possibly accounts in part for the discrepancies which exist between the values obtained[2]. The general properties of this limit are not in dispute. In heavily coated vessels it decreases very rapidly as the temperature is raised, it is reduced by addition of foreign gases such as N_2 or H_2O and is increased by decrease of the vessel diameter.

* The reaction is therefore auto-catalytic.

The hydrogen-oxygen reaction is most sensitive to traces of sensitizers and their effects have been subject to so much detailed scrutiny and theorizing that they are discussed separately in (c) below.

(b) *The Mechanism.* Although it cannot be said that there is one reaction scheme which accounts uniquely for all the known data, the principal features of the reaction mechanism are well established. A number of observations, not strictly kinetic in character, are strongly suggestive that atoms and radicals are present in reacting mixtures of hydrogen and oxygen and act as the chain carriers. The water bands which are due to the $^2\Pi \leftarrow {}^2\Sigma$ transition of free hydroxyl radicals are prominent in the emission spectrum of burning hydrogen. The tests for the presence of oxygen atoms devised by GAYDON[3] and WHITTING-HAM[4] (see Chapter II, section 2 *f* (ii)) when applied to this reaction yield positive results. HABER and co-workers[5] and NALBANDJAN[6] have shown that either oxygen or hydrogen atoms injected into $2H_2 + O_2$ mixtures have a powerful sensitizing action on the explosion. Mass spectroscopic examination of reacting mixtures has shown a unit of mass 33 to be present which may be the HO_2 radical[7].

The entities H, OH and O may be accommodated in a propagation and branching sequence as follows:

Propagation. (7) $\underline{OH} + H_2 \rightarrow H_2O + \underline{H}$; $\Delta E = -13$ k.cal

Branching. (8) $\underline{H} + O_2 \rightarrow \underline{HO} + \underline{O}$; $\Delta E = +14$,,

Branching. (9) $\underline{O} + H_2 \rightarrow \underline{HO} + \underline{H}$; $\Delta E = +0$,,

It is known that hydrogen atoms readily combine with oxygen molecules in an exothermic reaction which probably requires a third body (reaction (10)) and if the HO_2 radical is relatively unreactive so that a proportion of these radicals can diffuse to

Termination. (10) $\underline{H} + O_2 + M \rightarrow \underline{HO_2} + M$;

$HO_2 \rightarrow$ wall with possible formation of H_2O_2

the wall and there be destroyed, reaction (10) will be a chain terminating process. Since the rate of this reaction depends on the square of the total pressure whereas the branching reaction (8) and (9) proceed at rates dependent only on the first power, reaction (10) could account for the existence of an upper limit, but such a limit would be unusual in the respect that its values would be dependent on the size and condition of the reaction vessel. Those HO_2 radicals which are not destroyed at the wall continue the propagation of the chain by reaction with hydrogen according to equations (11) or (12). The former is 62 k.cal more exothermic than the latter and has frequently been assumed to

Propagation. (11) $HO_2 + H_2 \rightarrow H_2O + OH$
Propagation. (12) $HO_2 + H_2 \rightarrow H_2O_2 + H$

$\left.\begin{array}{l}\end{array}\right\}$ $\Delta E_{11} - \Delta E_{12} = -62$ k.cal

be the more probable reaction. However in flow systems at pressures greater than P_u hydrogen peroxide is found in analytically measurable amounts and an obvious merit of reaction (12) is that it provides a route to the formation of this compound. Whilst it is agreed that initiation occurs homogeneously in the gas phase there is no unanimity as to the precise reaction involved. HINSHELWOOD and WILLBOURN[2] favour reaction (13) because the order of reaction with respect to hydrogen is so high

Initiation. (13) $H_2 + M \rightarrow 2H + M$; $\Delta E = 103.4$ k.cal

and this view is supported by the high temperature coefficient of this reaction. LEWIS and VON ELBE[1] have objected to this suggestion on the grounds that the observed reaction rate demands an initiation rate far greater than could be accounted for by reaction (13). As an alternative they suggest the thermal

Initiation. (14) $H_2O_2 + M \rightarrow 2OH + M$; $\Delta E = \sim 58$ k.cal

decomposition of hydrogen peroxide (reaction (14)).

For the sake of argument we will assume that the reaction mechanism consists of reactions (13), (7), (8), (9), (10), (11) together with a wall termination reaction (15) which must be introduced to account for the lower limit. Hydrogen atoms have

Termination. (15) H + wall $\rightarrow$ destruction

been selected as the centres most likely to reach the wall because (a) they are the smallest and therefore diffuse most rapidly and (b) they react very slowly with oxygen (the bimolecular reaction (8) has a high energy of activation ca. 23 k. cal mole^{-1} and the termolecular reaction (10) will be of rare occurrence at low total pressures) whereas hydroxyl radicals and oxygen atoms react with hydrogen much more rapidly.

We may now inquire what properties such a reaction system

should possess. Using either of the methods outlined in Chapters IV and V we obtain the following expressions:

$$\theta = k_{13}[H_2][M] \quad . \quad . \quad . \quad . \quad (VI.10)$$

$$\phi = 2k_8[O_2] - \frac{\Sigma k_{10}[M][O_2]\Gamma_{HO_2}\bar{D}_0^{HO_2}/pd^2}{k_{11}[H_2] + \Gamma_{HO_2}\bar{D}_0^{HO_2}/pd^2} - \frac{\Gamma_H\bar{D}_0^H}{pd^2} \quad (VI.11)$$

and

$$2\bar{\iota} = \frac{k_{11}[H_2] + \Gamma_{HO_2}\bar{D}_0^{HO_2}/pd^2}{k_{11}[H_2]\Sigma k_{10}[M][O_2] + k_8[O_2](k_{11}[H_2] + \Gamma_{HO_2}\bar{D}_0^{HO_2}/pd^2)}$$

$$(VI.12)$$

where the subscript or superscript refers either to the reaction number or to the radical involved and

$$\Sigma k_{10}[M] = k_{10}^{H_2}[H_2] + k_{10}^{O_2}[O_2] + k_{10}^{H_2O}[H_2O] + \ldots k_{10}^{M}[M]$$

The steady state reaction rate is given by

$$\frac{d[H_2O]}{dt} = -\frac{\theta}{\bar{\iota}\phi} \quad . \quad . \quad . \quad (VI.13)$$

It is evident that at all pressures the reaction is subject to surface influences; at very low pressures principally due to the term containing Γ_H which corresponds to the loss of H atoms at the wall, and at higher pressures due to the loss of HO_2 radicals (term containing Γ_{HO_2}). Added gases will accelerate the reaction at very low pressures and at higher pressures will cause either an acceleration or a deceleration depending on whether their influence in impeding the diffusion of HO_2 radicals is outweighed by their effect in promoting reaction (10). Water may act as an added gas and therefore the reaction may be auto-inhibited at one pressure and auto-catalysed at a higher pressure as is indeed found to be the case. The rate will increase very sharply as the partial pressure of hydrogen is increased and will have a large temperature coefficient.

The expression (VI.11) for the net branching factor ϕ is of particular interest. For a mixture of constant composition containing no added gas it may be written

$$\phi = k_8'p - \frac{\alpha p^2}{\beta p^2 + \gamma} - \frac{\varepsilon}{p} \quad . \quad . \quad . \quad (VI.14)$$

and has certain interesting properties. Firstly at any temperature, even when the first term $k_8'p$ may be quite small, there will exist a critical pressure which will be the larger the smaller k_8, above which ϕ is positive (see Fig. VI.5). At this pressure, which is the third limit, the term ε/p is negligible and only a very small fraction of the HO_2 radicals formed in reaction (10) reach the wall and are destroyed. The value of this limit is approximately $3k_{10}\Gamma_{HO_2}\bar{D}_0^{HO_2}/4k_{11}k_8d^2$, from which we may deduce that it

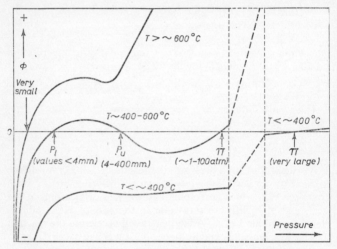

Fig. VI.5. Diagrammatic representation (not to scale) of the pressure dependence of ϕ in different temperature ranges for the hypothetical hydrogen-oxygen reaction involving reactions 13, 7, 8, 9, 10, 11, and 15 only

should decrease with increasing temperature according to π $= \pi^\circ \exp(E_8 + E_{11} - E_{10})/RT$ and therefore, since E_{10} is likely to be small[17] and E_{11} finite, the temperature coefficient of the third limit should be considerably larger, though of opposite sign to, that of the upper limit (see below). Further the third limit should diminish with increasing vessel diameter and be very sensitive to changes in surface coatings which differ in the efficiency with which they can remove HO_2 radicals. Added non-reactant gases serve both to impede diffusion of HO_2 radicals and to facilitate their formation by acting as third bodies in reaction (10) with predictable effects on the third limit which will depend on the nature of the gas added. All these phenomena have been observed experimentally.

There will also be a higher temperature zone corresponding to higher values of k_8' for which ϕ will have the value zero at each of three pressures as shown in Fig. VI.5. The lowest of these will be the lower limit P_l which for stoichiometric mixtures will be given by

$$P_l^2 = (P_{H_2} + P_{O_2})^2 = \frac{9\Gamma_H \bar{D}_0{}^{H}, _{H_2} \bar{D}_0{}^{H}, _{O_2}}{2k_8 d^2 (2\bar{D}_0{}^{H}, _{O_2} + \bar{D}_0{}^{H}, _{H_2})} \quad \text{(VI.15)}$$

and corresponds to the situation in which the pressures are so low that the termolecular reaction (10) is negligible and the major process competing with the branching reaction (8) is the loss of hydrogen atoms at the wall. The properties of this limit should therefore be (a) that it is inversely proportional to the vessel diameter, (b) that it diminishes with addition of gases which serve only to impede the diffusion of the hydrogen atoms to the wall, (c) that it is sensitive to the nature of the vessel wall and (d) if the wall termination reaction requires no activation energy, P_l decreases with temperature according to $P_l = P_l{}^\circ \exp(E_8/2RT)$. All these predictions are in accord with experiment.

As the pressure is further increased the rate of removal of hydrogen atoms at the walls declines and these chain centres are increasingly converted to HO_2 radicals in reaction (10) which reduces the chance of hydrogen atoms entering the branching reaction (8). Provided the HO_2 radicals are destroyed at the wall reaction (10) will constitute a termination reaction and the fraction, μ, of the HO_2 radicals which are removed in this way is $(\Gamma_{HO_2} \bar{D}_0{}^{HO_2}/pd^2)/\{k_{11}[H_2] + \Gamma_{HO_2} \bar{D}_0{}^{HO_2}/pd^2\}$. A second or upper pressure limit will then occur when

$$2k_8[O_2] = \mu \Sigma k_{10}[M][O_2] \quad \quad . \quad \text{(VI.16)}$$

and in the region where μ is close to unity it would be predicted (a) that for stoichiometric mixtures the upper limit would increase with temperature according to $P_u = P_u{}^\circ \exp(-E_8/RT)$, (b) that at constant temperature an added non-reactant gas M would depress the upper limit according to the equation, $aP_{H_2} + bP_{O_2} + cP_m = $ constant, where a, b, and c are in the same ratio as the products of the collision rate and efficiency as a third body in reaction (10) of hydrogen, oxygen and the added gas respectively, (*c*) that the upper limit would be much less dependent than the lower limit on vessel diameter and (*d*) that surface coatings which *increased* the efficiency of the wall in removing HO_2 radicals would have little influence on P_u, although those which drastically reduced this and thereby caused a substantial decrease in μ would cause P_u to increase. Experimental data are in harmony with these predictions.

If the pressure is increased above P_u the HO_2 radicals make more collisions with hydrogen before reaching the wall so that their chance of entering reaction (11) and propagating the chain rather than being removed at the surface is increased. μ therefore diminishes, ultimately becoming inversely proportional to the square of the pressure and in this region $\phi = 2k_8[O_2]$ $- \Sigma k_{10}[M][O_2]\Gamma_{HO_2}\bar{D}_0^{HO_2}/k_{11}[H_2]pd^2$, increases linearly with the pressure (as shown in Fig. VI.5) eventually becoming positive at the third limit, π, the properties of which have been described above.

The self-consistency of this reaction mechanism is further emphasized by the dependence on temperature of the various limits. Comparison of the theoretical and experimental temperature coefficients of P_u indicates that $20 < E_8 < 26$ k.cal mole^{-1} and the corresponding comparison for P_l indicates that $9 < E_8/2 < 14$. It follows that equation for the third limit should be $\pi = \pi^\circ \exp(E/RT)$, where $E > 23 \pm 3$ k.cal mole^{-1} and this corresponds to experimental observations.

The temperature range in which these limits have been observed is approximately 400 to 600°C. At higher temperatures than 600°C, $2k_8[O_2]$ always exceeds the second term in equation (VI.11) and only the lower limit, P_l, exists and is always much less than 1 mm Hg in reaction vessels of conventional shape and size. The relationship between these temperature regions and the pressure dependence of ϕ in each of them is illustrated in Fig. VI.5.

The only phenomena which are not obviously accounted for in this scheme are (*a*) the existence of hydrogen peroxide in the reaction products and (*b*) the widening of the explosion boundary by injection of H or O atoms. The former can be accommodated in the scheme without modifying appreciably the kinetic consequences by stating that reaction (12) also plays a part or by assuming that H_2O_2 is one of the decomposition products of adsorbed HO_2 radicals, produced by the well-known reaction.

$$(16) \qquad 2\underline{HO_2} \rightarrow H_2O_2 + O_2$$

or by the reaction given in section 7(*b*) of Chapter III. The latter phenomenon would appear to be an example of alteration of an explosion boundary by a change of the rate of initiation and this can occur in isothermal explosions only when there is quadratic branching (Chapter V, case (11)).

Whilst a mechanism in which two chain centres react to form three or more cannot be devised, the reaction

$$(17) \qquad \underline{H} + \underline{HO_2} \rightarrow 2\underline{OH}$$

has kinetic consequences somewhat similar to those of quadratic branching. In the region of the upper limit the HO_2 radicals are normally lost at the walls and the hydrogen atoms take part in either reaction (8) (i.e. branching) or reaction (10) (i.e. termination). Hydroxyl radicals always propagate chains via reaction (7) and therefore the interaction of a hydrogen atom and an HO_2 radical constitutes a diminution in the rate of termination. Injection of hydrogen atoms should therefore cause a raising of P_u, as is observed. Reaction (17) would also be expected to take place to a significant extent when a surface coating, such as boric acid, having a very low efficiency for removal of HO_2 radicals is applied so that the concentration of this radical is unusually high. It can be shown that if the reaction between H and HO_2 occurs, the partial pressures of hydrogen at the upper limit would be much larger in hydrogen-rich mixtures than that predicted by the simple relation $aP_{H_2} + bP_{O_2} =$ constant and this effect has been observed by EGERTON and WARREN[8].

The only alternative explanations for the effects observed by HABER and NALBANDJAN are that the highly exothermic recombinations of H and O atoms bring about local self-heating which cause inflammation at lower temperatures than the true ignition temperature, or that chain stopping properties of the surface of the reaction vessel are modified by exposure to high concentrations of atoms and radicals. Neither explanation is without its merits.

(*c*) *Retardation and Sensitization.* The hydrogen-oxygen explosion may be partially suppressed and this slow reaction reduced in rate by the addition of small amounts of halogens or organic iodides. Apart from the complicating influence of a heterogeneous reaction at high concentrations the effects are explicable in terms of the chain-terminating power of the additives which decreases in the expected order I_2, Br_2, Cl_2. These facts are readily accommodated in this theory by including an additional term $= -k_r[\text{Ret.}]$ in equation (VI.11).

Much effort has been directed towards the elucidation of the chemical reactions responsible for the dramatic lowering and subsequent raising of the ignition temperature which are observed when small but increasing amounts of various nitrogen compounds are added to hydrogen-oxygen mixtures. The problem is readily stated in general terms. In order to make the net branching factor positive in a region of pressure and composition where, in the absence of sensitizer, no ignition occurs, the sensitizer or some easily formed derivative must either be able to prevent the destruction of a chain centre or to react with it in a facile branching reaction, or possibly perform both these functions. Since at higher concentrations of sensitizer ϕ decreases as the sensitizer concentration is increased, the sensitizer must be presumed capable of terminating chains either directly or via an intermediate. Many reaction schemes have been proposed but that which gives the best description of the observed phenomena is that proposed by ASHMORE and co-workers[9], who proved, by direct photometric measurement of the concentration of nitrogen dioxide when this substance was used as a sensitizer, that it is slowly reduced to nitric oxide during the induction periods shown in Fig. VI.2. This reduction takes place via the reactions

(18) $$H_2 + NO_2 \rightarrow HNO_2 + H$$

(19) $$H + NO_2 \rightarrow HO + NO$$

(7) $$HO + H_2 \rightarrow H_2O + H$$

At very low initial pressures of sensitizer reaction (10) competes with reaction (19), the resultant HO_2 radicals being removed by reaction (16) or at the wall. All these factors mean that it takes longer to attain the critical concentration of nitric oxide necessary for ignition (see below) and consequently the induction periods are longer the lower the initial value of $[NO_2]$. At higher initial concentrations of NO_2, reaction (16) is less important and HO_2

radicals are destroyed by NO in reaction (20), which is extremely

(20) $$HO_2 + NO \rightarrow HO + NO_2$$

important because it results in the replacement of the poor chain propagating centre HO_2 by the active chain-propagating centre OH. However NO_2 also removes OH radicals in reaction (21) so

(21) $$HO + NO_2 + M \rightarrow HNO_3$$

that the critical concentration of nitric oxide is even lower and this fact together with the higher initial value of $[NO_2]$ makes the induction period pass through a minimum value as the initial $[NO_2]$ is increased (see Fig. VI.2).

The diminution of $[NO_2]$ during the induction period reduces the fraction of oxygen atoms which are removed by the rapid reaction (22) and enables a larger fraction to enter the branching reaction

(22) $$O + NO_2 \rightarrow O_2 + NO$$

(9). The decrease in termination caused mainly by this effect and to a lesser extent by the progressive replacement of (16) by (20) result in a steady increase in the net branching factor, ϕ, during the induction period. At low initial concentrations of NO_2, the absolute value of the nitric oxide concentration never attains a sufficiently high value to remove all the HO_2 radicals, some of which undergo mutual destruction in reaction (20), so that the development of chains with time corresponds to case (10) of Chapter V, i.e. $dn/dt = \theta + \phi n - \delta n^2$, where ϕ becomes positive at the end of the induction period. Consequently, at *low* initial pressures of sensitizer, ϕ, which has a negative value when the gases are admitted to the reaction vessel, becomes more positive during the induction period becoming greater than zero at the end of the induction period, when the nitric oxide concentration has attained a critical value. The reaction rate then rapidly increases but, as may be seen from reference to Fig. V.5, *a chain isothermal explosion is impossible*. It is assumed that ignition only occurs when the steady state rate $(= (\phi + \sqrt{\phi^2 + 4\delta\theta})/2\delta t)$ reaches a value at which the rate of heat production exceeds that of heat loss, i.e. the lower explosion limit is considered to be *chain-thermal* in nature. This view receives strong support from a very characteristic feature of this reaction, namely, the pressure pulse which marks the end of the induction period below the lower limit of sensitizer concentration and which increases in magnitude as the limit is approached.

At high NO_2 concentrations, loss of HO_2 radicals in reaction (16) is negligible, most of these species being converted to OH radicals via reaction (20) and the main termination process is removal of the latter by nitric oxide in reaction (23). Algebraic

$$(23) \qquad OH + NO + M \rightarrow HNO_2 + M$$

representation of the interplay of these processes indicates that as the sensitizer concentration is increased from a value between the limits, δ becomes zero and ϕ declines from positive values so that the explosion charges from chain-thermal to *chain-isothermal* and the upper limiting sensitizer concentration is defined by the condition $\phi = 0$, i.e. corresponding to that illustrated in Fig. V.2. In keeping with this conclusion is the fact that above this upper limit, pressure pulses at the end of the induction period are only very rarely observed and are always very small in magnitude. Further support for this interpretation is provided by the fact that the independently determined values of the rate constants k_7, k_9, k_{10}, k_{21}, k_{22}, and k_{23} are in quantitative agreement with those necessary to account for the properties of this system.

It seems probable that nitric oxide is the agent responsible for the branching when the other nitrogenous sensitizers are used but direct experimental verification of this assumption has not yet been obtained.

3. The Oxidation of Carbon Monoxide. This reaction is slightly more exothermic than the hydrogen-oxygen reaction, liberating 67·6 k.cal per mole of carbon dioxide formed. It resembles the latter reaction in having an explosion peninsula but differs in that, as shown in Fig. VI.6, there is a region at pressures less than P_l but greater than P_g where a blue glow may be observed, which is faint but protracted at pressures just greater than P_g and becomes more intense but of shorter duration at higher pressures[10]. The characteristics of this reaction suggest that P_g is that pressure at which the net branching factor becomes positive, i.e. the glow is a chain-isothermal 'explosion', that P_l is a chain-thermal explosion boundary and that P_u marks the pressure at which ϕ ceases to be positive, i.e. is a typical upper chain-isothermal explosion limit.

The identification of the kinetic characteristics of this reaction is made difficult by the very high sensitivity of the reaction to traces of water and hydrogen and to the condition of the surface of the reaction vessel and also by the fact that it is retarded by carbon dioxide, so that it is auto-retarded, and therefore the high

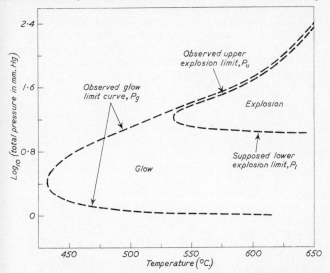

Fig. VI.6. The relation between the glow (P_g), lower explosion (P_l) and upper explosion (P_u) limits of dry stoichiometric mixtures of carbon monoxide and oxygen. Because of the great sensitivity of the values of the limits to the size and wall condition and to the method of measurement the figure should be regarded as expressing trends rather than posssessing absolute numerical validity.

pressure explosion is frequently auto-quenched. However the broad features of the 'dry' reaction are well established. The upper limit increases with increasing temperature according to $P_u = P_u{}^{\circ}e^{-E/RT}$, where E, though somewhat irreproducible, is about 30 k. cal. At this limit $[O_2] + a[CO] = $ constant and replacement of either oxygen or carbon monoxide by nitrogen has little influence on the total pressure below which explosion occurs. In the absence of added gas this total pressure decreases slightly as the ratio $[CO]/[O_2]$ is increased. The lower limit is much less sensitive to change of temperature than the upper limit; the glow limit is also less sensitive though the most recent measurements of the luminosity limit indicate that, contrary to previous views that P_g is almost independent of temperature, it obeys the relation $P_g = P_g^\circ e^{E/RT}$, where $E = 10 \pm 2$ k.cal[10]. Whilst P_g is lowered by decreasing the ratio $[CO]/[O_2]$ or by addition of foreign non-reactant gases, P_l is lowered by addition of argon and raised by addition of either nitrogen or carbon dioxide and is extremely sensitive to the nature of the wall-coatings.

Extensive measurements have been made on the light emitted by the combustion of carbon monoxide under various conditions. The visible luminosity when either nitric oxide or sulphur dioxide is present indicates that oxygen atoms are relatively plentiful in the 'dry' reaction. The infra-red emission indicates that vibrationally excited carbon dioxide molecules are formed and in fact as much as 24 per cent of the energy of the combustion may appear as infra-red radiation when cold CO—O_2 mixtures are ignited by a spark[11]. The emission spectrum of the carbon monoxide flame shows a continuum with a band system extending from 3000 to 4000 Å having two prominent intervals which suggests that transitions are occurring from a higher vibrationally and electronically excited state to a vibrationally excited ground state. HORNBECK and HOPFIELD[12] suggested that the banded emission was due to the $^3\Sigma_u^- \leftarrow {}^3\Sigma_g^-$ transition of oxygen but CLYNE and THRUSH[13] have recently shown that these bands are emitted when carbon monoxide and oxygen atoms react in the spin-allowed process (24) to form CO_2 in the $^3B_2$ state. This state may

$$(24) \qquad CO(^1\Sigma_g^+) + O(^3P) \to CO_2(^3B_2)$$

undergo slow intersystem crossing to the $^1B_2$ state which undergoes a radiative transition to the vibrationally excited ground $^1\Sigma_g^+$ state. Since the spin forbidden reaction (25) is exothermic to the extent of 127 k.cal and the emitted quantum is in the

$$(25) \qquad CO(^1\Sigma_g^+) + O(^3P) \to CO_2(^1\Sigma_g^+)$$

energy range 80 ± 100 k.cal there is ample energy for vibrational excitation. The carbon dioxide molecule formed in reaction (24) is in a triplet state and will persist sufficiently long to undergo collisions with both of the reagents. If the excited $CO_2(^3B_2)$

molecule produced in reaction (24) encounters an oxygen molecule, reaction (26), which is exothermic to the extent of 8 k.cal, may occur and if it encounters a carbon monoxide molecule

$$(26) \qquad CO_2(^3B_2) + O_2(^3\Sigma_g^1) \rightarrow CO_2(^1\Sigma_g^+) + 2O(^3P)$$

reaction (27) which is about 10 k.cal endothermic will occasionally take place. The initial carbon monoxide molecule emerging from

$$(27) \qquad CO_2(^3B_2) + CO(^1\Sigma_g^+) \rightarrow CO_2(^1\Sigma_g^+) + CO(^3\pi)$$

the latter reaction will undoubtedly react very rapidly with oxygen according to equation (28). This reaction, which may take place

$$(28) \quad CO(_3\pi) + O_2(^3\Sigma_g^-) \rightarrow CO_2(^1\Sigma_g^+) + O(^3P) \,(+ \, h\nu_{cont}?)$$

via the prior formation of CO_3, is so exothermic that radiation may be emitted and since it will involve a dissociative state of the CO_3^* this emission will be without structure and may perhaps be responsible for the continuum which is observed. The true origin of this continuum is still uncertain, the possibility that it arises from radiative combination of oxygen atoms is not excluded.

The highly exothermic nature of reaction (25) led SEMENOV[1] in 1934 to propose that reaction (26) was the branching reaction and this has been incorporated in all subsequent reaction mechanisms. The early schemes suffered from the disadvantage that the gas phase termination reaction was considered to be the bimolecular deactivation of $CO_2(^3B_2)$ and that this does not permit the net branching factor to become zero as the pressure is increased. Indeed, as has been stated by LEWIS and VON ELBE[1], 'branching and breaking reactions of the required (kinetic) orders are not possible . . . (unless) another intermediate is a chain carrier.' The electronically excited carbon monoxide molecules can fulfil this role and on this basis the complete mechanism becomes

(29) Initiation $\qquad\qquad CO + O_2 \rightarrow CO_2 + O$

(24) Propagation $\qquad\qquad O + CO \rightarrow CO_2(^3B_2)$

(26) Branching $\qquad\quad CO_2(^3B_2) + O_2 \rightarrow CO_2 + 2O$

(27) Propagation $\quad CO_2(^3B_2) + CO(^1\Sigma) \rightarrow CO_2 + CO(^3\pi)$

(28) Propagation $CO(^3\pi) + O_2 \rightarrow CO_2 + O$

(29) Termination $CO + O + M \rightarrow CO_2 + M$

(30) Wall termination $O + \text{wall} \rightarrow ?$

and the net branching factor is given by

$$\phi = \frac{k_{24}k_{26}[CO][O_2]}{k_{26}[O_2] + k_{27}[CO]} - \Sigma k_{29}[CO][M] - k_{30} \quad \text{(VI.17)}$$

corresponding to upper and lower glow limits defined by (VI.18) and (VI.19) respectively. Equation (VI.18) predicts that an increase

$$k_{24}k_{26}[O_2]/(k_{26}[O_2] + k_{27}[CO]) = \Sigma k_{29}[M] . \qquad \text{. (VI.18)}$$

$$k_{24}k_{26}[O_2][CO]/(k_{26}[O_2] + k_{27}[CO]) = \Gamma/d^2 \Sigma D_0^{-1}[M] . \quad \text{(VI.19)}$$

in the carbon monoxide content of the gas will lower the upper limit and that if nitrogen is as efficient a third body in reaction (29) as carbon monoxide or oxygen it should have little influence on the total pressure at the upper limit. Since E_{24} is known to be 3·7 k.cal[13] and E_{29} is likely to be zero, $E_{26} > 25$ k.cal. Correspondingly equation (VI.19) predicts the observed lowering of P_g when either $[O_2]/[CO]$ is increased or a foreign gas is added, and that for mixtures of constant composition, $P_g = P_g°e^{\dfrac{> 25 \text{ k.cal}}{2RT}}$.

The reaction between dry CO and O_2 is thus dominated by the great exothermicity of reaction (25) which makes possible an *energy-atom* chain. This great affinity of carbon monoxide for an oxygen atom is also important when substances are added which can give rise to hydroxyl or HO_2 radicals since the oxygen atom transfer reactions (31) and (32) are exothermic and presumed to be rapid. Consequently when carbon monoxide is added to a

(31) $CO + OH \rightarrow CO_2 + H + 26 \text{ k.cal}$

(32) $CO + HO_2 \rightarrow CO_2 + OH + 63 \text{ k.cal}$

fuel–oxygen mixture the rapid reactions (24), (26), (31) and (32) will ensure that the number of radicals will in no way be reduced and it would be expected that the carbon monoxide would be oxidized without substantially modifying the kinetics of the fuel-oxidation. When the fuel oxidation takes place below the tip of the CO—O_2 peninsula the fuel should behave as a sensitizer for the oxidation of carbon monoxide. In the case of hydrogen the participation of the carbon monoxide in the hydrogen-oxygen chain causes the minimum disturbance because CO can replace H_2 in each of the chain propagation steps (7) and (11) without altering the nature of the radicals formed, H and OH respectively. Small amounts of hydrogen will therefore cause CO–O_2 mixtures to explode between two pressure limits at temperatures down to 430°C, the two limits being dependent on temperature, added foreign gas, and vessel diameter in the usual way. The only differences in kinetics between this system and the hydrogen-oxygen reaction are attributable to the fact that large amounts of carbon monoxide can terminate chains by reaction (29). Perhaps the most striking evidence of the way in which the H_2–O_2 reaction chain controls the kinetics is the observation that although nitrogen dioxide does not sensitize the ignition of *dry* carbon monoxide, it is a very powerful sensitizer for the explosive combustion of carbon monoxide containing about 1 per cent of hydrogen. Thus a dry mixture of $2CO + O_2$ at a total pressure of 150 mm Hg was found by BUCKLER and NORRISH[14] to have an ignition temperature of 650°C but when it contained 3·3 mm H_2 and 0·10 mm NO_2 the ignition temperature was below 357°C. Moreover the phenomena which are so characteristic of the NO_2 sensitized hydrogen combustion, e.g. pressure limits of sensitizer, induction periods etc.—are here again in evidence.

4. **The Oxidation of Phosphorus Vapour**[15]. In the reactions discussed above examples have been given of lower pressure limits which were thought to be either *chain-isothermal* (P_l in the unsensitized hydrogen-oxygen reaction and P_g in the unsensitized carbon monoxide combustion) or *chain-thermal* (P_l in the unsensitized carbon monoxide combustion and the lower partial pressure of sensitizer in the NO_2-sensitized hydrogen-oxygen reaction). All the upper limits in these reactions were assumed to be chain-isothermal and this assumption receives *a posteriori* support from the agreement between the observed dependence of P_u on the experimental variables with that predicted from the postulated mechanisms. In these cases, as in many others which have not been cited, P_u increases exponentially with temperature because the energy of activation of the branching reaction is much larger than that of the gas phase termination

reaction. The oxidation of phosphorus vapour is unusual in that for a constant concentration of P_4 molecules the partial pressure of oxygen ($P_u{}^{O_2}$) above which the glow will not occur *diminishes* with increasing temperature, whilst the lower limit ($P_l{}^{O_2}$) is unaffected. A decrease in explodability as the temperature is increased is not easily accommodated in any theory in which the explosion condition is partly thermal, though it is not impossible to do this. To this extent there is therefore an additional reason for regarding the limits in this reaction as chain-isothermal.

The main characteristics of this reaction are well known. It is highly exothermic (see equation (33)). When phosphorus vapour and gaseous oxygen are mixed a yellow glow is observed if the pressure lies between two pressure limits. The reaction rate

$$(33) \qquad P_{4(g)} + 5O_{2(g)} \rightarrow P_4O_{10(g)}; \quad \Delta H^\circ = -714 \text{ k.cal}$$

outside these limits is very small and is undetectable by the usual techniques. At pressures between the limits it is very fast, being limited primarily by the supply of P_4 molecules. If solid white phosphorus is present the glow is initially seen throughout the vessel but quickly becomes localized as a diffusion flame close to the solid phosphorus, which, if sufficiently intense, will heat the phosphorus causing it first to melt and subsequently to inflame with deposition of solid phosphorus pentoxide and red phosphorus. Consequently there exist within the glow limits pressure limits of inflammation of solid phosphorus[16] with which we are not concerned. Various suboxides of phosphorus have been detected in the products of the glow reaction. The entity responsible for the light emission is not known with certainty but is probably a molecule of low atomicity, possibly PO.

At a constant partial pressure of phosphorus the lower glow limit is inversely proportional to the vessel diameter (see Fig. VI.7), is lowered by the addition of foreign non-reactant gases and is independent of temperature. The upper limit is unchanged by an alteration in vessel diameter. The most significant property of $P_u{}^{O_2}$ is that it decreases with rising temperature. There are technical difficulties which prevent an accurate delineation of the $P_u{}^{O_2}$-temperature curve for a preselected value of P_4 concentration but the effect can be strikingly demonstrated and the $P_u{}^{O_2}$-temperature curve can readily be deduced from that obtained in experiments when white phosphorus is present. If the withdrawal method for the determination of the upper limit is applied to a P_4-oxygen mixture contained in a vessel above room temperature a stage is often reached in which the gas in the colder connecting tubing through which the gas mixture is withdrawn glows whilst the same mixture at the same

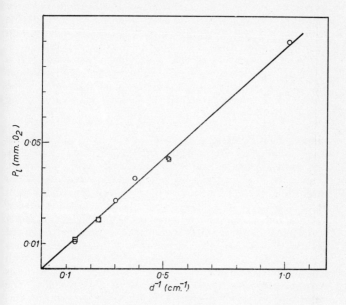

Fig. VI.7. The dependence of the lower limit ($P_l^{O_2}$) of the glow of phosphorus on vessel diameter (d)[16] when the partial pressure of P_4 is constant at 0·0042 mm

⊙ denotes values at 0°C

⊡   ,,   ,,   ,, 15°C

pressure in the reaction vessel does not. It is easily arranged to show the same effect in vessels of identical shape.

The dependence of $P_l^{O_2}$ and $P_u^{O_2}$ on temperature when white phosphorus is present is shown in Fig. VI.8 from which it may be deduced that, under these conditions, $P_l^{O_2} \propto \exp(7 \text{ k.cal}/\boldsymbol{R}T)$ and $P_u^{O_2} \propto \exp(-10 \text{ k.cal}/\boldsymbol{R}T)$.

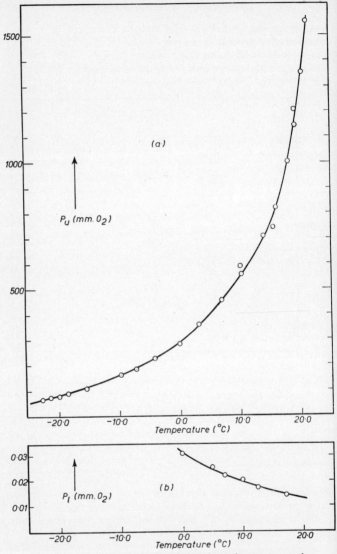

Fig. VI.8. The glow peninsula of phosphorus in a pyrex reaction vessel 3·75 cm internal diameter containing white phosphorus. (a) upper limit, (b) lower limit[15]

Although the chemical mechanism of the reaction cannot be regarded as established, the salient features are not in doubt. Small amounts of ozone are formed during the glow reaction which suggests that oxygen atoms are intermediates and react with molecular oxygen according to equation (34). Application of the NO and SO_2 tests for oxygen atoms gives positive results

$$(34) \qquad O + O_2 + M \rightarrow O_3 + M$$

although they are less clear cut than in other systems because of the overlap of the spectrum of the glow with the spectra emitted by NO_2^* and SO^*_3. The widening of the glow limits by increasing P_4 concentration indicates that branching depends, at least in part, on the encounter of a P_4 molecule with a chain carrier which is probably an oxygen atom. SEMENOV[15] suggested that such a collision could result in the formation of a P_4O molecule. In view of the high values of the bond energy terms for the bridge and apical P,O bonds in P_4O_{10} this reaction (35) is very highly exothermic and likely to involve a third body. For similar reasons any P_4O_n species (n having any integral value from 0 to

$$(35) \qquad P_4 + \underline{O} + M \rightarrow \underline{P_4O} + M$$

9) is expected to react rapidly with an oxygen molecule according to equation (36). On this

$$(36) \qquad \underline{P_4O_n} + O_2 \rightarrow \underline{P_4O_{n+1}} + \underline{O}$$

mechanism any oxygen atom not destroyed at the wall or in reaction (34) will cause the formation of one P_4O_{10} molecule and eight *additional* oxygen atoms in nine successive reactions of type (36). However, this scheme does not obviously lead to the formation of suboxides or of an emitter containing less than four phosphorus atoms per molecule. This difficulty can be overcome *either* by replacing (35) and (36) by reactions (35a), (37), and (38) and analogous processes *or* by involving propagation reactions such as $P_4O + O_2 \rightarrow 2PO$

$$(35a) \qquad P_4 + \underline{O} \rightarrow \underline{P_2O} + \underline{P_2}$$

$$(37) \qquad \underline{P_2} + O_2 \rightarrow \underline{P_2O} + \underline{O}$$

$$(38) \qquad \underline{P_2O} + O_2 \rightarrow \underline{P_2O_2} + \underline{O} \text{ or } \underline{PO} + \underline{PO_2}$$

+ P_2O, etc. Highly exothermic reactions in which ozone loses an oxygen atom to a small molecule such as P_2 or PO can easily be formulated and might well be chemiluminescent. However, the kinetics of the reaction require that, if the gas phase termination reaction is (34), the rate of the branching reaction should be proportional to $[M] \times [P_4]$ and we therefore prefer (35) as the main fate of oxygen atoms and reactions of the type (35a) as occurring much less frequently.

If the mechanism comprises the reaction sequence (36), (35), (34) and (39)

Initiation (36) $P_4 + O_2 \rightarrow \underline{P_4O} + \underline{O}$

Propagation $\begin{cases} (35) \\ \text{and Branching} \end{cases}$ (36) $P_4 + \underline{O} + M \rightarrow \underline{P_4O}$

$\underline{P_4O_n} + O_2 \rightarrow \underline{P_4O_{n+1}} + \underline{O}$

Termination (34) $\underline{O} + O_2 + M \rightarrow O_3 + M$

Termination (39) $\underline{O} + \text{wall} \rightarrow \text{destruction}$

then the net branching factor $\phi = 8[P_4]\Sigma k_{35}[M] - [O_2]\Sigma k_{34}[M] - k_{39}$. The lower glow limit will then be given by equation (VI.18) which reduces to (VI.19) in the absence of any added gas. These equations correctly predict the effects of vessel diameter and

$$8[P_4]\Sigma k_{35}[M] \,.\, \Sigma D_M^0{}^{-1}[M] = \Gamma/d^2 \qquad . \quad \text{(VI.18)}$$

$$[O_2]^2 = \Gamma D_{O_2}^0 / k_{35} d^2 [P_4] \qquad . \qquad . \quad \text{(VI.19)}$$

added foreign gas on the lower limit and since $P_l^{O_2}$ at constant $[P_4]$ is independent of temperature, E_{35} must be zero. Equation (VI.20), which is also deduced from this mechanism, adequately describes the properties of $P_u^{O_2}$ and predicts that in the absence of the

$$8[P_4]\Sigma k_{35}[M] = [O_2]\Sigma k_{34}[M] \qquad . \qquad . \quad \text{(VI.20)}$$

foreign gas and the presence of solid phosphorus equation (VI.21) should apply, where λ_v, the latent heat of vaporization of white

$$P_u^{O_2} = A \exp (E_{34} - \lambda_v - E_{35}) \qquad . \quad \text{(VI.21)}$$

phosphorus, is 14 k.cal. Since E_{35} is zero, the observed temperature coefficient of $P_u^{O_2}$ leads to the conclusion that $E_{34} \simeq 4$ k.cal mole^{-1}. Although other measurements[17] of the rate of reaction (34) suggest that it may have an apparent negative energy of activation of about 1·7 k.cal it should be mentioned that considerable O,O bond stretching is involved in reaction (34) which is only 24·2 k.cal exothermic and therefore a finite energy of activation might be expected and that for the similar but much more exothermic reaction (24), an energy of activation of 3·7 k.cal has been determined[13]. Another way out of this difficulty might be found if oxygen were presumed to destroy the centres P_4O_n in the reaction (4) and that this has a finite positive energy

$$(40) \qquad P_4O_n + O_2 \rightarrow P_4O_{n-1} + O_3$$

of activation. Mechanisms of this kind can be devised[18] but none have as yet been subjected to experimental test.

REFERENCES

1. Ref. 44, Chapter III; JOST, W.: *Explosion and Combustion Processes in Gases*, McGraw-Hill, London (1946); LEWIS, B. and VON ELBE, G.: *Combustion, Flames and Explosions of Gases*, Academic Press, London (1962); MINKOFF, G. J. and TIPPER, C. F. H.: *Chemistry of Combustion Reactions*, Butterworths, London (1962); HINSHELWOOD, C. N. and WILLIAMSON, A. T.: *The Reaction between Hydrogen and Oxygen*, Clarendon Press, Oxford (1934); *Le Mécanisme de l'Oxydation*, 8th Solvay Conference, Brussels, (1950). Nine international Symposia on Combustion have been held, the last seven of which have been published as follows: third (1949), fourth (1953), eighth (1962), WILLIAMS and WILKINS, Baltimore; fifth (1955) and sixth (1957), Reinhold, New York; seventh (1959) and ninth (1963), Butterworths, London. These contain many research papers relevant to the material of this chapter which are too numerous to list.

2. HINSHELWOOD, C. N. and WILLBOURN, A. H.: *Proc. Roy. Soc.*, A, **185**, 353, 368, 376 (1946).

3. Ref. 34, Chapter II.

4. Ref. 33, Chapter II.

5. Ref. 39, Chapter III.

6. Ref. 40, Chapter III.

7. Attributed to EISENHUTH, by HINSHELWOOD and WILLIAMSON (ref. 1, p. 19) but no reference given. HO_2 has been detected mass-spectroscopically in burning methane by ELTENTON, G. C.: *J. Phys. Coll. Chem.*, **52**, 469 (1948), in hydrogen peroxide decomposed by electron impact by ROBERTSON, A. J. B.: *Trans.*

Faraday Soc., **48**, 228 (1952) and in the reaction of atomic hydrogen with molecular oxygen by FONER, S. N. and HUDSON, R. L.: *J. Chem. Phys.*, **23**, 1364 (1955).

8. EGERTON, A. C. G. and WARREN, D. R.: *Proc. Roy. Soc.*, A, **204**, 465 (1951).

9. See ASHMORE, P. G. and TYLER, B. J.: *Ninth Symposium*[1] p. 201, where earlier references are given.

10. GAILLARD-CUSIN, F. and JAMES, F.: *J. Chim. Phys.*, **59**, 949 (1962), **60**, 1334, (1963). HOARE, D. E. and WALSH, A. D.: *Trans. Faraday Soc.*, **50**, 37 (1954).

11. GARNER, W. E. et al.: *Phil. Mag.*, **3**, 97 (1927), *J. Chem. Soc.*, 1123 (1929); 2037 (1930); 144 (1935).

12. HORNBECK, G. A. and HOPFIELD, R. W.: *J. Chem. Phys.*, **17**, 982 (1953).

13. CLYNE, M. A. A. and THRUSH, B. A.: *Ninth Symposium*, **177** (1963).

14. BUCKLER, E. J. and NORRISH, R. G. W.: *Proc. Roy. Soc.*, A, **167**, 292 (1938) and A, **172**, 1 (1939).

15. For papers earlier than 1934 see ref. 44, Chapter III. Almost all subsequent publications may be found in the lists of references given by DAINTON, F. S.: *Trans. Faraday Soc.*, **43**, 244 (1947) and DAINTON, F. S. and KIMBERLEY, H. M.: ibid., **46**, 629 (1950).

16. BEVINGTON, J. C. and DAINTON, F. S.: *Trans. Faraday Soc.*, **42**, 377 (1946).

17. CLYNE, M. A. A., MCKENNEY, J. C. and THRUSH, B. A.: *Disc. Faraday Soc.*, **37**, 214, (1964).

18. Unpublished work of the author.

CHAPTER VII

ADDITION POLYMERIZATION
AS AN EXAMPLE OF AN UNBRANCHED
CHAIN REACTION

UNBRANCHED chain reactions are extremely numerous and cover a great variety of types of chemical change, e.g. oxidation, halogenation, decomposition, in both liquid and gaseous media, each capable of initiation by several different processes. The many investigations which have been carried out on these frequently industrially important reactions have led to results of wide chemical significance. In this chapter we shall discuss briefly the kinetics of the addition polymerization of unsaturated compounds since this reaction exemplifies to a high degree very many of the principles, and the deductions made therefrom, which have been mentioned in earlier chapters. Moreover, in the past thirty years the field has been widely explored and during the latter half of this period a great deal of precise information has been obtained concerning the individual part processes. A thorough discussion of this field would fill a book and we have therefore omitted any aspect of the subject which does not have a direct bearing on the *kinetics* of the reactions in homogeneous systems. Thus no mention will be made of the size, shape and structure of polymer molecules, of the thermodynamics of the solutions or gels to which they give rise, or of the physical properties of polymeric substances. Excellent accounts of high polymer chemistry in which these subjects are treated *in extenso* are to be found in the works cited in reference 1. Detailed information concerning various monomers, their polymerization and the properties of the polymers and copolymers are to be found in a number of monographs[2].

1. Introduction. High polymeric substances are rarely pure compounds in the organic chemist's sense of the term pure, i.e. having a unique molecular weight. They generally consist of an ensemble of molecules of different molecular weights all of which are exact or near multiples of the molecular weight of the monomer. The monomer is unsaturated and may be classified as *bifunctional* or *polyfunctional*, according as to whether it is capable of joining with two or more other monomers respectively. Mono-olefines are clearly bifunctional. The polymer molecules may be simple chains of monomer molecules joined end-to-end in which case they are referred to as *linear* polymers, or they may possess some monomer units in side chains in which case they are called *branched* polymers, or the chains may be linked transversely either by chains of monomer-units or of added unsaturated materials called crosslinking agents, when the polymer is referred to as *cross-linked*. Since end-to-end addition of bifunctional monomers, e.g. ethylene ($CH_2{=}CH_2$) results in a saturated structure—polymethylene—(equation (1)), branched or cross-linked polymers can only be produced from bifunctional monomers by substitution reactions. Polyfunctional monomers,

$$\text{(1)} \qquad CH_2{=}CH_2 \rightarrow \frac{1}{n} (CH_2)_{2n}$$

e.g. isoprene ($CH_2{=}C(CH_3) - CH{=}CH_2$), are clearly not subject to this restriction.

When more than one monomer have been used to prepare the polymer, the latter is known as a *copolymer*. Because of the possibility of controlling the physical properties of copolymers by controlling the composition of the monomer feed, copolymers have been widely developed and investigated in industrial laboratories. Such polymers are divisible into four groups. Firstly, there are those copolymers in which the constituent monomers (A and B) are distributed randomly along the linear copolymer chains, the ratio of A to B in the polymer being capable of variation from 100 per cent A to a 100 per cent B solely by alteration of the ratio of A to B in the monomer mixture. An example of this is styrene-*p*-methoxystyrene copolymer. The second group comprises those copolymers in which at least one of the monomers will not undergo self-polymerization; the resultant polymer then *either* has the structure $(AB)_n$ (both monomers A and B incapable of polymerization, e.g. sulphur dioxide and cetene-1) *or* $(AB_xAB_y \ldots AB_z)_n$ where x, y and $z \nless 1$ (A incapable of polymerization, e.g. $A = SO_2$, $B =$ styrene). The third group, called *graft* copolymers, are those in which one polymer chain has been fused on to a second, i.e. $(A_{x-y}(B_n)A_y)$ and the fourth group contains the *block* copolymers in which block units A_x and B_y are joined to form chains containing the unit A_xB_y.

The overall polymerization of a bifunctional monomer (m_1) to form a polymer (m_n) of average degree of polymerization, n, may be represented by equation (2).

$$(2) \qquad m_1 \rightarrow \frac{1}{n} m_n$$

Bifunctional monomers include not only compounds containing a double bond, e.g. olefines, aldehydes, but also cyclic compounds such as S_8; $(PNCl_2)_3$; cyclic imines, oxides, esters, amides, disulphides, the rings of which can be opened and joined end-to-end to form linear polymers $\left(\text{e.g. } S_8 \rightarrow \frac{1}{n} S_{8n}\right)$. A necessary condition which must be satisfied for a substantial fraction of the monomer to be converted to polymer is that the free energy increment at the chosen monomer concentration and under the prevailing conditions of temperature, physical state of monomer and polymer, should be negative. The relevant standard thermodynamic functions are $\Delta G°$, $\Delta H°$ and $\Delta S°$, with a subscript which indicates the physical state (solid, liquid, gaseous or dissolved) of the monomer and the physical state (crystalline, amorphous, glassy, liquid or dissolved) of the polymer. Thus $\Delta H_{gc}° = -25\cdot4$ given in Table 3 signifies that 25·4 k.cal of heat are liberated when 1 mole of gaseous ethylene at one atmosphere pressure and 25°C is converted into the same weight of polyethylene in the condensed and largely amorphous solid form. For almost all polymerization reactions $\Delta G°_{25°C}$ is negative. This is because addition polymerization processes, in common with most aggregation reactions, are exothermic, due to the fact that the new bonds formed in the polymer are stronger than those which they replace in the monomer. The magnitude of this heat depends on structural factors as well as the state of aggregation of the monomer and polymer (see Table 2). Thus ΔH is made more positive (i.e. the reaction less exothermic) the more conjugated the monomer (compare styrene with vinyl acetate) and the more sterically strained is the polymer (compare the vinylidene compounds with the vinyl monomers, e.g. α-methyl styrene with styrene). Since fluid monomers are capable of free translation

TABLE 2

Heats of Polymerization

Data taken from DAINTON and IVIN[3]. Values in k.cal per mole of monomer polymerized.

Type	Monomer	$-\Delta H_{xy}$	xy	Remarks
Alkene	Ethylene	24·2	gc	
Alkene	Propene	20·1	lc	
Alkene	But-1-ene	20·0	lc	
Alkene	Hex-1-ene	19·8	lc	
Alkene	iso Butene	12·6	lc	Severe steric strain in polymer
Cyclo alkane	cyclo Propane	27·0	lc	Note influence of ring size: polymerization cannot be effected because no suitable ring opening reaction exists.
Cyclo alkane	cyclo Butane	25·1	lc	
Cyclo alkane	cyclo Pentane	5·2	lc	
Cyclo alkane	cyclo Hexane	− 0·7	lc	
Cyclo alkane	cyclo Heptane	5·1	lc	
Cyclo alkane	cyclo Octane	8·3	lc	
Unconjugated vinyl compound	Acrylamide	19·8	ss	
Unconjugated vinyl compound	Vinyl acetate	21·3	lc	
Unconjugated vinyl compound	Methyl acrylate	18·7	lc	
Conjugated vinyl compound	Styrene	16·7	lc	Resonance stabilized monomer
Conjugated vinyl compound	Substituted styrenes	16·0 to 16·7	lc	Resonance stabilized monomer.
Conjugated vinyl compound	Acrylonitrile	17·3	lc′	Resonance stabilized monomer
Unconjugated vinylidene compound	Methyl methacrylate	13·4	lc	Severe steric strain in polymer.
Unconjugated vinylidene compound	Vinylidene chloride	14·4	lc′	Severe steric strain in polymer.
Conjugated vinylidene compound	α Methyl styrene	8·4	lc	Resonance stabilized monomer and severe steric strain in polymer.
	Acenaphthylene	24·0	ss	Resonance stabilized monomer, steric strain in polymer and *severe* strain in monomer.
	Sulphur	− 3.2	ls	$\Delta S ls$ also positive, therefore 'floor' temperature.

and external rotation, whereas a monomeric segment of a polymer has lost these modes of energy storage and has gained only
some relatively inefficient vibrational modes plus two internal
rotational modes, most polymerization reactions are exentropic,
i.e. $\Delta S°$ is negative. The magnitude of this quantity seems to be
affected by structural changes to a lesser extent than the heat.
The heat and entropy changes are related to the free energy by
equation (VII.1).

$$\Delta G° = \Delta H° - T\Delta S° \quad . \quad . \quad . \quad (VII.1)$$

and it will therefore be generally true that when $\Delta G°_{25°C}$ is
negative an increase of temperature causes $\Delta G°$ to become more
positive. Hence, although most monomers are thermodynamically unstable with respect to their polymer at room temperature,
there may exist a higher temperature, which we shall later
identify with the 'ceiling temperature', above which the monomer
is stable and the polymer unstable.

In practice, a second condition must also be satisfied before
polymerization will occur. This condition is that a suitable
reaction mechanism exists for the conversion of monomer to
polymer at an appreciable rate. At room temperature in the
absence of radiation and catalysts this rate is in most cases very
slow and the monomer appears to be metastable. The same may
be true for the pure polymer at high temperatures. The reason
for this sluggishness is that the reaction proceeds by an unbranched chain mechanism which may be summarized

Initiation.   (3) $m_1 \to m_1{}^*$

Propagation.   (4) $m_1 + m_j{}^* \xrightarrow{k_p} m_{j+1}{}^*$

Termination.   (5) (i) Linear $m_j{}^* \xrightarrow{k_t{}'} m_j$

        or   (ii) Mutual $m_i{}^* + m_j{}^* \xrightarrow{k_t} m_{i+j}$ or $m_i + m_j$

where the $m_j{}^*$ denotes a polymer chain species containing j
monomeric segments and capable of entering into a propagation
reaction (4) with the monomer. Whatever the nature of the
activity denoted by the asterisk, it is evident that, provided the
degree of polymerization is sufficiently large for the properties

of a monomeric segment of the chain to be independent of the length, then the magnitude of the standard increment $(\Delta\chi^\circ)$ in any thermodynamic function χ accompanying the reaction (2) is equal to the value for the increment $(\delta\chi_p^{\ \circ})$ accompanying the propagation reaction, i.e.

$$\Delta\chi^\circ = \frac{1}{n}\left[\delta\chi_i^{\ \circ} + \delta\chi_t^{\ \circ} + (n-1)\delta\chi_p^{\ \circ}\right] = \delta\chi_p^{\ \circ} \ (n \text{ large}) \qquad \text{(VII.2)}$$

The chemical structure of the monomer is the major influence determining the nature of the entity $m_j{}^*$, which is either a free radical or a positive or a negative ion (see Chapter III, section 2). Unsaturated and cyclic monomers containing an atom other than carbon, e.g. H_2CO, CH_2—CH_2 are readily polymerized by an

$$\diagdown O \diagup$$

ionic mechanism; and when the route for the preparation of monomer involves the production of an acid, e.g. the hydrolysis of a dialkyl silicon dichloride, only the polymer can be isolated from the reaction mixture. Substituted olefines in which the substituent is strongly electrophilic are much more readily polymerized by a free radical mechanism ($* = \cdot$) or by an anionic mechanism ($* = -$) than by a cationic mechanism ($* = +$); whilst the reverse is true when the substituent is electrophobic. A limited number of compounds exists for which the reaction may proceed by any of the three mechanisms.

Except for instantaneously initiated, non-terminated, chain polymerizations (see Chapter V, case (15)) for which theory predicts that all the polymer chain centres will have the same length which increases progressively during the course of the reaction, all polymerization reactions will, at any instant, contain homologous polymer chain centres $(m_j{}^*)$ of all possible chain lengths. Although it might be thought that the reactivity of such chains would be dependent upon their length, there is evidence that in good solvents the majority of the chain centres react at the same rate unless the chains are extremely short (see Chapter II, ref. 25). It is fortunate that this should be so because otherwise the theoretical development of the reaction kinetics of addition polymerization would have been considerably retarded. Perhaps the most convincing evidence in favour of this result is the self-consistency of the data in this field when the principle is assumed. Because of this principle we may write for the rate of polymerization

$$- \frac{d[m_1]}{dt} = \sum_1^\infty k_{pj}[m_j{}^*][m_1] = k_p[m_1]\sum_1^\infty [m_j{}^*] . \quad \text{(VII.3)}$$

which is formally equivalent to equation (IV.1), and it will therefore be evident that $\sum_1^\infty (m_j{}^*)$ is determined only by the nature and rates of the initiation and termination reactions.

2. The Initiation of Chains: Use of Molecular Weight Measurements, Inhibitors and Retarders to Determine the Rate of Initiation. A variety of ways in which the monomer may be converted into the smallest chain centre, $m_1{}^*$, were discussed in Chapter III, section 5. From the kinetic point of view it is important to know the rate of initiation and whether or not it depends on the monomer concentration. Whilst the methods employed are to some extent determined by the particular reaction under investigation, certain general principles are applicable, which may be illustrated by reference to the following examples.

(a) Free Radical Polymerization. In polymerization reactions which proceed by the free radical mechanism *at least* one free-radical must be generated for each kinetic chain which is initiated. In the early stages of the subject it was commonly assumed that each free radical emerging from the reaction in which it was produced initiated one chain by adding to the monomer to form a substituted ethyl radical. For example, in the benzoyl peroxide catalyzed polymerization of styrene, it would have been assumed that each phenyl radical formed in reaction (27) of Chapter III would add to a styrene molecule according to reaction (6) to

$$\text{(6)} \quad C_6H_5\cdot + CH_2{:}CH.C_6H_5 \rightarrow C_6H_5.CH_2CH(C_6H_5)\cdot$$

form the adduct, a 1,2 diphenyl ethyl radical which could be equated with $m_1{}^*$. There are two consequences of this assumption: (i) that the number of chains started is equal to the number of initiating radicals chemically combined in the polymer and (ii) that the rate of initiation is equal to the rate of initiating radical production. Early results seemed to provide some confirmation of this assumption. In those cases where the initiating radical is produced by unimolecular dissociation of a catalyst or by the bimolecular interaction of two catalysts A and B (as in reaction (30) of Chapter III) and the termination is exclusively quadratic, the polymerization rate should be given by equation (VII.4), where k_{de} and k_{bi} are the rate constants of the corres-

$$- \, \mathrm{d}[m_1]/\mathrm{d}t = \theta^{\frac{1}{2}} \delta^{-\frac{1}{2}} \bar{\imath}^{-1}$$
$$= k_p[m_1]\{k_{de}[\text{catalyst}] \text{ or } k_{bi}[A][B]\}^{\frac{1}{2}}/k_t^{\frac{1}{2}} \quad . \quad \text{(VII.4)}$$

ponding reactions. A dependence of the rate on the first power of the monomer concentration and on the square root of either the catalyst concentration or product of the concentration of each catalyst is frequently observed and is exemplified in Fig. VII.1. Furthermore when the quadratic termination is by combination there should be *two* initiating radicals chemically bound to each polymer molecule and when it is by disproportionation only *one*. An early example of the former seemed to be afforded by the polymerization of styrene in aqueous solution where the resultant polymer was said to contain two catalyst fragments per molecule[4].

However, as the precision of methods of determining molecular weights and of measuring end-group concentrations by spectro-scopic or radioactive tracer techniques has improved, it has become clear that the basic assumption is often invalid and that there are many reasons why the rate of the catalytic process, whether it is unimolecular decomposition caused by heat or light or it is a bimolecular reaction, is not necessarily equal in rate to the chain initiation rate or to the rate of disappearance of the catalyst. In the first place the catalyst may be decomposing by reactions which do not involve radical production. Secondly, the catalyst be decomposed by radicals in the system without generating any additional radicals, i.e. the catalyst is merely acting as a chain transfer agent in the course of which it is des-troyed. This is called *induced decomposition* and may be recog-nized by a tendency for the order of reaction with respect to catalyst concentration to exceed unity. It is also frequently the case that some of the radicals which are formed in the catalytic process do not react with the monomer but disappear in other non-initiating processes. In liquid systems the cage effect will always operate to ensure that some of the radical fragments produced in photo-, radiation- or thermal-decom-positions will combine either before or after splitting into smaller

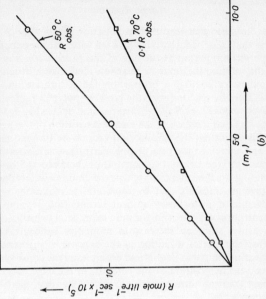

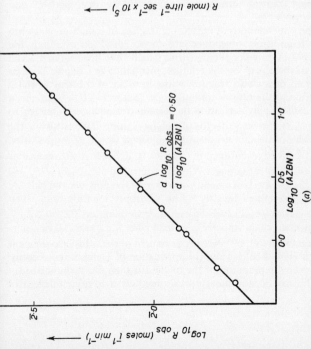

Fig. VII.1b. Initial rate of polymerization of methyl metha-crylate plotted against initial monomer concentration in benzene at 50°C and 70°C using 0·0413 M benzoyl peroxide as a catalyst.[15]

Fig. VII.1a. Log initial rate of polymerization of methyl metha-crylate plotted against log catalyst concentration. Solvent = benzene. Catalyst = AZBN (azo-bis-isobutyro-nitrile). Temperature = 50°C. Full line has slope of 0·50[14] units. In these cases the rate of initiation of polymer chain will be less than I_{abs} or k_{de}[catalyst]. Even when the primary radicals escape recombination at the site of their formation and diffuse into the solution they may be relatively inefficient in reacting with the monomer so that a proportion fail to initiate and act as terminators by reacting with the growing polymer radicals. This is called *primary radical termination* and is readily recognized by the fact that increase of the rate of generation of these primary radicals augments the termination rate as well as the initiation rate and therefore the rate of polymerization is proportional to a power of the catalyst concentration between 0·5 and zero, depending on the extents to which the chains are terminated by the primary radicals and by quadratic termination. Another manifestation of primary radical termination is a monomer concentration exponent in the rate expression which is greater than unity, since an increase in monomer concentration will increase the rate of initiation at the expense of primary radical termination. Further details and examples of the consequences of induced decomposition of the catalyst, of the cage effect and of primary radical termination are given by BEVINGTON[5] and BAMFORD[6].

The only methods of measuring the rate of initiation which are free from these objections are those based on counting the number of polymer chain centres which have been formed. The first of these rests on the relation, mentioned in Chapter IV, that the rate of a chain reaction is the product of the kinetic chain length and the rate of initiation, i.e. that $n/i = \theta \times k.c.l.$ In a free radical polymerization the kinetic chain length is related to the number average degree of polymerization, $\overline{DP_n}$, which is the quotient of the number average molecular weight of the polymer, $\overline{M_n}$, obtained as outlined in Chapter II, divided by the molecular weight of the monomer. When chain transfer is absent, $\overline{DP_n}$ will be equal to $k.c.l.$ in systems in which all the polymer radicals are either terminated linearly or by disproportionation and, when termination is exclusively by radical recombination $\overline{DP_n} = 2 \, k.c.l.$ Even when chain transfer does take place $k.c.l.$ can still be determined from $\overline{DP_n}$ by prior measurement of the transfer coefficient (see section 4 below) and the application of a suitable correction; however the precision of the method is then much diminished.

The second and most reliable method is to add sufficient of

a retarder to terminate all the growing polymer radicals in a reaction of well established stoichiometry. Compounds of transition elements are particularly valuable for this purpose[7] and equations (5) and (6) of Chapter II illustrate the kind of reactions involved. Provided ferric iron is not reduced in the initiation reaction, in both these reactions the rate of termination = rate of initiation = $d[Fe^{II}]/dt$, and this quantity is easily and precisely measurable by spectrophotometric methods.

The third method, which has also been mentioned in Chapter II, requires the addition of an inhibitor which, by reacting with the primary radicals prevents the initiation of polymer chains. If the stoichiometry of the reaction of the primary radical with the inhibitor is known the rate of initiation can be directly related either to the measured rate of disappearance of the inhibitor during the inhibition period or to the length of the inhibition period. For both methods it is necessary that the rate constant of the reaction between the primary radical and the inhibitor molecule, k_{in}, be much larger than that for reaction between the primary radical and the monomer, k_i, so that for a major part of the inhibition period the primary radical are almost entirely reacting with the inhibitor. At the same time the inhibitor concentration should not be so large that a significant fraction of the catalyst is destroyed during the inhibition period. The following example will indicate the stringency of these conditions. If the catalyst concentration at the beginning of the induction period is 10^{-2} M and not more than 5 per cent is to be destroyed the maximum permissible inhibitor concentration will be 5×10^{-4} M. Now the concentration of inhibitor at which 9 per cent of the primary radicals initiate chains will be $10k_i[m_1]/k_{in}$ and ideally this should correspond to as large a fraction of inhibitor destroyed as possible. Even if this fraction is only 90 per cent, $k_{in} = 2 \times 10^5 k_i[m_1]$. Since different monomers react at very different rates with the same radical, e.g. acrylonitrile reacts about fifty times more rapidly than vinyl acetate with methyl radicals, a substance which is a good inhibitor for the polymerization of one monomer may be much less suitable for use with another. Despite these differences it is still broadly true that the desirable qualities of an inhibitor are high reactivity towards the primary radicals to form a stable product, inertness towards monomer and easily measurable in low concentrations. Iodine and quinones are typical molecular inhibitors of free radical polymerizations. The former undoubtedly reacts according to equation (6), where $\underline{R}\cdot$ is the primary radical, and the

(6) $\underline{R}\cdot + I_2 \rightarrow RI + I\cdot \ (\rightarrow \tfrac{1}{2}I_2)$

resultant iodine atoms combine in pairs. The mechanism of action of the quinones is not thoroughly understood. They may form adducts of various semi-quinonoid structures, e.g.

RO—⬡—O· or HO—⬡(R)—O·, or abstract a hydrogen

atom from the radical to form the semiquinone HO—⬡—O·

and there is experimental evidence in support of all these possibilities[8]. Large conjugated free radicals having a highly delocalized odd electron, as expected, are highly coloured, form moderately stable adducts with primary radicals and do not react with monomer and several have been shown to act as inhibitors. The most commonly used are the hydrazyls, of which D.P.P.H. (diphenyl picryl hydrazyl) is typical. Although D.P.P.H. can be shown to be destroyed during the induction period by

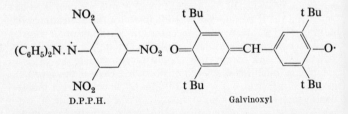

D.P.P.H.   Galvinoxyl

reaction with free radicals formed from a catalyst it has many serious limitations. Thus it does not react in the expected way with per-esters[9], it is sometimes incorporated into the polymer chain, it does not form the simple tetrahydrazine adduct but a variety of substituted hydrazines which are themselves radical scavengers. BAWN and VERDIN[10] have shown that 2-cyano 2-propyl radicals react with D.P.P.H. according to equation (7).

(7) $(CH_3)_2\dot{C}CN$ + D.P.P.H.

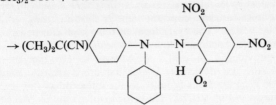

$\rightarrow (CH_3)_2C(CN)$

The most promising free radical inhibitor is the deep blue 'galvinoxyl' which reacts very efficiently with radicals to form the substituted cyclohexadienones *A* and *B*[11].

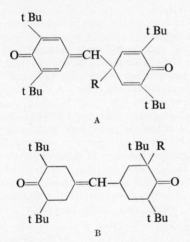

The rate of destruction of an inhibitor during the inhibition period will normally be $\alpha\theta$, where θ is the rate of initiation and α is the number of inhibitor molecules destroyed per primary radical formed. α is frequently taken as unity but complexities of the kind described above make this assumption untrue. As the inhibitor is destroyed an increasing fraction of primary radicals react with the monomer so that the rate of polymerization increases at first slowly and later rapidly, ultimately attaining the rate characteristic of the uninhibited reaction. Consequently the graph of percentage conversion against time should increase in slope from zero to a constant value as shown in the dotted lines of Fig. VII.2a. The exact form of this graph can be calculated for mixtures containing known amounts of inhibitor and monomer provided k_{in}/k_i and θ are known[12]. However the larger k_{in}/k_i the less detectable is this curvature and the inhibition period is conventionally taken as the intercept on the time axis, as shown in Fig. VII.2a. The error involved in this procedure is smaller the larger the inhibition period. To a first approximation the inhibition period, so defined, will be equal to the concentration, of added inhibitor divided by $\alpha\theta$ and hence θ may be obtained from the graph of inhibition period against initial inhibitor concentration which should be linear. An example of this is shown in Fig. VII.2b.

Emphasis has been placed on the importance of the ratio, k_{in}/k_i, and its dependence on the nature of the monomer and inhibitor. It will also depend on the character of the primary radicals. If, as is often the case in radiation-induced polymerization, there are two primary radicals this ratio may be very large for one and negligible for the other. A case in point is in the γ-ray induced polymerization of acrylamide in water. Here the two primary radicals are $\cdot OH$ and e^-, which becomes $H\cdot$ in acid solution, and various added ions such as Ag^+, Hg^{2+} and $(Co6NH^3)_3{}^+$ are inert to $\cdot OH$ but react very rapidly with e^- or $H\cdot$ so that increasing amounts of these additives progressively prevent chain initiation by one radical without interfering with that of the other. Small amounts of such substances therefore reduce the initial rate by a constant fraction as shown in curve (c) of Fig. VII.3, which may easily be shown to be equal to $\sqrt{G_H/(G_H + G_{OH})}$ or $\sqrt{G_{e^-}/(G_{e^-} + G_{OH})}$ at low and high pH respectively[13].

(b) *Ionic Polymerizations.* In homogeneous ionic polymerization processes the chain centre may be an ion-pair or a free-ion and in some cases both species may propagate simultaneously at different rates[18]. The creation of the initial ion or ion-pair may involve rapid or slow, production and subsequent addition to the monomer, of an electron or anion or proton or carbonium ion, some examples of which have already been given in Chapter III, section 5. If the initiation of all the chains is complete within a period which is shorter than the time for growth of a given centre,

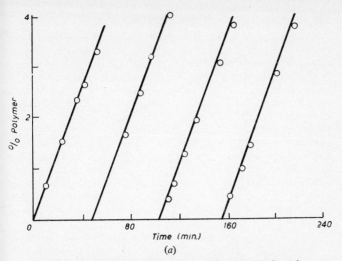

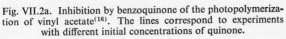

Fig. VII.2a. Inhibition by benzoquinone of the photopolymerization of vinyl acetate[16]. The lines correspond to experiments
with different initial concentrations of quinone.

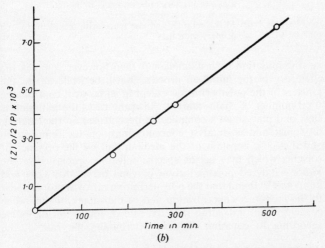

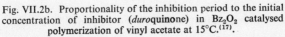

Fig. VII.2b. Proportionality of the inhibition period to the initial
concentration of inhibitor (*duro*quinone) in Bz_2O_2 catalysed
polymerization of vinyl acetate at $15°C$.[17].

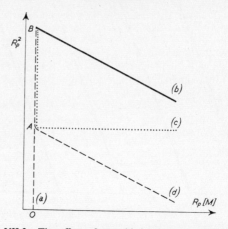

Fig. VII.3. The effect of an added substance, M, on the initial rate of a free radical polymerization, R_p.

Curve (a) M is an inhibitor but not a retarder.

(b) M is a retarder but not an inhibitor.

(c) M is not a retarder but reacts rapidly with one of a pair of primary radicals, i.e. is an inhibitor for one of the initiation processes.

(d) M is a retarder and also reacts with one of the primary radicals.

i.e. the initiation is 'instantaneous', then however complex the chemistry of the initiation process, it will be irrelevant to the kinetics of the polymerization except in so far as it controls the total number of chains started. In many cases the initiation is slow and may show a complicated dependence on the catalyst, monomer and co-catalyst concentrations, on the temperature and dielectric constant of the medium and on the presence of solvents which may act as specific solvating species. For the iodine catalyzed polymerization of vinyl octyl ether ELEY and RICHARDS[19] found that the polymerization rate was proportional to the monomer concentration and to the square of the iodine concentration, indicating that the rate of ionization of iodine according to equation (8) was determining the rate of the

$$(8) \qquad 2I_2 \rightarrow I^+ + I_3^-$$

initiation process, that each I^+ ion was captured by the monomer (equation (9)) and that the chains were linearly terminated.

(9) $$I^+ + m_1 \to Im_1^+$$

By contrast the rate of cationic polymerization of styrene may vary linearly with the first, second or third power of the concentration of the monomer depending on the medium, the catalyst and cocatalyst which are used[49].

In principle θ for ionic polymerizations which are slowly initiated may be measured by the same methods as are used for free-radical polymerization. In practice there are many difficulties. Cationic polymerizations often manifest marked chain transfer to monomer (see section 4) so that $\overline{DP}_n \ll k.c.l.$ Nevertheless the method can be applied in certain cases. The use of inhibitors is restricted by the fact that either their rate of disappearance may be so large that the inhibition period is too short to measure or the concentration of the inhibitor is often not easily measured.

3. Quadratic and Linear Termination: Retardation. Termination of a free-radical polymerization chain may occur by interaction with a similar chain (quadratic termination) or with a primary radical or with an additive, which is then referred to as a retarder. Quadratic termination does not occur in ionic polymerization where the chains are always linearly terminated by reaction either with the gegen ion or with an added retarder.

(*a*) *Quadratic Termination.* In Chapters IV and V it was pointed out that when quadratic termination is the sole mode of termination the reaction rate will be proportional to the square root of the rate of initiation. There are many instances of this in addition polymerization (e.g. Fig. VII.1a) and in photo- or radiation-chemically initiated reactions the rotating sector technique may be applied to measure k_t and E_t. The latter quantity usually lies in the range 2 to 5 k.cal whilst the frequency factor A_t is usually in the range $10^{9 \pm 1}$ l.mole^{-1} sec^{-1}. Consideration of these values in the light of the Transition State Theory (Chapter I) suggests that the reaction concerned is a metathesis rather than a bimolecular association reaction. Experimental evidence in favour of either one of these possibilities is usually based either on end-group analysis or on molecular weight distribution. The former method depends on the deduction mentioned in the previous section that when initiation occurs solely by addition to the monomer of an identifiable initiation fragment and there is no chain transfer there will be two initiation fragments in each polymer molecule formed by combination of two growing radicals and only one fragment when the polymer molecule has resulted from a disproportionation. The end-groups in the polymer may be measured spectroscopically or by tracer techniques when a radioactive initiator is used[5]. If an initiating radical which contains a functional group such as COOH is used, the resultant end-group in a polymer molecule will be able to form an acid anydride with the end-group of another molecule. Hence if there is only one catalyst fragment per molecule, formation of the anhydride will at most double the molecular weight, whereas if there are two end groups per molecule, anhydride formation will cause a very large increase in molecular weight[20]. The second method is laborious and tedious because it involves the measurement of the number average molecular weight distribution in a polydisperse sample of polymer. It can be shown that if the curve of the number of polymer molecules per unit weight of each polymer fraction plotted against its $\overline{DP}$ shows a maximum then the chain termination must be by combination[21]. Inherent in this deduction is the assumption that the rate of initiation and the monomer concentration are constant, and it therefore only relates to polymer samples obtained from experiments allowed to proceed to low conversions.

These different kinds of investigation indicate that polymer radicals derived from different monomers behave differently. Thus polyacrylonitrile and polystyryl radicals combine, whereas polymethyl methacrylate radicals disproportionate, doubtless partly because of strains involved in combination and partly because of the greater number of readily accessible H atoms (one of which may be transferred during disproportionation) in polymer radicals having a heavily substituted end group such as $-\dot{C}(CH_3) CO.OCH_3$.

Whereas the initiation, propagation and transfer reactions always involve at least one reactant of molecular weight of the order of 50–150, mutual termination requires the encounter of two radicals which, on the average, may be very large, e.g. with molecular weights between 10^4 and 10^5. Such large entities will move sluggishly and it would be expected that their movement would be impeded by increases in viscosity of the medium brought about either by added polymer molecules or by those which are produced in the system as the reaction proceeds. The movement of smaller molecules would be much less affected by changes in the viscosity of the medium. We would therefore expect that although the rates of initiation, propagation and transfer would be relatively insensitive to increases in the viscosity of the medium, the diffusion of the large radicals might become so slow as to be rate determining in the mutual termination reaction. This is found to be the case. TROMMSDORF[22] has

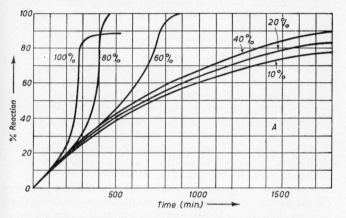

Fig. VII.4. 'Peaking' in the polymerization of methyl methacrylate in benzene solution at 50°C. Catalyst = 10 g.litre^{-1} benzoyl peroxide; initial monomer concentration given on each curve[15].

shown that when liquid methyl methacrylate is thickened before polymerization by the addition of polymers the rate of polymerization is considerably increased. This explanation had previously been offered by NORRISH and SMITH[23] for the characteristic auto-acceleration of methyl methacrylate polymerization known as 'peaking', which is marked in methyl methacrylate polymerization in solution at concentrations exceeding 40 per cent and which is accompanied by a simultaneous increase in the molecular weight of the polymer. This phenomenon is illustrated in Fig. VII.4. Confirmation of this explanation is provided by the observations (a) that when transfer agents are added which substantially decrease the molecular weight of the polymer this 'peaking' is very much reduced, (b) that the chain lifetime, which is inversely proportional to the square root of k_t, increases rapidly during the auto-acceleration phase[24] and (*c*) by the observation that k_t for methyl methacrylate polymerization is directly proportional to the reciprocal of the viscosity of the reaction medium, in accordance with the formula given in Chapter I for a diffusion controlled reaction[25].

If the polymerization is carried out in a bad solvent for the polymer the growing radicals will be precipitated and thereby immobilized and prevented from undergoing quadratic termination. They therefore survive long after initiation ceased and, as described in section (*g*), Chapter V, give rise to persistent after-effects.

If the monomer contains an acidic or basic function and is water soluble, a change in pH may cause both the monomer and polymer radical to become charged. An example of this is methacrylic acid, $CH_2:C(CH_3)COOH$, the pK_a of the carboxylic group of which is about 6, so that above pH6 both the monomer and the polymer radical are negatively charged and BLAUER has shown[26] that both k_t and k_p are much smaller at pH > 6 than in acid solution. This effect is presumably due to the powerful electrostatic repulsion between the charged reactants in both the propagation and termination reactions.

(*b*) *Primary Radical Termination*. At high rates of primary radical generation and low concentrations of relatively unreactive monomer not all the primary radicals will be able to react with monomer before encountering a growing polymer radical. The remainder may combine with one another or react with a growing polymer radical. If this primary radical termination occurs to the exclusion of quadratic termination then the rate of polymerization is given by equation (VII.5) in which k_i is the rate constant

$$- \,\mathrm{d}[m_1]/\mathrm{d}t = k_i k_p [m_1]^2 / k_{t''} \qquad . \qquad . \quad \text{(VII.5)}$$

of the primary radical + monomer reaction and $k_{t''}$ that of the primary radical + polymer radical interaction[27]. In practice, if only one kind of primary radical is formed, it is unlikely that this situation will be exactly achieved. However if two different primary radicals are formed one of which reacts efficiently with the monomer and inefficiently with the polyradical whilst for the other radical the position is reversed, this kinetic situation should be more easily attainable. There are indications that this may be the case when γ-rays are used to initiate the polymerization of acrylonitrile in dimethyl formamide solution[28].

When termination is partly quadratic and partly by primary radicals which are also disappearing in pairs the reaction mechanism comprises the following stages.

(10) Primary Radical Production   *Rate*

$$\rightarrow R\cdot \qquad\qquad\qquad \theta$$

(3) Initiation $R\cdot + m_1 \rightarrow m_1\cdot$ $k_i[R\cdot][m_1]$

(4) Propagation

$$m_j\cdot + m_1 \rightarrow m_{j+1}\cdot \qquad\qquad k_p[m_1][m_j]$$

(5.ii) Quadratic Termination

$$2m_j\cdot \rightarrow \text{dead polymer} \qquad\qquad k_t[m_j\cdot]^2$$

(11) Primary Radical Termination

$$R\cdot + m_j \rightarrow \text{dead polymer} \qquad\qquad k_{11}[R\cdot][m_j\cdot]$$

(12) Primary Radical Combination

$$2R\cdot \rightarrow R_2 \qquad\qquad\qquad k_{12}[R\cdot]^2$$

It is frequently true that when two different radicals react in pairs the rate constant for dissimilar members of a pair interacting is close to the geometric mean of the rate constants for each of the two like pairs reacting. Making this assumption in this case, i.e. $k_{11} = \sqrt{k_t k_{12}}$, and applying the stationary state principle the equation (VII.6) is obtained[29], and for the example cited the graphs of polymerization rate (*a*) against $\sqrt{\theta}$ at constant

$$- \mathrm{d}(m_1)/\mathrm{d}t = k_p[m_1]^2 \sqrt{\theta k_t}/\{[m_1] - k_{11}\theta^{\frac{1}{2}}/k_i k_t^{\frac{1}{2}}\} \qquad . \quad \text{(VII.6)}$$

monomer concentration and (*b*) against monomer concentration at constant θ, are in accord with this equation[28]. However it must be emphasized that this does not provide a sensitive test of primary radical termination and the data fit equally well an equation based on degradative chain transfer to solvent (see section 4 below).

(*c*) *Spontaneous Linear and Primary Ion Termination in Ionic Polymerization.* Termination by a primary species is the normal mode of termination in ionic polymerization. Two cases may be distinguished: (i) that in which the oppositely charged ion is a poor terminator and travels along the growing polymer chain as a counter ion and (ii) that in which ions of either sign are fed into the system and one ion initiates whilst the other, or some species derived from it, terminates. The first case is characteristic of most cationic polymerizations and the termination may be treated kinetically as a unimolecular reaction of the ion-pair terminating its growth, so that the polymerization rate is $= k_p[m_1]\theta/k_t$, where θ is a function of $[m_1],T$, catalyst, etc., which is determined by the initiation process. This spontaneous termination reaction may involve ester formation or cyclization. In the second case which is exemplified by the radiation-induced anionic polymerization of acrylamide in liquid ammonia at $-65°C$, the ions of one sign (e_{am}^-) initiate and the oppositely charged ions (NH_3^+) are unstable and react according to (13) within about 10^{-14} sec. The growing polymer anions are terminated on encounter with either NH_4^+ or NH_2 according to equation (14).

$$(13) \qquad NH_3^+ + NH_3 \rightarrow NH_4^+ + NH_2$$

$$(14) \qquad m_j^- + NH_4^+ \text{ or } NH_2 \rightarrow P_j + NH_3 \text{ or } NH_2^-$$

This corresponds exactly to the conditions necessary for equation (VII.5) to hold and it has been found that the monomer exponent is $1\cdot8 \pm 0\cdot3$ and the dose-rate exponent close to zero[30].

(*d*) *Retardation.* Strictly this merely means deceleration of the reaction as distinct from inhibition which implies its total cessation. However deceleration can be achieved either by an increase in the termination rate or by a partial decrease in the initiation rate and, as pointed out earlier in this chapter, a substance which reacts competitively with the monomer for initiating species will, if present in sufficient concentration, reduce the initiation rate effectively to zero for a period of time until this additive has been destroyed. If this is the only function of the added substance it is called an *inhibitor* and may have the effects on the initial rate of polymerization illustrated in the curves (*a*) and (*c*) of Fig. VII.3. A *retarder* may be defined as a substance which does not affect the initiation process but does introduce an additional termination step. In practice, because the initiating species and the propagating species are both either free-radical, cationic or anionic in nature, there are many chemical substances which can react with both the initiating entity and the growing centre. Simple examples of this duality of function are (*a*) carbon dioxide which readily reacts with the green naphthalenide radical ion $C_{10}H_8^-$ and the red polystyryl anion$(CH_2-CH(C_6H_5))_n^-$ in both cases discharging the colour, thereby preventing initiation by the former and further growth by the latter, and (*b*) ferric chloride which can react with the initiating 2-cyano 2-propyl radical and with the growing polyacrylonitrile radical. When both processes operate during a polymerization the kinetic pattern becomes rather complex[6], but there are certain simpler kinetic situations which it is instructive to discuss.

Consider first the case of free-radical polymerization in which the substance, M, merely destroys growing centres according to

(15) $\qquad m_j\cdot + M \overset{k_r}{\rightarrow}$ dead polymer + product

equation (15) in which the product is stable and incapable of reacting with the monomer. The reaction sequence (3), (4), (5.ii), and (15) corresponds to case (9) of Chapter V and if the chains are sufficiently long equation (VII.3) is valid. Substituting $n = \Sigma[m_j\cdot] = R_p/k_p[m_1]$ in equation (V.28), where R_p is the initial rate of polymerization, we obtain (VII.7) as the expression for the initial steady-state rate, where $R_{p,0}$ is the value of the

$$R_p^2 = R_{p,0}^2 - k_p k_r[m_1]R_p[M]/k_t \qquad . \quad \text{(VII.7)}$$

initial polymerization rate when no retarder is present. Curve (*b*) of Fig. VII.3 corresponds to this equation and there are many examples of this behaviour, especially in radiation-induced polymerizations where the retarder is a compound of a transition metal which can oxidize the polymer radical, e.g. ferric, cupric, auric, cobaltic and tungstic compounds, or reduce it, e.g. titanous, europous, chromous, hypovanadous and molybdenous compounds[31].

In radiation-initiated free radical polymerization two major initiating radicals are often produced and if the retarder can also react very rapidly with one of these then small amounts of M will suffice to suppress initiation by this radical. It is readily shown that the graph of R_p^2 against $R_p[M]$ will have the form of curve (*c*) of Fig. VII.3, in which the negative slope of the second, linear, segment is $k_p k_r[m_1]/k_t$ and the rapid initial drop enables the ratio k_{in}^M/k_i to be measured, where k_{in}^M and k_i are the rate constants for reaction of this initiating radical with M and monomer respectively. Some of the values of k_r for inorganic retarders are given in Table 3. They cover a very wide range and show marked dependence on the detailed structure of the retarder in ways which provide valuable information concerning inorganic oxidation and reduction mechanisms.

TABLE 3. RATE CONSTANTS FOR RETARDATION (k_r) BY INORGANIC COMPOUNDS OF FREE RADICAL ADDITION POLYMERIZATION

(a) In Aqueous Solution at 25°C

Monomer	Reaction Type	Inorganic Species (M_x)	$k_r\,(M^{-1}s^{-1})$	Ref.
Acrylamide	Oxidation i.e. $m_j \cdot + M\bar{x} \rightarrow P_j + M\overline{x-1}$	Fe^{3+}	2.8×10^3	a
Methacrylamide	"	Fe^{3+}	5.3×10	b
Acrylamide	"	$FeOH^{2+}$	2.1×10^4	a
Methacrylamide	"	$FeOH^{2+}$	6.1×10^3	b
Acrylamide	"	$FeCl^{2+}$	8×10^4	a
"	"	$FeBr^{2+}$	1.7×10^6	a
"	"	FeN_3^{2+}	1.6×10^6	a
"	"	$FeSCN^{2+}$	1.4×10^7	a
"	"	$Fe(o\ phen)_3^{3+}$	3.1×10^5	a
"	"	$Fe(CN)_6^{3-}$	8.5×10^5	a
"	"	Cu^{2+}	1.2×10^3	a
"	"	Hg^{2+}	1.0	c
"	"	Ag^+	0.0	a
"	"	Tl^{3+}	0.34	a
"	"	Substitution stable octahedral complexes of CrIII and CoIII	0.0	a
"	Reduction i.e. $m_j \cdot + M\bar{x} \rightarrow P_j + M\overline{x+1}$	Fe^{2+}	$0 < k_r < 1$	a
"	"	Ti^{3+}	5.8×10^2	a
"	"	Eu^{2+}	8×10^4	a
"	"	V^{2+}	1.1×10^5	a
"	"	Cr^{2+}	2.8×10^5	a

(b) Non-aqueous Solution

Monomer	Solvent	Reaction Type	Inorganic Species	Temp.	$k_{tr}(M^{-1}s^{-1})$	Ref.
Acrylonitrile	Dimethyl formamide	Oxidation	$FeCl_3$	25°C	8×10^2	c, d, e
,,	,,	,,	$CuCl_{2+x}^{x-}$	,,	$6 \cdot 1 \times 10^3$	f
,,	,,	,,	$Fe(acac)_3$	,,	2×10^2	f
,,	,,	,,	$Co(acac)_3$	,,	3×10^2	f
,,	,,	,,	$RuCl_3$	,,	$1 \cdot 1 \times 10^4$	f
,,	,,	,,	$HAuCl_4$	,,	$1 \cdot 1 \times 10^4$	f
,,	,,	,,	$HgCl_2$	,,	0	f
Methyl methacrylate	,,	,,	$CuCl_{2+x}^{x-}$	60°C	$6 \cdot 6 \times 10^5$	g
,,	,,	,,	$FeCl_3$	,,	3×10^3	h
Methyl acrylate	,,	,,	$FeCl_3$	,,	4×10^3	h
Methacrylonitrile	,,	,,	$FeCl_3$	,,	3×10^2	h
Styrene	,,	,,	$FeCl_3$	,,	5×10^4	h

References: (a) Colinson, Dainton, Mile, Tazuke, and Smith, *Nature*, **198**, 26 (1963); (b) Dainton and Sisley, *Trans. Faraday Soc.*, **59**, 1377 (1963); (c) Bamford, Jenkins and Johnston, *J. Polymer Sci.*, **29**, 355 (1958); (d) Colebourne, Collinson, Currie and Dainton, *Trans. Faraday Soc.*, **59**, 1357 (1963); (e) R. G. Jones, unpublished work; (f) Dainton and Reilly, to be published; (g) Bengough and Fairservice, *Trans. Faraday Soc.*, **61**, 1206 (1965); (h) Bamford, Jenkins and Johnston, *Trans. Faraday Soc.*, **58**, 1212 (1962).

If the product in reaction (15) is not chemically inert to the monomer so that some of the product molecules reinitiate fresh polymerization chains the efficiency of M as a retarder is diminished. If the retarder is a molecule the product of reaction (15) must be a radical with some capacity, however small, for initiation. The retarder is then better described as a *degradative chain transfer agent* (see following section) and the efficiency with which the radical product initiates the fresh chain will depend on the competitive reactions which it can enter. Various complex kinetic situations may be envisaged, some of which have been realized[32]. They involve no novel chemical principles and the results indicate that, as expected, if the product radical is stable the molecule will be a good retarder (e.g. triphenyl methane) but that the retardation and re-initiation efficiencies depend on the monomer, e.g. triethylamine is a good retarder of vinyl acetate and acrylonitrile polymerization but not of styrene polymerization[5,6].

An interesting category of retarders includes those substances containing a C—H bond adjacent to a C,C double bond, e.g. allyl esters. Such compounds readily surrender an H atom to a growing chain to form a resonance stabilized allylic radical which is a very inefficient chain initiator (16).

(16) $m_j^* + Cl \cdot CH_2 {-} CH {=\!=} CH_2 \rightarrow m_j H + Cl \cdot CH {=\!=} CH {=\!=} CH_2$

Allyl compounds are particularly interesting in that they are themselves polymerizable by the free-radical mechanism and must therefore always be auto-retarded. These substances do in fact polymerize unusually slowly and when detailed kinetic analysis has been made it has been found that the rate of polymerization is proportional to the first power of the catalyst concentration[33].

4. Chain Transfer. The number average degree of polymerization $\overline{DP}_n$ is defined as the average number of monomeric units incorporated in each polymer molecule produced. If each kinetic chain which is initiated results in the formation of *one* polymer molecule, as would be the case if the termination process were either linear or by disproportionation, the degree of polymerization is then equal to the kinetic chain length, i.e. the ratio of the rate of polymerization to the rate of initiation. The expressions appropriate to the various chain sequences are:

(3), (4), (5(i)) $\qquad\qquad \overline{DP}_n = k_p[m_1]/k_t' \quad . \quad . \quad . \quad$ (VII.8)

(3), (4), (5(ii)) disproportionation

$$\overline{DP}_n = k_p[m_1]/[\theta k_t]^{\frac{1}{2}} = \frac{k_p{}^2[m_1]^2}{k_t R_p} \quad . \quad . \quad \text{(VII.9)}$$

(3), (4), (5(ii)) combination

$$\overline{DP}_n = 2k_p[m_1]/[\theta k_t]^{\frac{1}{2}} = \frac{2k_p{}^2[m_1]^2}{k_t R_p} \quad . \quad \text{(VII.10)}$$

where R_p is the observed rate of polymerization $= k_p[m_1]\Sigma(m_j{}^*)$. These relations are rarely obeyed in practice. Thus for catalysed reactions subject to mutual termination it is found that when polymer samples are taken at low conversion from reaction mixtures containing the same monomer concentration but different amounts of catalyst and therefore polymerizing at different rates, the reciprocals of their average degrees of polymerization are proportional to the observed rate only for a

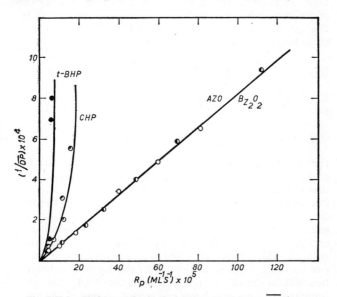

Fig. VII.5. Chain transfer by hydroperoxy catalysts. $\overline{DP}^{-1}$ for polymethyl methacrylate samples from bulk polymerization of monomer plotted against R_{obs} for various catalysts[34]
○ Bz_2O_2 ◑ AZBN   ● t BuO_2H ◐ cumene O_2H

limited range of catalysts including the azonitriles and benzoyl peroxide. When other catalysts, particularly hydroperoxides, are used, the polymer molecules have a lower molecular weight and therefore the curve of $\overline{DP}_n^{-1}$ versus R_p shows positive deviations from linearity. These effects are illustrated in Fig. VII.5. If the catalyst concentration is maintained constant and the monomer concentration increased, then, according to equations (8), (9), and (10) the $\overline{DP}_n$ should increase proportionally. It is commonly the case that the increase is much less than would be expected and that the reciprocal of $\overline{DP}_n$ is often proportional to the ratio of the concentration of the solvent and monomer (Fig. VII.6). In cationic polymerization it has also been frequently found that $\overline{DP}_n^{-1}$ is independent of the monomer concentration.

The explanation of effects of this kind was first proposed by FLORY in 1937[35]. He suggested that a growing polymer chain might be capable of transferring its capacity for growth to a chain transfer agent. Denoting the latter substance by S, the chain transfer reaction may be written

$$(17) \qquad m_j^* + S \xrightarrow{k_{tr}} m_j + S^*$$

If this reaction is always followed by reaction of S^* with a monomer molecule (reaction (20))

$$(18) \qquad S^* + m_1 \to Sm_1^*$$

then no chain centres will be destroyed. The lifetime of the chains and also their kinetic chain length will be unaltered, so that the reaction rate will not be affected. If, however, only a fraction of the S^* species activate fresh monomer, the remaining S^* disappearing in some other manner not influencing the reaction, the substance S will act partly as a chain transfer agent and partly as a retarder since the kinetic chain length will be reduced. This process is referred to as *degradative chain transfer* (see also section 3 (*d*)). In either event the degree of polymerization will be the rate of polymerization divided by the rate of formation of pairs of polymer end groups. A pair of end groups is produced whenever a chain centre is created and destroyed, i.e. either when the chain transfer reaction (17) and (18) occur in succession or when a chain is initiated, since at the steady state

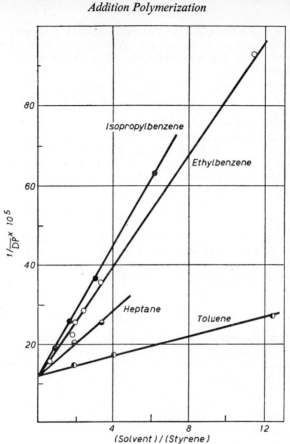

Fig. VII.6. Chain Transfer by Solvent. $\overline{DP}^{-1}$ for samples of polystyrene prepared by thermal polymerization at 60°C in various solvents plotted against solvent/monomer ratio, $[S]/[m_1]$[(36)]

one chain centre is destroyed for every new centre created in an initiation reaction. Hence

$$\overline{DP}_n = \frac{k_p[m_1]}{w + \Sigma k_{tr}[S]} \quad \text{and} \quad \text{k.c.l.} = \frac{k_p[m_1]}{w}. \quad \text{(VII.11)}$$

where $w = k_t'$ or $(\theta k_t)^{\frac{1}{2}}$, and k_{tr} is the velocity constant of the transfer reaction. When mutual termination is occurring and the catalyst is also acting as a chain transfer agent, i.e. $\theta = k_{de}[\text{cat}]$ equation (11) gives

$$\overline{DP}^{-1} = \frac{k_t}{k_p^2[m_1]^2}\left[R_{\text{obs}} + \frac{k_{tr}R_{\text{obs}}^2}{k_{de}k_p[m_1]}\right] \quad . \quad \text{(VII.12)}$$

The shape of the plot of DP_n^{-1} versus R_p would therefore be parabolic and the experimental observations depicted in Fig. VII.5 do lie on such a curve. The exact nature of the transfer reaction with a catalyst has not been established with certainty. One possibility is summarized in reactions (19) and (20).

(19) $\qquad m_i{}^* + \text{HOOR} \rightarrow m_j\text{OH} + \underline{\text{RO}}\cdot$

(20) $\qquad\qquad \underline{\text{RO}}\cdot + m_1 \rightarrow \text{RO}m_1{}^*$

and suggests that any compound containing a weakly bound atom or group might be an effective transfer agent, and this has in fact proved to be the case. The alkyl mercaptans are in this category, presumably due to the reactions

(21) $\qquad m_j{}^* + \text{HSR} \rightarrow m_j\text{H} + \underline{\text{RS}}\cdot$

(22) $\qquad\qquad \underline{\text{RS}}\cdot + m_1 \rightarrow \text{RS}m_1{}^*$

and are employed in industry, where they are known as 'regulators' or 'modifiers', to limit the average chain length of polymer molecules to the desired value. Chain transfer reactions may also involve (*a*) substitution in an aromatic nucleus or (*b*) when the chain transfer agent is unsaturated, detachment of an atom or group from the growing polymer chain. The latter class of reactions includes the rather special case of monomer transfer, which may be written

(23) $\qquad\qquad m_j{}^* + m_1 \rightarrow m_j + m_1{}^*$

and is clearly an alternative to propagation to which it is kinetically equivalent. This process seems to occur very freely in cationic polymerization[15] where it presumably involves proton transfer of the type

(24) $\quad \text{$\sim$CH}_2\overset{+}{\text{---CH}} + \text{CH}_2{=}\text{CH} \rightarrow \text{$\sim$CH}{=}\text{CHX} + \text{CH}_3\overset{+}{\text{---CH}}$
$\qquad\qquad\quad\;\; | \qquad\qquad\; | \qquad\qquad\qquad\qquad\qquad\qquad\quad |$
$\qquad\qquad\quad\;\; \text{X} \qquad\qquad\; \text{X} \qquad\qquad\qquad\qquad\qquad\qquad\quad \text{X}$

(25) or if $X = CH_3 \rightarrow \text{\textasciitilde\textasciitilde\textasciitilde}CH_2\text{---}CH + CH_3\text{---}\overset{+}{CH}$
$$\qquad\qquad\qquad\qquad\qquad \underset{CH_2}{\|} \qquad\quad \underset{CH_3}{|}$$

The ease of this type of reaction may be one of the principal factors which prevent the formation of very large polymers by the cationic mechanism at room temperatures and necessitates the use of low temperatures in the industrial utilization of Friedel-Crafts catalysts in polymerization.

The ratio of the rate constant for chain transfer to that for propagation is sometimes known as the *transfer constant* and denoted by C_s for transfer to S and C_m for transfer to monomer. Modifying equation (VII.11) to include monomer transfer and the possibility that of the radicals which terminate quadratically a fraction l disproportionate we obtain (VII.13). Hence if k_t' or k_t (whichever is relevant)

$$\overline{DP}_n{}^{-1} = \frac{1+l}{2} \cdot \frac{w}{k_p[m_1]} + C_s \frac{[S]}{[m_1]} + C_m. \quad \text{(VII.13)}$$

is known and the rate of initiation can be measured, C_s and C_m may be determined. In the special cases where w is proportional to $[m_1]$, i.e. when the rate of initiation of a free-radical polymerization is proportional to the square of the monomer concentration this equation reduces to (VII.14), where $\overline{DP}_n{}^\circ$ is the

$$\overline{DP}_n{}^{-1} = \overline{DP}_n{}^{\circ-1} + C_s[S]/[m_1] \qquad . \quad \text{(VII.14)}$$

value of $\overline{DP}_n$ when no chain transfer agent has been added. The uncatalysed thermal polymerization of styrene involves a bimolecular initiation step so that $\theta = k_{bi}[m_1]^2$ and GREGG and MAYO[36] have shown that equation (VII.14) holds for this system in a variety of solvents over wide ranges of monomer concentration, as shown in Fig. VII.6. A very large number of transfer constants has been evaluated for free-radical and cationic polymerizations, some of which are given in Table 3 on page 194 where the structural factors which control their magnitude is briefly discussed. In passing it may be noted that, in cationic polymerization, chain transfer by aromatic substances, ArH, probably involves substitution in the aromatic nucleus. In the case of styrene polymerization this reaction may be represented by (26) in which A^- denotes the gegen anion

(26) $\sim\!\sim\!\sim\overset{+}{CH_2CH}.C_6H_5\!:\!A^- + ArH$

$\rightarrow \sim\!\sim\!\sim CH_2CH(C_6H_5)Ar + HA$ or $CH_3CHC_6H_5\!:\!A^-$

and this system therefore offers a convenient means of investigating the relative reactivities of different carbonium ions to different aromatic compounds. This aspect has been extensively investigated by OVERBERGER[37] and OKAMURA[38] and their colleagues who have elucidated the steric and electronic factors which influence the rate.

Compounds containing tertiary CH groups, such as isopropyl benzene are good chain transfer agents (see Fig. VII.6) and, since all polymers based on vinyl monomers contain this grouping, it would be expected that polymer molecules could act as chain transfer agents. If this occurs during homopolymerization, the growing radical may either chain transfer on to its own chain or on to the chain of an adjacent polymer radical or molecule and the radical so formed will propagate, so that the resultant polymer will be branched. In the former case, depicted in (27), a flexible

(27)

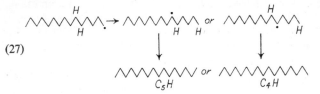

radical is statistically more likely to attack the 4th or 5th C—H group and thus a short side-chain will be formed. In the latter case long branches will be produced. If, during the homopolymerization of a monomer A a polymer B_n is present which acts as a chain transfer agent, the product will comprise the homopolymers A_n and B_n together with branches or grafts of polymeric side chains of A on the polymer B_n. Since transfer reactions frequently have larger activation energies than propagation reactions the formation of branched polymers is favoured in high temperature polymerization.

5. The Influence of Temperature: Depropagation. The overall energy of activation in a polymerization reaction should be given by

$$E = RT^2 \frac{\partial \ln R_p}{\partial T} = E_p + E_i - E_t' \text{ for sequence 3, 4, 5(i)}$$
(VII.15)

and
$$= E_p + \frac{E_i - E_t}{2} \text{ for sequence 3, 4, 5(ii)} \quad \text{(VII.16)}$$

corresponding to a straight line for the plot of the log R_p versus T^{-1} the magnitude and sign of the slope of which is determined by the values of the energies of activation of the part processes of initiation (E_i), propagation (E_p), and termination (E_t or E_t'). E_p is usually small, lying between 4 and 10 k.cal for most free radical and ionic polymerizations (see pp. 51 and 213). E_t and E_t' are also small, being generally slightly less than E_p in free radical polymerization. Consequently $E_p - E_t'$ and $E_p - \dfrac{E_t}{2}$ are often positive in sign and the reaction rate should then increase with temperature. For most systems in easily accessible temperature ranges this is true. The exceptional cases are discussed below. When light or ionizing radiation is used to initiate the reaction $E_i = 0$ and the overall energy of activation is very small, but when a catalyst is employed E_i has a magnitude not less than the dissociation energy of the catalyst into the radicals or the endothermicity of the appropriate ionic initiatory reaction. The bond dissociation energies of the peroxy- and azo-nitrile catalysts are about 30 k.cal and the values of $RT^2 \dfrac{\partial \ln R_p}{\partial T}$ when these catalysts are used are therefore usually of the order of 20 k.cal.

The effect of a temperature rise on the molecular weight is more or less complicated depending on whether chain transfer is playing a major part. When chain transfer can be neglected the appropriate equation will be

$$RT^2 \frac{d \ln (\overline{DP}_n)}{dT} = E_p - E_t' \text{ or } E_p - \frac{E_i + E_t}{2}$$
(VII.17, 18)

from which it is seen that in the absence of mutual termination the molecular weight is likely to show a slight increase with temperature. Combining either equations (15) and (17) or equations (16) and (18) we obtain

$$RT^2 \frac{\mathrm{d} \ln (\overline{DP}_n/R_p)}{\mathrm{d}T} = - E_i \quad . \quad . \quad \text{(VII.19)}$$

an equation which is particularly valuable in ionic polymerization, since it offers the only currently known method of finding the energy of activation of this initiation reaction. The values obtained by this method are only a small fraction of the values appropriate to catalysed free radical polymerization, where in the few cases where this method has been applied it has yielded results in accord with those obtained from direct measurements of the rate of initiation. It will be noticed that in photochemical polymerization, which is essentially radical in character and where $E_i = 0$, the molecular weight will increase with

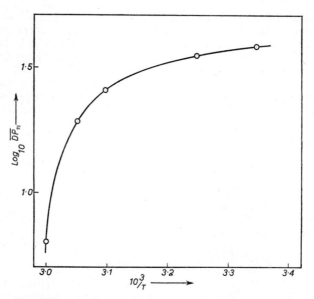

Fig. VII.7. The effect of temperature on DP_n. Monomer = vinyl octyl ether. Catalyst = silver perchlorate. Solvent = diethyl ether. Plotted from data of ELEY and RICHARDS[19].

temperature in a similar manner to the rate. This has been observed in the photopolymerization of several monomers[39].

The chain transfer reaction generally has a larger energy of activation than E_t or E_t' and hence as the temperature increases, $\Sigma k_{tr}[S]$ will usually increase more rapidly than w. The difference in the energies of activation of these two terms may be such that within a small temperature range a system may pass from a state in which polymer molecule growth is controlled by chain termination to one in which it is controlled almost entirely by transfer. The graph of the log $\overline{DP}_n$ against T^{-1} then shows considerable curvature as for example in the ionic polymerization of vinyl octyl ether. (See Fig. VII.7.)

At the beginning of this chapter it was stated that almost all addition polymerizations are considerably exothermic and exentropic and therefore there is a temperature above which the monomer, at a specified concentration, ceases to be thermodynamically unstable with respect to the polymer. At this temperature ΔG is zero and hence δG_p must be zero and $k_p[m_1] = k_d$ where k_d is the velocity constant of the reverse of the propagation reaction. This 'unzipping' reaction (28) is called

$$(28) \qquad m_j{}^* \xrightarrow{k_d} m_{j-1}^* + m_1$$

the *depropagation* reaction. The frequency factor (A_d) and energy of activation (E_d) of this reaction may be readily proved to be related to A_p and E_p in a system giving high polymers by equations (VII.20) and (VII.21)[40].

$$E_d = E_p - \Delta H \qquad . \quad . \quad . \quad \text{(VII.20)}$$

$$\Delta S° = R \ln (A_p/A_d) \text{ (standard state } [m_1] = 1M) \text{ (VII.21)}$$

Table 2 shows that, except for relatively strain free cyclic monomers, heats of polymerization are generally in the range of 8 to 24 k.cal and therefore, whatever the mechanism of polymerization, E_d is ways much larger and frequently several times larger than E_p. If the reasonable assumption is made that A_d, which is the frequency factor of a simple unimolecular dissociation process, lies in the range 10^{12} to 10^{14} sec^{-1} (see Chapter I), then since $\Delta S°$ is negative, $A_p \ll A_d$ and the probability factor of the propagation reaction *must* necessarily be very much less than unity. Thus we have a ready explanation of the appropriate data in Table 1 of Chapter III. Taking into account the de-propagation reaction, equation (VII.3), for the rate of polymer-ization should be replaced by

$$R_p = -\frac{d[m_1]}{dt} = \Sigma[m_j^*]\{k_p[m_1] - k_d\}$$

$$= A_p e^{\frac{-E_p}{RT}} \Sigma[m_j^*]\{[m_1] - e^{\frac{-\Delta S^\circ}{R}} \cdot e^{\frac{\Delta H}{RT}}\}. \quad \text{(VII.22)}$$

Hence, whatever may be the nature of $[m_j^*]$ and the reactions by which it is created and destroyed, the rate of a polymerization reaction must increasingly fall below the curve corresponding to a simple Arrhenius expression as the temperature is raised, ultimately falling to zero at a 'ceiling temperature', T_c, obtained by equating the term in brackets in equation (VII.20) to zero and therefore given by

$$T_c = \frac{\Delta H}{\Delta S^\circ + R \ln [m_1]} = \frac{\Delta H}{R \ln \dfrac{A_p[m_1]}{A_d}} \quad . \quad \text{(VII.23)}$$

The ceiling temperature should be independent of the mode or rate of initiation, i.e. ionic or free radical nature of the catalyst and its concentration, or the type of radiation and its intensity. It should decrease with monomer concentration in a way which recalls the Clausius-Clapeyron equation, a fact which focuses attention on the essential similarity of the two aggregational processes of polymerization and condensation. All these pre-dictions have been fully confirmed experimentally for the 1:1 interpolymerization of olefines with sulphur dioxide from which T_c is in an easily accessible region. Rate-temperature curves for formation of three different polysulphones are shown in Fig. VII.8 and indicate that T_c is dependent on the olefine, the struc-ture of which controls the magnitude of ΔH and, to a much less degree, of ΔS°.

Equation (23) may be tested quantitatively. If the reciprocal of the ceiling temperature corresponding to a given monomer concentration is plotted against the logarithm of that monomer concentration a straight line is obtained from the slope and intercept of which ΔH and ΔS° may be calculated. The heat of

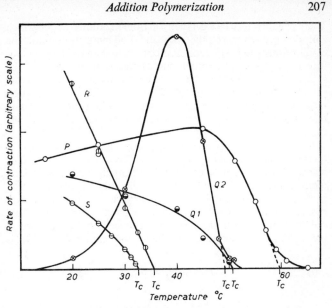

Fig. VII.8. Ceiling temperatures for polysulphone formation from various olefines. (DAINTON and IVIN[41]).

P : hexene-1; *Q* : hexadecene-1; *R* : *cis* butene-2; *S* : *trans* butene-2;

P, *Q*1, *R* and *S* refer to photochemical initiation; *Q*2 to azo *bis iso* butyro nitrile initiation.

reaction may also be measured by direct adiabatic or isothermal calorimetry and there is excellent agreement between the values obtained by all these methods[3]. A further simple verification of the existence of a depropagation reaction is obtained when the pure *cis* or *trans* isomer of a 1,2, dialkylethylene is used. Free rotation is possible in the polymer and therefore the monomer which is shed from the polymer chain m_j^* during depropagation may possess either a *cis* or *trans* configuration, as illustrated in equation (29).

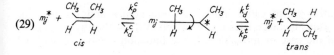

There will therefore be a geometrical isomerization reaction which will proceed concurrently with the polymerization until the equilibrium ratio [cis]/[trans] appropriate to the ambient temperature is attained. The initial rate of this isomerization will be $k_d{}^t\Sigma[m_j{}^*]$ or $k_d{}^c[m_j{}^*]$ and thus affords a ready measure of the rate of depropagation and of $E_d{}^c$ and $E_d{}^t$. The isomerization rate, unlike the polymerization rate, should show no ceiling temperature and Fig. VII.9 shows that this is indeed the case.

It should be emphasized that although the monomer is thermodynamically stable only above T_c and the polymer stable below T_c the existence of an experimentally realizable ceiling temperature does not necessarily imply that depolymerization of dead polymers will begin at any temperature above T_c or that monomer will be the sole product in the temperature range where polymer breakdown does occur. The ceiling temperature is merely that temperature at which the equilibrium (30) is

$$(30) \qquad m_j{}^* + m_1 \underset{k_d}{\overset{k_p}{\rightleftharpoons}} m_{j+1}{}^*$$

established for a selected monomer concentration, and above it dead polymer is metastable whilst below it monomer is metastable. In non-terminated polymerization systems, such as the anionic polymerization of α-methylstyrene, there is no dead polymer and the only polymeric species is $m_j{}^*$ and equilibrium (30) can be kept mobile indefinitely[43]. If in terminated systems a means is available for eventually converting monomer to $m_1{}^*$ and polymer to $m_j{}^*$, then a rather sluggish equilibrium between dead monomer and polymer may be attained as illustrated in equation (31). Light, free-radical and cationic catalysts have been

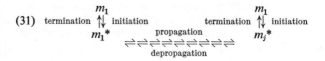

$$(31) \quad \text{termination} \overset{m_1}{\underset{}{\uparrow\downarrow}} \text{initiation} \qquad \text{termination} \overset{m_1}{\underset{}{\uparrow\downarrow}} \text{initiation}$$
$$m_1{}^* \underset{\text{depropagation}}{\overset{\text{propagation}}{\rightleftharpoons\rightleftharpoons\rightleftharpoons\rightleftharpoons}} \qquad m_j{}^*$$

employed to cause initiation of monomer and polymer for various methacrylates and equation (VII.23) thereby verified[44]. In the case of formaldehyde the initiation catalyst is 'built-in'

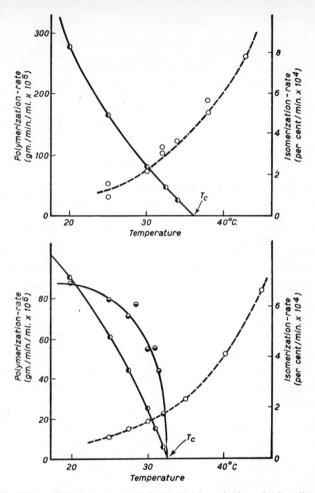

Fig. VII.9. (i) Full line, ● — ● —, photopolymerization; broken line, ○ — ○ —, Bz₂O₂ catalysed isomerization (*cis → trans*)

(ii) Full line: ● — ● —, photopolymerization: ◐ — ◐ —, Bz₂O₂ catalysed polymerization. Broken line: Bz₂O₂ catalysed isomerization (*trans → cis*)

Variation with temperature of the rates of interpolymerization (full lines) of *cis* butene-2 (i) and *trans* butene-2 (ii) with sulphur dioxide; and the initial rates of concurrent isomerization (dotted lines) *cis → trans* (i) and *trans → cis* (ii). Initial mol. fraction of olefine = 0·091 in each case[42] to the polymer and the mobile equilibrium can only be avoided and a metastable polymer of usefully long life obtained by ingenious 'end-capping' or copolymerization techniques.

The propagation reaction only increases with increasing temperature more rapidly than the propagation reaction when the polymerization is exothermic. For endothermic reactions the reverse is true and if the reaction is also endentropic there will exist a temperature T_f, also given by equation (VII.23), *below* which the polymer is metastable. This is the case for elementary sulphur for which the 'floor' temperature is 168°C and the monomeric units are S_8 and S_6 rings.[45]

6. Rate Constants for each of the Steps in Addition Polymerization. (*a*) *Measurement*. In the preceding sections we showed that, when stationary state conditions prevail, measurements of the rate and of the number average degree of polymerization of the polymer formed at low conversion enable the following to be determined: (i) θ and hence ϕ_i or G_i for photo- and radiation-initiated; and k_{de} for catalysed, polymerization (ii) the rate constant ratios: k_{in}/k_i; k_p/k_d; k_{tr}/k_p; k_p/k_t' or k_p/k_r or $k_p/\sqrt{k_t}$ and (iii) whether combination or disproportionation is the mode of any quadratic termination. Absolute values of k_p, k_d, k_{tr}, k_r, k_t or k_t' can only be obtained from measurements of the polymerization rate under non-stationary state conditions for which it is certain that the non-stationary state is not due to the presence of small amounts of adventitious impurity acting as an inhibitor or retarder or to changing values of the rate constants caused by progressively decreasing viscosity of the medium or to physical occlusion or isomerization of the growing centres. Under these circumstances the non-stationary states arise from a change in the rate of initiation which is more rapid than the time necessary for the chain centre concentration to respond to the changed initiation rate. In Chapter V it was explained how either acceleration of reaction after the onset of initiation or the deceleration after cessation of initiation or the average reaction rate during intermittent initiation can be used to evaluate the chain lifetime and hence $\delta = k_t$ or $g = k_t'$ or both (see cases 5, 6, 8, 9, 12, and 13). The necessity to start and stop the initiation at prescribed moments is the reason why photochemical initiation has so often been used in lifetime studies. However a given number of chains can be very rapidly initiated by rapid mixing of the monomer and a solution containing a very active catalyst and it was shown in case (14) of Chapter V that the non-stationary state which ensues can be used to evaluate $g = k_t$.

When the polymer chains are 'living' k_p can always be easily measured. In the discussion of case (15) of Chapter V two situations were envisaged corresponding to a steady rate of initiation and to 'instantaneous' initiation respectively, and in each instance k_p is easily calculated from the decrease of monomer concentration with time provided the rate of initiation or the number of chains started is known. Only the latter case has been realized and in the systems studied the major factor limiting the precision of the results is the measurement of the number of growing chains or 'living ends', as they are termed. None the less the method has been extensively and successfully used for values of k_p up to about 10^3 l.mole^{-1} sec^{-1}.

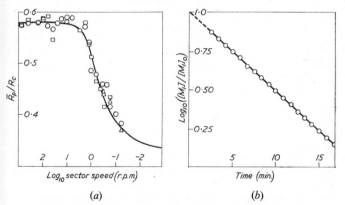

(a)   (b)

Fig. VII.10. (a) Rate of photosensitized polymerization of 0.2 or 0.4 M aqueous solutions of acrylamide at 25°C under intermittent illumination using a 1 in 3 sector. Full line denotes theoretical curve for $\delta = k_t = 3.3 \times 10^6$ l mole^{-1} sec^{-1}.

(b) Variations of styrene concentration with time at 25°C for a solution in dioxane containing 6×10^{-5} M "living ends" and initially M styrene. The line corresponds to $k_p = 30$ l mole^{-1} sec^{-1}.

Fig. VII.10 exemplifies the data which are typical of (a) intermittently initiated free-radical polymerization, i.e. a non-stationary state and (b) the stationary state polymerization of an instantaneously initiated 'living' polymerization.

(b) *Values.* Table 4 contains a few of the rate constants and Arrhenius parameters which have been obtained and these will suffice to illustrate the wide range of type of chemical reaction which can be studied in polymerization reactions.

The dependence of A_p and E_p on the solvent polarity, general or specific solvating power and on the structure of the monomer are easily studied and provide insights into the mechanisms of attack on double bonds and cyclic compounds by free radicals or ions or ion-pairs. The corresponding quantities for the transfer and retardation reactions likewise give very valuable details concerning the reactions of radicals or ions with added substances. These reactions include such diverse processes as hydride-, proton- and hydrogen-atom transfer, nucleophilic substitution in aromatic nuclei and the oxidation and reduction of polymer radicals by inorganic compounds in aqueous and non-aqueous media. Similarly the data regarding termination reactions are a rich source of information concerning the structural factors which control combination or disproportionation of two identical radicals and the spontaneous unimolecular reactions of ions and ion-pairs. The techniques of addition polymerization thus constitute a most powerful tool for the quantitative exploration of the reactivities of free radicals and ions. The underlying causes of the patterns thus revealed are now becoming apparent and for details of these, which it is inappropriate to discuss here, the reader should consult references 5, 6, 13, 18, and 46.

7. Addition Copolymerization[(47)]. In a mixture of x monomers undergoing polymerization there will also be x types of growing chain m_j^* each of which may react with each of x monomers. The number of possible propagation reactions which may occur is therefore x^2, and each of these will have a characteristic velocity constant. Although the overall rate of polymerization may be a very complicated expression involving a variety of initiation and termination processes, the percentage composition of the resultant copolymer which is determined by the relative values of $-\,\mathrm{d}[m_1]/\mathrm{d}t$ for each monomer, will be controlled solely by the composition of the monomer feed and the values of the propagation constants. In the case of a two-monomer system extensive experimental and theoretical investigations have been made. Denoting the monomers as α and β and the growing chains with α and β ends as α_j^* and β_j^* respectively, where j is

TABLE 4. ARRHENIUS PARAMETERS FOR SELECTED REACTIONS INVOLVED IN ADDITION POLYMERIZATION

(a) Anionic Propagating Species i.e. m_j^- or $m_j^- M^+$

Polymeric Anion	Solvent	Gegen Ion (M^+)	Other Reactant	Reaction Type	$k(M^{-1}s^{-1})$	At Temp. $(°C)$	$log_{10}A$	E $(kcal\ mole^{-1})$	Ref.
Styrene	Tetrahydropyran	Na$^+$	Styrene	Addition	11	25	6·1	6·7	a
,,	,,	K$^+$	,,	,,	68	,,	5·7	5·3	a
,,	,,	Rb$^+$	,,	,,	78	,,	5·5	4·9	a
,,	,,	Cs$^+$	,,	,,	49	,,	5·3	4·9	a
,,	Tetrahydrofuran	K$^+$	,,	,,	70	,,	—	—	a
,,	Dioxan	K$^+$	,,	,,	28	,,	5·9	6·1	a
,,	Benzene	K$^+$	,,	,,	47	,,	6·8	7·2	a
,,	cyclo-Hexane	K$^+$	,,	,,	~7	,,	—	—	a
,,	Tetrahydrofuran	Na$^+$	2 vinyl pyridine	,,	~4 × 10^4	,,	—	—	b
,,	,,	Na$^+$	p Me styrene	,,	20	,,	—	—	b
,,	,,	Na$^+$	α Me styrene	,,	3	,,	—	—	b
,,	,,	Na$^+$	β Me styrene	,,	2	,,	—	—	b
p Me styrene	,,	Na$^+$	Styrene	,,	130	,,	—	—	b
2 vinyl pyridine	,,	Na$^+$	,,	,,	v. low	,,	—	—	b
styrene	,,	Na$^+$	O$_2$	,,	v. high	,,	—	—	a

(b) Free Radical Propagating Species, $m_j \cdot$

Notes: (i) Values of k, A and E for propagation and mutual termination reactions of typical vinyl polymerization in organic media are given on pages 52 and 53. (Table 1, Chapter III).

(ii) Values of k_r for the oxidation or reduction of polymer radicals by inorganic compounds are given on page 194 (Table 3, Chapter VII).

Radical ($m_j \cdot$)	Other Reactant	Reaction Type	$k(M^{-1}s^{-1})$	At Temp. (°C)	Ref.
Polystyryl	Styrene	Addition	$1 \cdot 7 \times 10^2$	60	c
,,	Methyl methacrylate	,,	$3 \cdot 4 \times 10^2$	60	c
,,	Vinyl acetate	,,	$3 \cdot 2$	60	c
Polymethyl methacrylate	Methyl methacrylate	,,	$7 \cdot 3 \times 10^2$	60	c
,,	Styrene	,,	$1 \cdot 6 \times 10^3$	60	c
,,	Vinyl acetate	,,	$3 \cdot 7 \times 10$	60	c
Polystyryl	Toluene	H atom abstraction?	$2 \cdot 2 \times 10^{-3}$	60	d
,,	Ethyl benzene	,,	$9 \cdot 2 \times 10^{-3}$	60	d
,,	Diphenyl methane	,,	$8 \cdot 1 \times 10^{-2}$	60	d
,,	Triphenyl methane	,,	$1 \cdot 4 \times 10^{-1}$	60	d
,,	n-butyl mercaptan	,,	$3 \cdot 9 \times 10^3$	60	e
,,	Tri-ethyl amine	,,	$1 \cdot 2 \times 10^{-1}$	60	f

References: (a) unpublished work by Dainton, East, Hurworth, Harpell, Ivin and LaFlair; (b) Smid and Szwarc, J. Polymer Sci., 61, 31 (1962) normalised to fit (a); (c) Bamford, Barb, Jenkins and Onyon, "The Kinetics of Vinyl Polymerizations by Radical Mechanisms" Butterworth, London (1958); (d) Gregg and Mayo, Disc. Faraday Soc., 2, 328 (1947); (e) Walling, J. Amer. Chem. Soc., 70, 2561 (1948); (f) Bamford and White, Trans. Faraday Soc., 52, 716 (1956).

the total number of all types of monomeric units in the chain, we have

			Rate
(32)	$\alpha_j{}^* + \alpha \rightarrow \alpha_{j+1}{}^*$		$k_{\alpha\alpha}[\alpha_j{}^*][\alpha]$
(33)	$\alpha_j{}^* + \beta \rightarrow \beta_{j+1}{}^*$		$k_{\alpha\beta}[\alpha_j{}^*][\beta]$
(34)	$\beta_j{}^* + \alpha \rightarrow \alpha_{j+1}{}^*$		$k_{\beta\alpha}[\beta_j{}^*][\alpha]$
(35)	$\beta_j{}^* + \beta \rightarrow \beta_{j+1}{}^*$		$k_{\beta\beta}[\beta_j{}^*][\beta]$

whence at the stationary state

$$\left.\begin{aligned}
d[\alpha_j{}^*]/dt &= \theta_\alpha - k_{t\alpha}[\alpha_j{}^*]^2 - k_{t\alpha\beta}[\alpha_j{}^*][\beta_j{}^*] \\
&\quad - k_{\alpha\beta}[\alpha_j{}^*][\beta] + k_{\beta\alpha}[\beta_j{}^*][\alpha] = 0 \\
d[\beta_j{}^*]/dt &= \theta_\beta - k_{t\beta}[\beta_j{}^*]^2 - k_{t\alpha\beta}[\alpha_j{}^*][\beta_j{}^*] \\
&\quad + k_{\alpha\beta}[\alpha_j{}^*][\beta] - k_{\beta\alpha}[\beta_j{}^*][\alpha] = 0
\end{aligned}\right\} \qquad \text{(VII.24)}$$

and
$$\left.\begin{aligned}
-d[\alpha]/dt &= [\alpha]\{k_{\alpha\alpha}[\alpha_j{}^*] + k_{\beta\alpha}[\beta_j{}^*]\} \quad (a) \\
-d[\beta]/dt &= [\beta]\{k_{\beta\beta}[\beta_j{}^*] + k_{\alpha\beta}[\alpha_j{}^*]\} \quad (b)
\end{aligned}\right\} \qquad \text{(VII.25)}$$

For long chain systems the rates of propagation will greatly exceed the rates of initiation and termination and we may write

$$k_{\alpha\beta}[\alpha_j{}^*][\beta] = k_{\beta\alpha}[\beta_j{}^*][\alpha] \qquad . \qquad \text{(VII.26)}$$

Using (VII.26) to eliminate $[\alpha_j{}^*]$ from (VI.25 (a)) and (VII.25 (b)) we obtain

molar ratio of α to β in copolymer

$$= \frac{-d[\alpha]}{-d[\beta]} = \frac{[\alpha]}{[\beta]} \left\{ \frac{1 + r_\alpha \dfrac{[\alpha]}{[\beta]}}{\dfrac{[\alpha]}{[\beta]} + r_\beta} \right\} \qquad . \qquad . \qquad \text{(VII.27)}$$

where $r_\alpha = \dfrac{k_{\alpha\alpha}}{k_{\alpha\beta}}$ and $r_\beta = \dfrac{k_{\beta\beta}}{k_{\beta\alpha}}$ and are called the *monomer re-activity ratios* since they are the relative reactivities of the two monomers towards a growing polymer chain with either an α or β ending.

In deducing equation (27) it has been assumed that each of the velocity constants has a value which is independent of the

overall composition of the chain apart from the terminal monomer unit, an assumption which is justified by experience. Equa-
tion (27) may be used to find r_α and r_β in two ways; the α/β
ratio is carefully determined from polymer samples obtained
from experiments carried either to very low conversions or to
appreciable conversion. In the former, equation (27) is applied
assuming that the composition of the feed stays constant and
therefore has its initial value. In the latter method it is necessary
to take account of the fact that except in the very rare case
where the ratio of the monomer concentration and composition
of the copolymer are unaffected during the polymerization (i.e.
when $r_\alpha[\alpha] + [\beta] = r_\beta[\beta] + [\alpha]$), the composition of the monomer
feed and the composition of the copolymer being formed will be
different at different stages of the reaction. This involves rather
tiresome graphical integration. The analogy has been made
between copolymerization and distillation of the miscible liquids,
for example, *ideal* copolymerization is said to occur when the
ratio of the reactivities of given monomers is the same whatever
the radical to which they are being added. For the two component systems covered by equation (27) this implies $r_\alpha r_\beta = 1$
and equation (27) becomes

$$\frac{d[\alpha]}{d[\beta]} = r_\alpha \frac{[\alpha]}{[\beta]}. \qquad \text{(VII.28)}$$

when $r_\alpha > 1$, the polymer contains more of α than the feed and
conversely when $r_\alpha < 1$ it contains more of β than the feed. A
special case is when $r_\alpha = r_\beta = 1$, i.e. the reactivities of the
monomers with either end are identical, when the copolymer
formed has the same percentage of α and β as the monomer
mixture from which it is being produced.

It is most usual to find that a change in the nature of the
terminal group of the growing polymer influences to different
degrees the reaction of the two monomers towards it, i.e.
$r_\alpha r_\beta \neq 1$. Several cases must then be considered, which are
illustrated in Fig. VII.11. An extreme case is when $k_{\alpha\alpha}$ and $k_{\beta\beta}$
are both zero, i.e. each monomer will not undergo self polymeriz-
ation and will only react with chain ends of opposite type. In
this case the only polymer which can be formed is one containing
equal amounts of each monomer. The alkyl polysulphones are
of this type and the copolymer of maleic anhydride and α-methyl
styrene approaches it very closely. If only one of the monomers

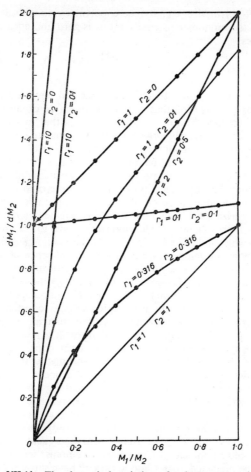

Fig. VII.11. The theoretical variation of polymer composition with monomer feed composition for various monomer reactivity ratios according to equation (27). (Taken from MARK and TOBOLSKY, page 427.)

H. Mark and A. V. Tobolsky, *Physical Chemistry of High Polymeric Systems* Interscience, New York (1950) will self-polymerize, e.g. styrene copolymerizing with SO_2, then one of the monomer reactivity ratios is zero and equation (27) becomes

$$\frac{- \, d[\alpha]}{- \, d[\beta]} = 1 + r_\alpha \frac{[\alpha]}{[\beta]} \quad \text{if } r_\beta = 0 \quad . \quad . \quad \text{(VII.29)}$$

from which it is seen that the polymer can never contain less than 50 per cent of that monomer which *is* capable of self polymerization. The most extreme case is that in which both r_α and r_β are extremely large when the tendency to copolymerize will be extremely small and a large proportion of the polymer molecules produced will be pure polymers of α or of β.

The ratios for cationic polymerization are quite different from the values for free radical polymerization (see CUNDALL)[47]. A very considerable range of 2-component free radical and ionic copolymerizations have now been investigated and the data obtained provide a reliable empirical guide to the structural factors which influence r_α and r_β. Since these ratios generally tend to unity as the temperature is raised, the influence of structure must be more marked on the energy of activation than on the frequency factor. The reactivity ratios enable the evaluation of the effects of structure on reactivity of different monomers with a given radical. When the propagation velocity constant of self-polymerization is also known the effect of changing the structure of a radical chain end on its reactivity with a given monomer may also be found. Where this has been done, namely, for styrene, vinyl acetate, methyl acrylate and methyl methacrylate, the order of reactivity for monomers has been shown to be exactly the opposite of the order of reactivity for the radicals. Thus vinyl acetate monomer is much less reactive than styrene to any radical, but a radical with a vinyl acetate ending is much more reactive to any monomer than are radicals with a styryl ending. The result is in accordance with theoretical expectations.

It would be immensely convenient if monomer reactivity ratios could be predicted. PRICE and ALFREY[48] have suggested that the cross propagation constant $k_{\alpha\beta}$ can be factorized to give $(P_\alpha \, e^{\frac{-\varepsilon_\alpha}{RT}})$ $(Q_\beta \, e^{\frac{-\varepsilon_\beta}{RT}})$ in which the first term is characteristic of the radical and the second term of the monomer. Values can be assigned to P_α, Q_β, ε_α, and ε_β for different radicals and monomers which are in approximate agreement with known monomer reactivity ratios. This is a useful empirical result, of which the precise significance is still obscure. Attempts to relate ε_α and ε_β to charges on the two reagents are open to serious objection. None the less, the polarity of the substituents on the copolymerizing monomers is a factor of the greatest importance; for example, when ε_α and ε_β have opposed signs, as might be the case with two monomers containing electrophilic and electrophobic substituents respectively, $k_{\alpha\alpha}$ and $k_{\beta\beta}$ would be small and $k_{\alpha\beta}$ and $k_{\beta\alpha}$ large, and there would therefore be a strong tendency to form a 1:1 alternating copolymer.

The precision with which transfer constants have been determined has enabled BAMFORD *et al.*[46] to make a somewhat different approach to this problem. Taking the rate constant of the reaction of a polymer radical with toluene, k_T, as the standard and σ as the algebraic sum of the Hammett constants for any substituents on the terminal monomer group, the rate constant, k, for the reaction of this radical with any other reagent can be written as (VII.30), in which A and B are characteristic of the

$$\log k = \log k_T + A\sigma + B \qquad . \qquad \text{(VII.30)}$$

reagent, the former being a polar factor. The monomer reactivity ratios in a copolymerization are then given by

$$\log r_\alpha = (A_\alpha - A_\beta)\sigma_\alpha + (B_\alpha - B_\beta) \qquad . \qquad \text{(VII.31)}$$

and $$\log r_\beta = (A_\beta - A_\alpha)\sigma_\beta + (B_\beta - B_\alpha) \qquad . \qquad \text{(VII.32)}$$

The A and B factors for homo- and co-polymerization are self-consistent, which enables the various influences on the rate constants to be factorized and related to the detailed reaction mechanisms.

REFERENCES

1. BAWN, C. E. H.: *The Chemistry of High Polymers.* Butterworths, London (1948); FRITH, E. M. and TUCKETT, R. F.: *Linear Polymers.* Longmans, London (1951); MARK, H. and TOBO-LSKY, A. V.: *Physical Chemistry of High Polymeric Systems.* Interscience, New York, Second Edition (1950); FLORY, P. J.: *Principles of Polymer Chemistry.* Cornell University Press, New York (1953); TOMPA, H.: *Polymer Solutions.* Butterworths, London (1956); STILLE, J. K.: *Introduction to Polymer Chemistry.* John Wiley, New York (1962).

2. BLOUT, E. R. and MARK, H. F.: *Monomers*. Interscience, New York (1949); BOUNDY, R. H. and BOYER, R.: *Styrene*, Reinhold, New York (1952); RENFREW, A. and MORGAN, P.; *Polythene*, Iliffe and Sons, London (1957). CERESA, R. J.: *Block and Graft Copolymers*. Butterworths, London, (1962); SORENSON, W. R. and CAMPBELL, T. W.: *Preparative Methods of Polymer Chemistry*. Interscience, New York (1961); GAYLORD, N. G. and MARK, H. F.: *Linear and Stereoregular Addition Polymers*, Interscience, New York (1959).

3. DAINTON, F. S. and IVIN, K. J.: *Experimental Thermochemistry*, Volume II, Chapter 12, pp. 251–280, Interscience, London (1962).

4. EVANS, M. G.: *J. Chem. Soc.*, 272 (1947).

5. BEVINGTON, J. C.: *Radical Polymerization*, Academic Press, London (1961) contains a recent summary of this work.

6. BAMFORD, C. H., BARB, W. G., JENKINS, A. D. and ONYON, P. F.: *The Kinetics of Vinyl Polymerization by Radical Mechanisms*, Butterworths, London (1958); BAMFORD, C. H., JENKINS, A. D. and JOHNSTON, R., *Trans. Faraday Soc.*, **55**, 1451 (1959).

7. Refs. 20, 25 and 27 of Chapter II.

8. BARTLETT, P. D., HAMMOND, G. S. and KWART, H.: *Disc. Faraday Soc.*, **2**, 342 (1947); COHEN, S. G.: *J. Polymer Sci.*, **2**, 511 (1947).

9. BARTLETT, P. D. and RÜCHARDT, C.: *J. Amer. Chem. Soc.*, **82**, 1756 (1960).

10. BAWN, C. E. H. and VERDIN, D.: *Trans. Faraday Soc.*, **56**, 815 (1960).

11. BARTLETT, P. D. and FUNAHASHI, T.: *J. Amer. Chem. Soc.*, **84**, 2596 (1962).

12. BAMFORD, C. H., JENKINS, A. D. and JOHNSTON, R.: *Proc. Roy. Soc.*, **A, 239**, 214 (1957).

13. Ref. 51 of Chapter III.

14. ARNETT, L. M.: *J. Amer. Chem. Soc.*, **74**, 2027 (1952). Drawn from table IV.

15. SCHULZ, G. W. and HARBORTH, G.: *Makromol. Chem.*, **1**, 106 (1947). Drawn from Table 2.

16. Modified Fig. 6 from BURNETT, G. M. and MELVILLE, H. W.: *Proc. Roy. Soc.*, **A, 189**, 456 (1947).

17. BARTLETT, P. D. and KWART, H.: *J. Amer. Chem. Soc.*, **72**, 1057 (1950); Fig. 3.

18. WALLING, C., BRIGGS, E. R., CUMMINGS, W., and MAYO, F. R.: *J. Amer. Chem. Soc.*, **72**, 48 (1950), and SZWARC, M.: *Anionic Polymerization* (to be published).

19. ELEY, D. D. and RICHARDS, A. W.: *Trans. Faraday Soc.*, **45**, 425 (1949).

20. BAMFORD, C. H. and JENKINS, A. D.: *Nature*, **176**, 78 (1955).

21. HERINGTON, E. F. G. and ROBERTSON, A.: *Trans. Faraday Soc.*, **38**, 490 (1942); **40**, 236 (1944).

22. TROMMSDORFF, E., KOHLE, H. and LAGALLY, P.: *Makromol. Chem.*, **1**, 169 (1948).

23. NORRISH, R. G. W. and SMITH, R. R.: *Nature*, **150**, 336 (1942).

24. MATHESON, M. S., AUER, E. E., BEVILACQUA, E. B. and HART, E. J.: *J. Amer. Chem. Soc.*, **73**, 5395 (1951); BENGOUGH, W. I. and MELVILLE, H. W.: *Proc. Roy. Soc.*, **A, 230**, 249 (1955).

25. BENSON, S. W. and NORTH, A. M.: *J. Amer. Chem. Soc.*, **81**, 1339 (1959).

26. BLAUER, G.: *Trans. Faraday Soc.*, **56**, 606 (1960).

27. DAINTON, F. S.: *Nature*, **160**, 268 (1947)

28. COLEBOURNE, N., COLLINSON, E. and DAINTON, F. S.: *Trans. Faraday Soc.*, **59**, 1357 (1963).

29. BAMFORD, C. H., JENKINS, A. D. and JOHNSTON, R.: *Trans. Faraday Soc.*, **55**, 1451 (1959).

30. Ref. 34, Chapter III.

31. Ref. 10, Chapter III and DAINTON, F. S. and REILLY, P. J.: *J. Polymer Sci.* (1964).

32. KICE, J. L.: *J. Amer. Chem. Soc.*, **76**, 6264 (1954); *J. Polymer Sci.*, **19**, 123 (1956).

33. BARTLETT, P. D. and ALTSCHUL, R.: *J. Amer. Chem. Soc.*, **67**, 816 (1945).

34. BAYSAL, B. and TOBOLSKY, A. V.: *J. Polymer Sci.*, **8**, 529 (1952).

35. FLORY, P. J.: *J. Amer. Chem. Soc.*, **59**, 241 (1937).

36. GREGG, R. A. and MAYO, F. R.: *Disc. Faraday Soc.*, **2**, 328 (1947).

37. ENDRES, G. F. and OVERBERGER, G. C.: *J. Amer. Chem. Soc.*, **77** 2201 (1955); **78**, 1969 (1956).

38. SAKURADA, Y., HIGASHIMURA, T. and OKAMURA, S.: *J.Polymer Sci.*, **33**, 496 (1958).

39. See MATHESON et al[24] and MACKAY, M. H. and MELVILLE, H. W.: *Trans. Faraday Soc.*, **45**, 330 (1949).

40. DAINTON, F. S. and IVIN, K. J.: *Quart. Rev.*, **12**, 61 (1958); and earlier paper cited therein.

41. DAINTON, F. S. and IVIN, K. J.: *Disc. Faraday Soc.*, **14**, 199 (1955).

42. DAINTON, F. S. and BRISTOW, G. M.: *Proc. Roy. Soc.*, **A, 229**, 509, 525 (1955).

43. DAINTON, F. S., HARPELL, G. and IVIN, K. J.: *Makromol Chem.*, (1965)

44. IVIN, K. J.: *Trans. Faraday Soc.*, **51**, 1273 (1955); BYWATER, S.: *Trans. Faraday Soc.*, **51**, 1267 (1955); SMALL, P. A.: *Trans. Faraday Soc.*, **49**, 441 (1953).

45. FAIRBROTHER, F., GEE, G. and MERRALL, G. T.: *J.Polymer Sci.*, **16**, 459 (1955).

46. BAMFORD, C. H., JENKINS, A. D. and JOHNSTON, R.: *Trans. Faraday Soc.*, **55**, 179 (1959).

47. Reviews of this subject have been given by MAYO, F. R. and WALLING, C.: *Chem. Rev.*, **46,** 191 (1950); Chapter IV of ref. 5; Chapter 5 of ref. 6 and by CUNDALL, R. B. in Chapter 15 of PLESCH[18].

48. ALFREY, T. and PRICE, C. C.: *J. Polymer Sci.*, **2,** 101 (1947).

49. COLCLOUGH, R. O. and DAINTON, F. S.; *Trans. Faraday Soc.*, **54,** 886 (1958).

INDEX

Page numbers in italics refer to figures; on pages in heavy type
the definition is given.